WAVE MECHANICS FOR CHEMISTS

WAVE MECHANICS
FOR CHEMISTS

C. W. N. CUMPER, M.A., Ph.D. (Cantab.), F.R.I.C.

Principal Lecturer, Woolwich Polytechnic, London

ACADEMIC PRESS   NEW YORK/LONDON

1966

Academic Press Inc.
111 Fifth Avenue
New York, New York 10003

Library of Congress Catalog Card Number: 66-15263

Printed in Great Britain

To

Mark and Hugh

PREFACE

The intention of this book is to cover the needs of students preparing for University Degree Examinations though some of the courses may not require a detailed knowledge of each of the problems discussed in Part I. In addition it is hoped that many chemists will find a lead in the latter chapters to understanding many problems on valency and molecular structure. The mathematical arguments have been kept to a minimum and should present no real difficulties to a person with an A level pass in the General Certificate of Education.

Until the start of this century chemists were content to know that two molecules could react to form a third molecule; it is now necessary to know how and why the molecules react and to be able to predict the nature and properties of the product. To this end it is first necessary to understand the electronic structure of atoms and then to consider how they combine to form molecules. Not only must we inquire, for example, why hydrogen atoms combine to form H_2 whereas oxygen atoms can form both O_2 and O_3, but also why more energy is required to separate the two atoms in H_2 than in O_2, and more still to remove a hydrogen atom from a molecule of water. Also, why are the lines joining the hydrogen and oxygen nuclei in water inclined at $104\frac{1}{2}°$ whereas in another triatomic molecule, carbon dioxide, they are linear? Not until the answers are known to these and similar questions is it possible to reflect on the changes which occur in two molecules as they approach one another, collide, and then separate into the same or different molecules.

Molecules are a collection of atoms in a very definite relationship with one another; atoms with a diameter of a few ten millionths of a millimetre are built from electrons and nuclei which are themselves minute in comparison with the size of the atom. It is tempting to assume that these extremely small bodies behave in the same way as particles which can be seen and studied by direct observations.

That is to say that they obey Newton's laws of motion. Unfortunately this 'billiard ball' model is *not* applicable to fundamental particles. A new concept and new mathematical equations are required to correlate the behaviour of these minute objects; the concept is that of a wave, the mathematical relationship is the Schrödinger equation.

In Part I of this book the Schrödinger equation is discussed and then applied to some imaginary 'box problems', the object being to illustrate the inadequacies of the billiard ball model with examples which are mathematically simple, yet provide valid models for actual atoms and molecules. Some atomic problems are then discussed.

Unfortunately, rigorous solutions of the Schrödinger equation cannot be obtained for most atoms or for any molecule; its approximate solutions, however, provide a detailed and reliable theory of valency and molecular structure. This constitutes the subject matter of Part II.

Finally in Part III, the techniques developed previously are applied to selected chemical systems. The object being to discuss a wide range of chemical problems without embarking on an exhaustive coverage of each class of molecule, and without elaborate mathematical analysis.

I could not conclude this Preface without expressing my thanks to my colleagues Professor S. R. Landor and J. Bassett who read part of the typescript, and to L. Blight who kindly read the whole manuscript. I am also indebted to G. D. Pickering, R. F. Rossiter, and A. Singleton for reading the galley proofs. It is too much to hope that no errors or obscurities remain and the responsibility for them is entirely mine.

Finally, I wish to express my very great debt to my wife for her assistance and her constant encouragement in the preparation of this book.

CHARLES W. N. CUMPER

CONTENTS

ix

APPENDICES

PART I

EXACT SOLUTIONS OF THE SCHRÖDINGER WAVE EQUATION

CHAPTER 1

INTRODUCTION

What is wave mechanics? It is the application of a fundamental concept in physics to describe the behaviour of assemblies of small particles. The concept in question is that of a wave—characterized by its measurable attributes of wavelength and frequency and expressed by a mathematical function describing the variation of its amplitude in space and time. We are naturally more familiar with another physical concept, that of a particle, which is characterized by mass and velocity. This is because the results of most experiments involving particles are readily interpreted in terms of mass and velocity by utilizing Newton's laws of motion, but for *some* experiments the classical approach is inadequate. It was to explain the results of experiments which appeared to contravene Newton's laws that the concept and theory of wave mechanics were introduced. Like all good theories, it has done more than explain a few experimental observations—it has provided us with a unifying theory enabling us to correlate numerous observations on fundamental particles, atoms, and molecules and, what is just as important, to plan new experiments and foresee many results. Chemistry is particularly well served by wave mechanics since it provides the only adequate explanation of chemical binding and valency, and hence of the structure, chemical behaviour, and reactivity of molecules.

Fundamentally, wave mechanics is a mathematical treatment of the behaviour of small particles but we need not be frightened by the mathematics involved provided we are prepared to accept a few purely mathematical results, and concentrate more on understanding their significance. The mathematics has been developed in several alternative ways but undoubtedly the most popular approach is that initiated by Schrödinger in 1926 and developed by Heitler and London, Lennard-Jones, Pauling, Mulliken, and Coulson to name but a few. The popularity of this approach resides in the fact that a physical picture of the results can usually be presented. In practice, experimental observations are used to guide the development of the mathematical treatment when, as is nearly always the case, only approximate calculations can be carried out. Wave mechanics cannot obviate the necessity to measure by experiment such things as the binding energy between atoms, bond angles, bond lengths, and the rates of chemical reactions. What it does is to furnish a theory which enables us to correlate and understand the experimental values of these quantities. Their numerical values can only be estimated in most cases as the mathematical equations can seldom be solved exactly.

1.1. The Nature of Light

To understand the origin of wave mechanics let us first consider the nature of light. Newton was particularly impressed by the fact that light travelled in straight lines and at very high speeds. He concluded that light must consist of a stream of small but fast moving corpuscles. At an interface, or where there is a change in the density of the medium through which the corpuscles pass, Newton proposed that they underwent 'fits' of refraction or reflection. This was subsequently attributed to a force acting upon the corpuscles normal to the interface. The nature of this force was mysterious and though it offered an explanation of the phenomena of refraction and reflection it was unable to explain the origin of interference patterns. The suggestion that light was a wave motion enabled Huygens to give a simple explanation of the interference of light waves as well as providing an explanation of refraction and reflection. It is not so easy, however, to explain what is undergoing the vibrations, or to see why light should be propagated in straight lines. In spite of these limitations the validity of the theory was not questioned until the advent of the quantum theory of Planck at the commencement of this century.

Planck suggested that radiation, thermal as well as light rays, was emitted by bodies in discrete 'packets', now known as photons. This return to a corpuscular theory enabled phenomena such as atomic and X-ray spectra, the photoelectric effects, and the Compton effect to be understood and interpreted.

There are therefore two theories of the nature of light. The photon or corpuscular theory which offers a ready explanation of quantum phenomena and the fact that light can be propagated great distances in straight lines, and the wave theory, which seems to be the only reasonable way to explain the interference of light beams. There is one very important difference between the *types of experiment* requiring the different theories. Photons must be extremely small and it is only when they encounter very small objects, or the closely spaced lines of a diffraction grating, that the photon theory is inadequate and wave theory has to be employed. In other words, it is the nature of the experiment that determines which theory should be used to explain it, and fortunately there is a very simple quantitative relationship between them. According to the quantum theory, the energy ε of each photon is directly proportional to the frequency ν of the radiation

$$\varepsilon = h\nu = hc/\lambda$$

where h is Planck's constant of action, c the velocity of light, and λ the wavelength. On the other hand, the relativity theory of Einstein shows that $\varepsilon = mc^2$, where m is the mass of the photon. Hence $\varepsilon = h\nu = mc^2$, or the momentum of the photon characteristic of a particle, is related to the frequency, a characteristic wave property, by

$$p = mc = \frac{h\nu}{c} = \frac{h}{\lambda}$$

In the photon theory the intensity of a light beam at a particular point would be given by the density of photons in a small volume element around the point. In the wave theory the amplitude of the wave ψ is adjusted so that $|\psi|^2$ is equal to the light intensity. The two theories do not attempt to explain either the nature of the matter comprising a particle or the nature of the medium which vibrates to propagate a wave disturbance. They are two different physical concepts which can be given mathematical formulations enabling the motion of a 'particle' to be represented and its future behaviour discussed.

1.2. The de Broglie Relationship

We have just seen that light, for long considered to be a wave disturbance, has to be considered to be corpuscular if the results of some experiments are to be understood. This naturally poses the question: 'does an object normally considered to be a particle (e.g. an electron or atom) ever have to be treated as a wave disturbance?'

Particles obey Newton's laws of motion. At least, particles which we can see and handle have been found experimentally to obey these laws. Newton even applied them to explain the orbits of planets and other bodies in the solar system. When extremely

small objects were detected (electrons, protons, atoms, etc.) nothing
was more natural than to suppose they also followed the classical
laws of motion. However difficulties soon arose. Bohr, for example,
had to introduce several arbitrary (quantum) restrictions in order
to explain the atomic spectrum of hydrogen. More refined experiments showed that his postulates were still not adequate to explain
all the observed phenomena and additional ones had to be introduced. In other words, experimental results demonstrated that the
classical laws of motion would require some rather drastic revision
if they were to apply to the fundamental particles of nature.

In view of this situation, and as a result of some mathematical
analogies between the *principle of least action* of Maupertius and
the *principle of least time* of Fermat, de Broglie[1,2] in 1924 suggested
that in certain situations the behaviour of particles can only be
explained by employing wave equations. These situations arise
either when the particle encounters objects which are very close
together or when it is confined to a very small region of space. The
connexion between the particle and wave concepts is the same as
for light rays, namely

$$p = mv = \frac{h}{\lambda} = \frac{h\nu}{c} \tag{1.1}$$

where v is now the velocity of the particle of mass m. This rather
startling postulate of de Broglie has been verified experimentally,
and since it constitutes one of the basic facts of wave mechanics
we must outline these experiments.

Equation (1.1) was first verified for a beam of electrons. Under
an accelerating potential V, electrons acquire the kinetic energy

$$\tfrac{1}{2}mv^2 = Ve$$

where e is the electronic charge. Hence their momentum is given by

$$p = mv = (2mVe)^{1/2}$$

If we assume that the de Broglie relationship is correct, electrons
with this momentum would have a wavelength associated with their
motion equal to

$$\lambda = \frac{h}{p} = \frac{h}{(2mVe)^{1/2}} \simeq \left(\frac{150}{V}\right)^{1/2} \text{Å} \quad \text{(if } V \text{ is in volts)} \tag{1.2}$$

Electrons accelerated by potentials of 1·5 to 15,000 volts should
therefore be associated with wavelengths of about 10–0·1 Å. These
distances are comparable with the spacing between the lattice
planes of crystals, which should therefore be able to act as a diffraction grating for a suitably accelerated beam of electrons. The vital
experiments were performed a few years later by Davisson and
Germer, and by Thomson.

Davisson and Germer

Davisson and Germer[3-5] were engaged in the study of secondary electron emission from electrodes in vacuum tubes. The essential features of their apparatus are shown in Figure 1.1.

Electrons accelerated at potentials of less than 370 volts were directed normally† at the octahedral (111) faces of a polycrystalline nickel target. The intensity of the electrons scattered by the nickel

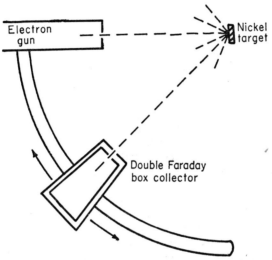

FIGURE 1.1   Reflection of a beam of slow electrons.

at various angles was measured with a double Faraday box collector and found to vary in a fairly regular manner. During one experiment a bottle of liquid air exploded and oxidized the surface of the hot nickel target. Subsequent treatment of this target to remove the oxide film changed the nature of the nickel specimen from being polycrystalline to one consisting of a few large nickel crystals. This produced a dramatic change in the scattering curves obtained in subsequent experiments. In addition to a general scattering the electrons were also selectively reflected at certain angles to the surface—just as if the incident beam had consisted of X-rays which were being reflected by the regularly spaced layers of atoms in the crystal at angles given by Bragg's law. Twenty sets of electron beams were in fact associated with twenty sets of Laue beams that would have issued from the same crystal with X-rays of a wavelength given by equation (1.2). The numerical correspondence was not exact but

† In later experiments a small angle of incidence was employed.

the discrepancy was later attributed to the refractive index inside the crystal being different for X-rays and electron 'waves.'

Here was clear evidence that a beam of low-energy electrons behaved as if it was a wave disturbance when the de Broglie wavelength was comparable with the spacing between the lines on a reflection grating. Two months after their preliminary announcement, Thomson and Reid reported that high-energy electrons were diffracted on passing through a thin metal film.

Thomson

In Thomson's experiments[6–8] high-energy cathode rays, accelerated through potentials of between 10 and 60 kV, were collimated by a narrow tube of 0·23 mm diameter and then passed through very thin films of aluminium, gold, platinum, or celluloid. A photographic plate exposed 32 cm behind the film showed the characteristic concentric (Debye–Scherrer) rings of a diffraction pattern (Figure 1.2). In some cases diffraction spots were also observed, implying that the minute crystals in the film were partially orientated.

In applying the de Broglie relationship a correction had to be made for the relativistic change of electron mass with velocity and, as in Davisson and Germer's experiments, different refractive indices had to be adopted for the electron waves and X-rays.

These experiments prove that an accelerated beam of electrons can be reflected and diffracted, and the wavelength associated with this behaviour is given by the same equation as relates the wave and photon theories of light. This relationship has since been verified experimentally with beams of neutrons and atoms, so that the

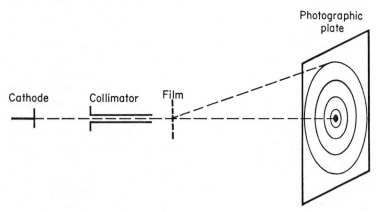

FIGURE 1.2   Diffraction of a beam of fast electrons.

wave–particle duality is established as a characteristic feature of matter and independent of any charge the particle might carry.

1.3. The Heisenberg Uncertainty Principle

Let us consider some implications of the observation that electrons may be diffracted, bearing in mind that the significance of all wave equations is that the square of the wave amplitude is proportional to the intensity of the disturbance at the point in question.

What would happen if Thomson's experiment could be performed with single electrons instead of a continuous beam? Would the whole diffraction pattern appear each time an electron struck the screen? This is hardly possible as the screen is of moderate size and there would be still further diffraction rings at greater angles. An electron cannot be of infinite size; each electron would strike the screen at one particular point and it would not be until a very large number of electrons had been diffracted that the complete pattern would be obtained. The important point is that the electron can leave the diffraction grating along an infinite number of paths. It is impossible to say which route a particular electron will follow after it has been diffracted or where it will strike the screen, it may be anywhere within the extension of the mathematical wave employed to describe its behaviour. Obviously the intensity of the diffraction pattern depends upon the diffraction angle, so there is a greater chance of the electron striking the screen at some points than at others. In fact, all that we can say about the diffracted electron is that there is a certain probability of its striking the screen at a particular point. This is proportional to the value of the square of the wave amplitude $|\psi|^2$ at the point in question.

The momentum acquired by the electron in Thomson's experiment is known with considerable precision, it is a *sharp* quantity, but until it strikes the screen the direction it takes on leaving the diffraction grating is completely unknown, it is an *unsharp* quantity. Once it strikes the screen its position and direction of motion are known, they both become sharp quantities. At the same time, however, varying amounts of kinetic energy are lost to the atoms in the screen, and the momentum of the electron after the collision is correspondingly uncertain. If it was measured a range of values would be found, each having a certain probability. The existence of conjugate sharp and unsharp quantities is a characteristic feature of wave mechanics. Quantities measured by experiment are forced to have sharp values, but the process of measurement must cause an uncertain change in some other property so that its value becomes unsharp. This feature of wave mechanics is embodied in the *uncertainty principle* of Heisenberg[9] which may be expressed in the forms

$$\Delta q \, \Delta p \geqslant ah$$

or

$$\Delta \varepsilon \, \Delta t \geqslant ah \qquad (1.3)$$

where Δq represents the uncertainty in our knowledge of a particle's position when its momentum is known with an accuracy of Δp. The errors in the simultaneous knowledge of the energy of the particle and the time are likewise $\Delta \varepsilon$ and Δt respectively. The number a is usually between $1/4\pi$ and $1/\pi$, depending upon the exact definition of the uncertainties and the nature of the experiment. Planck's constant h is the absolute limit to the accuracy with which two conjugate properties may be simultaneously known, a limit which we might be able to reach but which can never be lowered.

A detailed analysis of all actual and hypothetical experiments designed to measure simultaneously q and p, or ε and t, lead to the above mathematical result. Two of these experiments are considered in Appendix 2. We may therefore take it that the Heisenberg uncertainty principle is a fundamental feature of the physical world as we know it. Some prominent scientists and philosophers maintain that if we knew more about fundamental particles and were able to measure some of their other properties, as yet unknown, then the direction they take after being diffracted could be calculated and precise values for q and p could be known simultaneously. Until such time as these unspecified properties are discovered and measured we must accept the Heisenberg relationship as a principle of nature.

In the diffraction experiment considered above, the momentum is known with great accuracy—consequently there must be a great error in our knowledge of the position of the electron. We must realize however that since equation (1.3) may be written in the form

$$\Delta q \, \Delta(mv) \geqslant ah$$

or

$$\Delta q \, \Delta v \geqslant ah/m$$

if the mass of the particle is large the uncertainty in the simultaneous knowledge of its position and velocity is extremely small. We are back in the domain of classical mechanics. Whenever large particles or freely moving small particles are considered wave mechanically, the results obtained are identical with those from classical mechanics. Wave mechanics includes classical mechanics and at the same time extends the theoretical treatment of motion to very small particles. In this book we are concerned with the structure and properties of atoms and molecules and these cannot be discussed adequately by classical mechanics.

The emission spectra of atoms consist of radiation at a large number of well-defined wavelengths. Since this radiation is produced by an electron jumping from one energy level to another, these energy levels must also have very well-defined, or sharp, values. This very important experimental fact will be utilized in subsequent theoretical treatments of atomic systems. At the moment, note just one consequence; according to the Heisenberg principle we can never know the exact position of an electron in an atom. There is no means of knowing the trajectory of any electron inside an atom or molecule and so it is impossible to distinguish between different electrons. All that can ever be calculated is the probability of finding an electron at a particular point in the space around the nucleus.

BIBLIOGRAPHICAL REFERENCES

1. de Broglie, L., *Phil. Mag.*, 1924, **47**, 446.
2. de Broglie, L., *Ann. Phys.*, 1925, **3**, 22.
3. Davisson, C. J., and Germer, L. H., *Nature*, 1927, **119**, 558.
4. Davisson, C. J., and Germer, L. H., *Phys. Rev.*, 1927, **30**, 705.
5. Davisson, C. J., and Germer, L. H., *Proc. Nat. Acad. Sci. U.S.A.*, 1928, **14**, 317, 619.
6. Thomson, G. P., and Reid, A., *Nature*, 1927, **119**, 890.
7. Thomson, G. P., *Proc. Roy. Soc.*, 1928, A117, 600.
8. Thomson, G. P., *Nature*, 1927, **120**, 802.
9. Heisenberg, W., *Z. Phys.*, 1927, **43**, 172.

CHAPTER 2

THE SCHRÖDINGER WAVE EQUATION

2.1. Wave Motion in One Dimension

Before discussing the Schrödinger wave equation it is desirable to consider certain aspects of wave motion. As we saw in the previous chapter, the results of many experiments involving electrons and other small particles can only be correlated by employing mathematical equations known as wave equations. The simplest waves are those which extend in just one dimension—say the x direction.

A monochromatic wave is characterized by an amplitude ψ and a constant wavelength λ or frequency ν, since $\lambda\nu = v_w$, the wave velocity. The wave amplitude, or *wave function*, is the dependent variable, it depends upon the distance along the x coordinate, and frequently also upon the time t. A convenient equation which expresses this dependence is

$$\psi = A \sin \left[2\pi \left(\frac{x}{\lambda} - \nu t \right) \right]$$

$$= A \sin (2\pi\theta) \qquad (2.1)$$

where A is the maximum amplitude of the wave (Figure 2.1). The nodes n, points of zero displacement, and antinodes a, points of maximum displacement, move along the x axis with time in a periodic manner, the whole wave appearing to move forward with the wave velocity v_w.

The corresponding cosine expression

$$\psi = B \cos (2\pi\theta) \qquad (2.2)$$

describes the same wave but with a phase shift of $\frac{1}{2}\pi$ in the angle. To be more general, the angle θ can be replaced by $\theta + \alpha$, where α

12

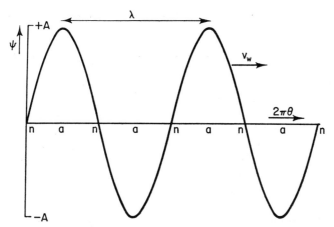

FIGURE 2.1 A monochromatic sine wave.

is an arbitrary phase shift, or the wave form can be represented by a linear combination of equations (2.1) and (2.2)

$$\psi = A \sin (2\pi\theta) + B \cos (2\pi\theta) \qquad (2.3)$$

This type of wave can also be expressed in an alternative mathematical form which involves exponentials.

$$\psi = A\, e^{2\pi i\theta} \equiv A \cos (2\pi\theta) + iA \sin (2\pi\theta)$$

or $$\psi = B\, e^{-2\pi i\theta} \equiv B \cos (2\pi\theta) - iB \sin (2\pi\theta)$$

where $i = \sqrt{(-1)}$. As before a more general expression is obtained by their linear combination giving

$$\psi = A\, e^{2\pi i\theta} + B\, e^{-2\pi i\theta}$$
$$\equiv (A + B) \cos (2\pi\theta) + i(A - B) \sin (2\pi\theta) \qquad (2.4)$$

In these equations the real and imaginary parts of the wave function are separated. This is particularly valuable when dealing with problems in which the wavelength can become an imaginary quantity.

All the equations mentioned above represent *travelling waves*, the nodes and antinodes moving along the x axis periodically with time. There are also *standing waves* in which the positions of the nodes and antinodes are stationary, the amplitude between the nodes varying as before with distance and time. This type of wave is important for the applications considered in this book where the particles are 'bound' and are not free to escape from the system.

Corresponding to equations (2.3) and (2.4) they would be represented by

$$\psi = \left[A \sin\left(\frac{2\pi x}{\lambda}\right)\right] \cos(2\pi \nu t) + \left[B \cos\left(\frac{2\pi x}{\lambda}\right)\right] \sin(2\pi \nu t) \quad (2.5)$$

and

$$\psi = [A\, e^{2\pi i x/\lambda} + B\, e^{-2\pi i x/\lambda}]\, e^{-2\pi i \nu t} \quad (2.6)$$

The terms inside the square brackets describe how ψ varies with the distance x and can be referred to as the *space part* of the wave function, the other factors constitute the *time part* of ψ. The time factor is important, for example, when magnetic properties associated with the movement of bound electrons are being considered, or when the experiment involves translation of the particle from one part of the apparatus to a different part. In most cases, however, we are only interested in how the average value of ψ over an appreciable time interval depends upon the value of x. Under these circumstances it is legitimate to consider only the space part of the wave function, and when the symbol ψ is written it will, unless otherwise stated, refer to the space factor alone. The results obtained for standing wave amplitudes should be multiplied by a time factor, but unless this furnishes valuable information about the system under consideration it will not be done.

The equations discussed above apply to harmonic motion; those adopted to portray the variation of ψ with position in the majority of practical problems are more complex mathematically. Virtually all types of wave equations have one very important feature in common, they satisfy the differential equation (e.g. Coulson[1])

$$\frac{d^2\psi}{dx^2} + \left(\frac{2\pi}{\lambda}\right)^2 \psi = 0 \quad (2.7)$$

That this is the case for the wave forms discussed so far may easily be verified; it will be illustrated by considering the space part of equation (2.5).

$$\psi = A \sin\left(\frac{2\pi x}{\lambda}\right) + B \cos\left(\frac{2\pi x}{\lambda}\right)$$

$$\frac{d\psi}{dx} = \frac{2\pi}{\lambda} A \cos\left(\frac{2\pi x}{\lambda}\right) - \frac{2\pi}{\lambda} B \sin\left(\frac{2\pi x}{\lambda}\right)$$

and

$$\frac{d^2\psi}{dx^2} = -\left(\frac{2\pi}{\lambda}\right)^2 A \sin\left(\frac{2\pi x}{\lambda}\right) - \left(\frac{2\pi}{\lambda}\right)^2 B \cos\left(\frac{2\pi x}{\lambda}\right)$$

$$= -\left(\frac{2\pi}{\lambda}\right)^2 \psi$$

This equation is characteristic of waves, and constitutes one of the fundamental features of wave mechanics.

2.2. Translational Motion of a Particle

To conclude this discussion of one dimensional waves we show how the translational motion of a small particle can be described by wave equations.

In terms of a wave disturbance the movement of a particle is represented by superimposing a large number of infinitely long monochromatic waves. If the parameters for each wave are suitably

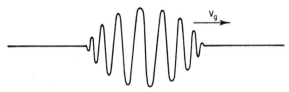

FIGURE 2.2   A travelling wave pulse.

chosen, a wave pulse (Figure 2) results, the different waves interfering with one another on either side of the pulse to produce zero amplitude. (This summation of waves is known as a Fourier series.)

The velocity v of the particle, mass m, is readily identified with the group velocity of the waves forming this pulse. When there is a large dispersion, the wavelength varying rapidly with the particle velocity ($\lambda = h/mv$), the phase velocity of each wave v_w and the group velocity v_g of a number of waves differ. They are defined by the relationships

$$v_w = \lambda \nu = \frac{\nu}{1/\lambda}$$

$$v_g = \frac{\mathrm{d}\nu}{\mathrm{d}(1/\lambda)} = \frac{\mathrm{d}\nu}{\mathrm{d}(mv/h)} = \frac{h}{m}\frac{\mathrm{d}\nu}{\mathrm{d}v}$$

where v, the particle velocity, may be equated to the group velocity v_g. Hence,

$$\nu = \frac{m}{h}\int v\,\mathrm{d}v = \frac{mv^2}{2h}$$

or

$$h\nu = \tfrac{1}{2}mv^2 = T$$

where T is the kinetic energy of the particle. The integration constant is omitted as it would only add a constant to the energy and has no physical meaning. If the particle has no potential energy this would also be its total energy. It will be recalled that the same connexion exists between energy and frequency for a photon.

2.3. The Schrödinger Wave Equation

This equation may be formulated by combining two relationships, on the one hand, the purely mathematical property of waves (equation (2.7)), and on the other, de Broglie's equation relating the particle and wave concepts of matter. The latter has been tested by experiment and its incorporation implies that some of the information will be statistical in character.

The total energy E in atomic and molecular systems has normally a well-defined value (i.e., it is a sharp quantity). It is equal to the sum of the potential V and kinetic T energies, both of which depend upon the relative positions of the individual particles which constitute the system. However, whereas V can, in principle, be expressed in terms of coulombic or other forces acting upon the system, this is often not possible for T. The total and potential energies are consequently taken to be the more fundamental properties. Consider a mass m moving with a velocity v. Then

$$E - V \equiv T = \tfrac{1}{2}mv^2 = \frac{p^2}{2m} = \frac{h^2}{2m\lambda^2}$$

In other words, the de Broglie wavelength associated with the particle is related to the difference between the total and potential energies by the equation

$$\lambda^2 = \frac{h^2}{2m(E - V)} \tag{2.8}$$

For virtually all waves equation (2.7) is satisfied, and substituting the above value of λ^2 we obtain

$$\frac{d^2\psi}{dx^2} + \frac{8\pi^2 m}{h^2}(E - V)\psi = 0 \tag{2.9}$$

This is the very celebrated equation† described by Schrödinger[2] in

† It is ultimately experiment which verifies that the energy term in equation (2.9) is the kinetic energy $T = E - V$ and not the total energy E. It is worth while noting that had it been the total energy, then ψ, and with it the probability of finding the particle at a given point, would be independent of the potential energy. This is unlikely.

1926 for motion in one dimension. It describes in very general terms the motion of a particle of mass m under a potential V.

The above might appear to be a derivation of the wave equation—at least for translational motion. This is not true. There is no proof of the Schrödinger equation any more than there is a proof of Newton's laws of motion. They are fundamental relationships which give logical coherence to a vast amount of experimental observation. With Newton's laws, the experimental observations were restricted to those upon macroscopic bodies and later experiments proved they were not completely valid when applied to atomic systems. The deductions which have been made from the Schrödinger equation about atomic systems have, however, been confirmed experimentally. Further, when macroscopic bodies are considered, the Schrödinger equation leads to the same conclusions as are obtained from classical theory. Though Newton's laws have therefore become superfluous, nobody would dream of abandoning them since they are much easier to apply and appreciate and, for objects large compared with atoms, equally accurate.

Equation (2.9) is for motion in one dimension. In three dimensions it is not difficult to appreciate that

$$\frac{d^2\psi}{dx^2} \quad \text{is replaced by} \quad \frac{\partial^2\psi}{\partial x^2} + \frac{\partial^2\psi}{\partial y^2} + \frac{\partial^2\psi}{\partial z^2}$$

and $V_{(x)}$ and $\psi_{(x)}$ are replaced by $V_{(x,y,z)}$ and $\psi_{(x,y,z)}$. The three-dimensional wave equation is consequently

$$\frac{\partial^2\psi_{(x,y,z)}}{\partial x^2} + \frac{\partial^2\psi_{(x,y,z)}}{\partial y^2} + \frac{\partial^2\psi_{(x,y,z)}}{\partial z^2} + \frac{8\pi^2 m}{h^2}(E - V_{(x,y,z)})\psi_{(x,y,z)} = 0$$

or

$$\nabla^2\psi + \frac{8\pi^2 m}{h^2}(E - V)\psi = 0 \qquad (2.10)$$

where the subscripts have been dropped and the Laplacian operator ∇^2 employed as an abbreviation for

$$\frac{\partial^2}{\partial x^2} + \frac{\partial^2}{\partial y^2} + \frac{\partial^2}{\partial z^2}$$

In this book equation (2.10) will be referred to as the *Schrödinger equation* or the *wave equation*. For a number of particles it becomes

$$\frac{1}{m_1}\nabla_1^2 + \frac{1}{m_2}\nabla_2^2 + \ldots + \frac{8\pi^2}{h^2}(E - V)\psi = 0$$

The Schrödinger equation is a differential equation of the second order, and in applying it to a particular problem the mathematical task is first to find a suitable expression for ψ, showing how the wave amplitude depends upon the distances along the x, y, and z axes, and then to solve the differential equation. In every case we shall find there are many expressions for ψ which satisfy the Schrödinger equation. Only some of the solutions will however be acceptable; they will be called *eigenfunctions* (or well-behaved wave functions) and the corresponding energies E the *eigenvalues* of the system. The conditions the wave functions must satisfy before they are acceptable are best seen from definite examples, and this is one of the objectives in Chapter 3. These conditions are summarized, and an alternative formulation of the wave equation is given in Chapter 4.

The only dependent variable in the Schrödinger equation is ψ—it depends upon the coordinates of the particle. In some cases it turns out to be a complex function of the form $\psi = u + iv$, where u and v are real functions of the coordinates. Neither ψ, nor its complex conjugate $\psi^* = u - iv$, has any physical significance whatever. Their product, $\psi\psi^* = |\psi|^2 = u^2 + v^2$, or if ψ is a real function of the coordinates ψ^2, has a physical significance. The interpretation of all forms of wave motion, whether they be of light waves, sound waves, electric fields, or matter waves, is that the square of the wave amplitude at a particular point gives the 'intensity' of the effect at that point. A particle can only be in one position at a given instant, but according to the Heisenberg uncertainty principle we can never know precisely where this position is, we can only state the probability of it being at a given point in space. $|\psi|^2$ is interpreted as being a direct measure of this probability P. The greater the wave amplitude the greater is the probability of finding the particle at that point or, during a given time interval, the longer on average is the total time spent at that point.

The Schrödinger equation we have been considering involves the space part of the wave function, and only applies to stationary states in which the particles are bound together and the energy is a sharp quantity. The energy and the probability distribution are not dependent upon time, and when, as is frequently the case, these are the only quantities of experimental and theoretical interest, the time factor can be ignored. Otherwise the complete wave function must be employed. It is the product of a space and a time factor and is a solution of the more general time-dependent wave equation

$$\nabla^2\psi_{(x,y,z,t)} + \frac{8\pi^2 m}{h^2}\left[\frac{2\pi i}{h}\frac{\partial}{\partial t} - V_{(x,y,z)}\right]\psi_{(x,y,z,t)} = 0$$

This equation also applies to non-stationary states where E is not a sharp quantity (e.g. the scattering of electrons), but its consideration would take us beyond the scope of this book.

2.4. The Charge-cloud Concept

This is a very valuable concept for a charged particle which is not free to escape from the system (e.g. an electron in an atom or molecule). During a time interval sufficiently long for an electron to travel a considerable distance, $|\psi|^2$ would give the net charge density ($\rho_{(x,y,z)}$) at each point in space. Over this time interval the electron could be pictured as spread out in the form of a charged cloud. This interpretation gives a physical description of the 'position' of an electron in an atom which is easy to appreciate but unfortunately it is not strictly accurate. If the electron is a particle it can only occupy a very small region of space and cannot extend over regions of a few ångström units in all directions. Were it possible to photograph the electron in an atom it would be found to be in a certain position; if a very large number of three dimensional photographs were taken on the same negative a charge-cloud picture of the electron would be obtained.

This approach enables contours of electron density to be drawn for each eigenvalue of an atom. Contours could also be constructed such that the electron spends 95% (or any other percentage) of its time within the contour; alternatively we might say that 95% of the electronic charge is within the contour. Wave functions for atoms stretch to an infinite distance from the nucleus and consequently their size might be considered infinite! The 95% (or 99%) contour gives a more realistic value for atomic and molecular dimensions, the probability of finding an electron more than a few ångströms from the nucleus is extremely small. (The average distance of an electron from the nucleus provides a different measure of atomic size—see Sections 4.4 and 7.4.) Finally, this idea gives a concept of shape to the probability distribution of an electron around a nucleus. This, in turn, is of the utmost significance for we shall find that this shape is the main factor controlling the stereochemical disposition of atoms in a molecule.

What is the situation if the wave function refers to more than one electron? For two electrons ψ depends upon the coordinates of both, and $|\psi|^2 \, d\tau_1 \, d\tau_2$ is the probability of electron 1 being in a volume element $d\tau_1$ and *at the same time* electron 2 being in the volume element $d\tau_2$. This function will give the resultant charge-cloud for both electrons. The charge density ρ_1 will be dependent upon the position of the second electron, because of the mutual repulsion between them. We must therefore average over all positions of electron 2. Consequently, the function

$$\rho_1 = \int |\psi|^2 \, d\tau_2$$

integrated over all values of τ_2 gives this one electron density in a two-electron system and permits its distribution to be computed. The extension to more than two electrons is obvious.

BIBLIOGRAPHICAL REFERENCES

1. Coulson, C. A., *Waves*, Oliver and Boyd, London, 1958.
2. Schrödinger, E., *Ann. Phys.*, 1926, **79**, 361.

CHAPTER 3

PARTICLE IN A BOX

The Schrödinger equation will be applied first of all to some hypothetical 'particle in a box' problems. The reason for considering these artificial problems is that in spite of their great simplicity they provide clear illustrations of the basic procedures adopted in obtaining exact and acceptable solutions of the wave equation. Furthermore we shall, by drawing analogies, obtain many qualitative results for the mathematically more complex problems which arise when the equation is applied to atoms and molecules. For the non-mathematical reader this alone is of value if the wave mechanical description of atomic systems is to be fully appreciated.

A 'box' in the sense of this chapter is a potential box. That is, a particle is subjected to sudden and discontinuous changes in potential at positions which constitute the walls of the box. If the particle is charged one can imagine these to take the form of electrostatic potential barriers.

3.1. A Particle in a One-dimensional Box with Infinite Potential Walls

This is the simplest of the box problems and will be considered in detail. Suppose the particle of mass m is restricted to motion along the x axis. Further, suppose that between $x = 0$ and $x = a$ it is subjected to a zero potential and outside this range to an infinite one. In other words, the walls of the box are at $x = 0$ and $x = a$ and at these positions the potential energy of the particle changes suddenly from zero to infinity.

Inside the box $V = 0$ and the one-dimensional wave equation assumes a particularly simple form

$$\frac{d^2\psi}{dx^2} + \frac{8\pi^2 m}{h^2} E\psi = 0 \qquad (3.1)$$

21

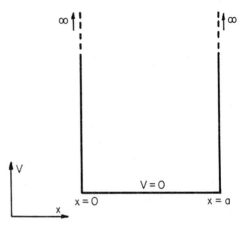

FIGURE 3.1   A one-dimensional potential box with walls of infinite height
at $x = 0$ and $x = a$.

The general solution of this differential equation is

$$\psi = A \sin\left(\frac{2\pi x}{\lambda}\right) + B \cos\left(\frac{2\pi x}{\lambda}\right) \qquad (3.2)$$

Differentiating twice with respect to x we obtain equation (2.7)

$$\frac{d^2\psi}{dx^2} = -\left(\frac{2\pi}{\lambda}\right)^2 \psi$$

and substituting into equation (3.1)

$$E = \frac{h^2}{2m\lambda^2} \qquad (3.3)$$

According to this equation the energy of the particle is unrestricted and can vary continuously with the parameter λ. What is the effect of the potential barriers?

Outside the box the particle would be subjected to an infinite potential and would therefore acquire an infinite energy. This is clearly impossible; the probability of finding the particle outside the box is consequently zero. In other words ψ^2, and hence ψ, must be zero when $0 \geqslant x \geqslant a$. In addition to satisfying the Schrödinger equation the wave functions must comply with boundary conditions at the walls of the box.

At $x = 0$, $\psi = 0$. Hence in equation (3.2) the parameter B must be zero, since $\cos 0 = 1$, and the wave function reduces to

$$\psi = A \sin\left(\frac{2\pi x}{\lambda}\right)$$

Also at $x = a$, $\psi = 0$ and

$$\psi = A \sin \left(\frac{2\pi a}{\lambda}\right) = 0$$

so that

$$\frac{2\pi a}{\lambda} = n\pi \qquad (n = 0, 1, 2, 3 \ldots)$$

In other words λ is restricted to the values $2a/n$ and may be identified with the de Broglie wavelength since, for the motion of the particle inside the box to persist, there must be an integral number of half-wavelengths between $x = 0$ and $x = a$. More significant however is the fact that this restriction upon the values of λ limits the wave functions (or eigenfunctions) to the values†

$$\psi_n = A \sin \left(\frac{n\pi}{a} x\right) \tag{3.4}$$

and the corresponding energies (or eigenvalues) of the particle to

$$E_n = \frac{n^2 h^2}{8ma^2} \qquad (n = 1, 2, 3 \ldots) \tag{3.5}$$

The integer n may be termed a *quantum number*. We note that it cannot be zero because the eigenfunction would then be zero and the de Broglie wavelength infinite, and this could not describe a particle.

The energy cannot vary continuously but is quantized in units of $h^2/8ma^2$, the multiples being $1, 4, 9, 16 \ldots n^2$. The minimum energy the particle can possess is $h^2/8ma^2$; this is known as the *zero-point energy* of the system and its existence is a general feature of systems where the motion would be described as vibrating. The presence of this zero-point energy is consistent with the uncertainty principle. Since the particle must be between $x = 0$ and $x = a$ the error in our knowledge of its position is finite, consequently there must also be a finite error in our knowledge of its momentum or energy which cannot therefore be zero. We shall see later that there is no zero-point energy associated with rotatory motion.

† This can also be written as

$$\psi_n = \frac{A}{2i} [e^{in\pi x/a} - e^{-in\pi x/a}]$$

which expresses better the idea that the particle is equally likely to be travelling in either direction along the x axis.

2

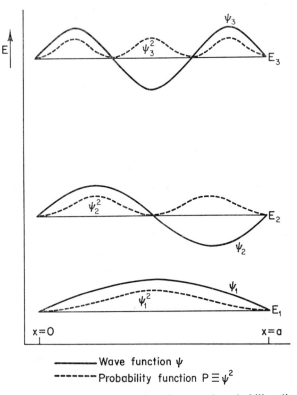

—————— Wave function ψ

- - - - - -Probability function $P \equiv \psi^2$

FIGURE 3.2   Energy levels, wave functions, and probability distributions of a particle in a box with walls of infinite height.

Reference to Figure 3.2 shows that for the lowest or ground state one half-wavelength fits into the box; there are no internal nodes. The wave functions for the higher energy states however have $n - 1$ internal nodes, in addition to those at the walls of the box. According to the Sturm–Liouville theorem[1] this is a general property of differential equations of the Schrödinger type when $V \rightarrow \infty$ at $x = \pm \infty$. We note in passing that the kinetic energy of the particle, equal to its total energy in this particular problem, is greater the more nodes or the greater the curvature in the wave function.

Normalization. So far nothing has been said about A, the maximum amplitude of the wave function. The solutions of the wave equation are independent of its magnitude so it may be chosen to satisfy any condition we like to impose, provided the eigenvalues are unaffected. It is customary to adjust A so that ψ^2, instead of being proportional to the probability of finding the particle at a particular value of x, is actually equal to $P_{(x)}$. The probability of finding the particle between x and $x + dx$ is $P_{(x)}\, dx$. The particle however must be somewhere between $x = 0$ and $x = a$ so that the integral of the probability between these limits must be unity, i.e.

$$\int_0^x P_{(x)}\, dx = \int_0^x \psi^2\, dx = 1$$

This process is referred to as normalizing the wave function to unity, or more simply as *normalization*. It must always be done when absolute probabilities are required. For the particle in a box

$$\int_0^a \left[A \sin \left(\frac{n\pi x}{a} \right) \right]^2 dx = 1$$

$$A^2 \int_0^a \tfrac{1}{2} \left[1 - \cos \left(\frac{2n\pi}{a} x \right) \right] dx = 1$$

and

$$\tfrac{1}{2} A^2 \left[x - \frac{a}{2n\pi} \sin \left(\frac{2n\pi}{a} x \right) \right]_0^a = 1$$

To satisfy this relationship A must be $\sqrt{(2/a)}$. The normalized wave functions are therefore

$$\psi_n = \sqrt{\left(\frac{2}{a} \right)} \sin \left(\frac{n\pi}{a} x \right)$$

and the absolute probability of the particle being found at a particular value of x is

$$P_{(x)} \equiv \psi_n{}^2 = \frac{2}{a} \sin^2 \left(\frac{n\pi}{a} x \right)$$

The probability of finding the particle at the nodes is zero and it passes through a maximum of $2/a$ in between them (Figure 3.2). The total area under each probability curve must be unity by the normalization condition.

A question often asked is: How does the particle pass from one side of the box to the other when there is a node in between? The reply is that the question should not be asked! The energy of the particle is a well-defined and sharp quantity; consequently, according to the Heisenberg uncertainty principle, it is useless to inquire about the position or motion of the particle. In the case of atoms, where we shall encounter spherical nodes, a complete treatment which includes the effect of electron spin (Dirac) shows that the probability of finding the electron on a nodal surface is extremely small, but not zero.

Since the potential is uniformly zero inside the box, classical theory maintains that there should be an equal probability of finding the particle at any value of x. Consequently

$$\int_0^a P_{(x)}\, dx = P_{(x)} \int_0^a dx = P_{(x)}a = 1$$

and $P_{(x)} = 1/a$, one-half the maximum value indicated by wave theory.

Orthogonality. Before leaving this discussion of a particle in a one dimensional box it is convenient to introduce a mathematical property of eigenfunctions which is a general feature of all exact solutions of the wave equation. It is that any two eigenfunctions are *orthogonal* to each other. That is

$$\int_0^a \psi_n \psi_m\, dx = 0 \qquad (n \neq m)$$

Orthogonal wave functions are completely independent of one another. In many chemical problems only approximate solutions are obtained and these are not necessarily orthogonal, that is, one solution will involve part of another solution. We shall return to this point in subsequent chapters.

If the wave functions illustrated in Figure 3.2 are examined it will be seen that if the quantum number n is odd $\psi_{(x)} = \psi_{(a-x)}$, whereas if it is even $\psi_{(x)} = -\psi_{(a-x)}$. Consequently if n is even and m odd the integral of the product $\psi_n \psi_m$ over all values of x must necessarily be zero. That this is true whatever the values of n and m can be shown as follows:

$$\int_0^a \psi_n \psi_m\, dx = \int_0^a \left[\sqrt{\left(\frac{2}{a}\right)} \sin\left(\frac{n\pi}{a}x\right) \sqrt{\left(\frac{2}{a}\right)} \sin\left(\frac{m\pi}{a}x\right) \right] dx$$

$$= \frac{2}{a} \int_0^a \tfrac{1}{2}\left\{ \cos\left[(n-m)\frac{\pi}{a}x\right] \right.$$

$$\left. - \cos\left[(n+m)\frac{\pi}{a}x\right] \right\} dx$$

$$= \frac{1}{a}\left\{ \frac{a}{(n-m)\pi} \sin\left[(n-m)\frac{\pi}{a}x\right] \right.$$

$$\left. - \frac{a}{(n+m)\pi} \sin\left[(n+m)\frac{\pi}{a}x\right] \right\}_0^a$$

Since the difference and sum of the two quantum numbers, $n - m$ and $n + m$ respectively, must be integers the sines of the angles in this expression are all zero and the integral is also zero. Any two eigenfunctions for a particle in a box must therefore be orthogonal.

Wave functions which are both normalized and orthogonal are sometimes said to be *orthonormal*.

3.2. Particle in a Rectangular Three-dimensional Box

The previous problem will now be extended to three dimensions. Consider a rectangular box of sides a_x, a_y, and a_z, the potential energy of the particle inside the box being zero and outside the box infinite. In other words, the particle must remain inside the box and satisfy the three-dimensional Schrödinger equation

$$\frac{\partial^2\psi}{\partial x^2} + \frac{\partial^2\psi}{\partial y^2} + \frac{\partial^2\psi}{\partial z^2} + \frac{8\pi^2 m}{h^2}E\psi = 0$$

To solve this differential equation we first see if it is possible to separate the wave function, which depends upon the three coordinates x, y, and z, into the product of three factors $X(x)$, $Y(y)$, and $Z(z)$, each dependent upon only one coordinate. We assume that,

$$\psi_{(x,y,z)} = X(x)\,Y(y)Z(z)$$

or, to simplify the following expressions,

$$\psi = XYZ$$

Since Y and Z are independent of x

$$\frac{\partial\psi}{\partial x} = YZ\frac{\partial X}{\partial x}\ ;\qquad \frac{\partial^2\psi}{\partial x^2} = YZ\frac{\partial^2 X}{\partial x^2}\ \text{etc.}$$

The Schrödinger equation becomes

$$YZ\frac{\partial^2 X}{\partial x^2} + ZX\frac{\partial^2 Y}{\partial y^2} + XY\frac{\partial^2 Z}{\partial z^2} + \frac{8\pi^2 m}{h^2}EXYZ = 0$$

and dividing throughout by $(8\pi^2 m/h^2)XYZ$

$$\frac{h^2}{8\pi^2 m}\left(\frac{1}{X}\frac{\partial^2 X}{\partial x^2} + \frac{1}{Y}\frac{\partial^2 Y}{\partial y^2} + \frac{1}{Z}\frac{\partial^2 Z}{\partial z^2}\right) + E = 0$$

The first term is a function of x only, the other terms being independent of the value of x. Consequently if y and z remain constant whilst x is varied (i.e. motion parallel to the x axis), the last three terms in the above equation remain constant, and so therefore must the first. Let the constant be $-E_{(x)}$, i.e.

$$\frac{h^2}{8\pi^2 m}\frac{1}{X}\frac{\partial^2 X}{\partial x^2} = -E_{(x)} \tag{3.6a}$$

Likewise

$$\frac{h^2}{8\pi^2 m}\frac{1}{Y}\frac{\partial^2 Y}{\partial y^2} = -E_{(y)} \tag{3.6b}$$

and

$$\frac{h^2}{8\pi^2 m}\frac{1}{Z}\frac{\partial^2 Z}{\partial z^2} = -E_{(z)} \tag{3.6c}$$

where

$$E_{(x)} + E_{(y)} + E_{(z)} = E \tag{3.6d}$$

Factorization of the wave function into the product of three factors is therefore permissible, because by so doing the wave equation can be written in a form which involves the sum of terms each dependent upon only one of these same variables.

The equations (3.6) are of the same form as equation (3.1) in the previous problem and the solution is therefore

$$\psi \equiv XYZ = \sqrt{\left(\frac{2}{a_x}\right)}\sin\left(\frac{n_x\pi}{a_x}x\right)\sqrt{\left(\frac{2}{a_y}\right)}\sin\left(\frac{n_y\pi}{a_y}y\right)$$

$$\times \sqrt{\left(\frac{2}{a_z}\right)}\sin\left(\frac{n_z\pi}{a_z}z\right)$$

$$= \sqrt{\left(\frac{8}{V}\right)}\sin\left(\frac{n_x\pi x}{a_x}\right)\sin\left(\frac{n_y\pi y}{a_y}\right)\sin\left(\frac{n_z\pi z}{a_z}\right)$$

where $V = a_x a_y a_z$ is the volume of the box. The total energy is

$$E = E_{(x)} + E_{(y)} + E_{(z)} = \frac{h^2}{8m}\left(\frac{n_x^2}{a_x^2} + \frac{n_y^2}{a_y^2} + \frac{n_z^2}{a_z^2}\right)$$

In this three-dimensional problem the three quantum numbers n_x, n_y, and n_z specify the component kinetic energies associated with the directions of the cartesian axes.

(In Chapter 7 we deal with another three-dimensional problem, the hydrogen atom, and we shall again factorize the wave function into the product of three factors. In this case however it is convenient to work with polar coordinates and the three quantum numbers which are automatically introduced in its mathematical solution no longer specify the same property in different directions.)

In the particular case of a particle in a *cubic box*, $a_x = a_y = a_z = a$ and

$$E = \frac{h^2}{8ma^2} [n_x^2 + n_y^2 + n_z^2]$$

The energy depends upon $n_x^2 + n_y^2 + n_z^2$ so that it is possible for different states, each specified by a unique set of the three quantum numbers, to have the same energy. This is illustrated in Figure 3.3 where the numbers above each line are the values of n_x, n_y, and n_z respectively for that state. When several states have the same energy they are said to be *degenerate*. Degeneracy in this problem arises through the particle being able to possess different components of its quantized kinetic energy along the three cartesian axes, whilst its total energy remains constant. Some of the degeneracy is removed if only two sides of the box are of equal length and all degeneracy is lost when the three sides are unequal.

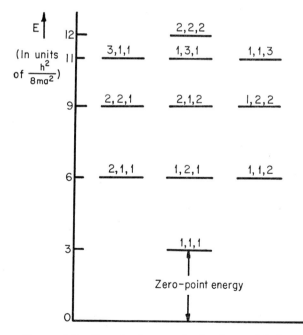

FIGURE 3.3   Quantized energy levels of a particle in a cubic box.

3.3. Particle in a One-dimensional Box with One Finite and One Infinite Potential Wall

As an extension of the first problem discussed consider the case where one of the potential walls is of finite height equal to U (Figure 3.4).

In region 1, $0 < x < a$, the particle has no potential energy but in region 2, $a < x < \infty$, it possesses the potential energy U. By

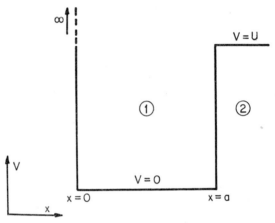

FIGURE 3.4   A one-dimensional box with one finite and one infinite potential wall.

combining the de Broglie relationship ($\lambda = h/p$) with that for the kinetic energy of the particle ($T = p^2/2m$), we obtained equation (2.8)

$$\lambda^2 = \frac{h^2}{2m(E - V)} \tag{3.7}$$

In region 2 there are two possibilities. If the energy of the particle is greater than its potential energy U, the de Broglie wavelength λ_2 associated with the motion of the particle is real (equation (3.7)). If on the other hand its total energy is less than U, λ_2^2 is negative and λ_2 would be an imaginary quantity. In this case the kinetic energy $T = E - U$ would also be negative. According to classical theory this is impossible and the particle could never be found in region 2 with $E < U$. The Schrödinger equation however is only concerned with the total energy (eigenvalue) of the system and with its potential energy—governed by the various attractive and repulsive forces operating in the system. There is no specific mention of the quantity we know as kinetic energy and no restriction is placed upon the relative values of E and U. From our knowledge of the motion of large bodies obeying the laws of classical mechanics, the probability of finding the particle in a situation where $E < V$ must be small, but the Schrödinger equation does not exclude this situation completely with small particles.

We have to face the possibility of λ being an imaginary quantity, in which case it is more convenient to employ expressions for the wave functions which involve exponentials. The one-dimensional wave equation is

$$\frac{d^2\psi}{dx^2} + \frac{8\pi^2 m}{h^2}(E - V_{(x)})\psi = 0$$

In region 1 let the wave function ψ_1 satisfying this differential equation be

$$\psi_1 = A_1 \exp\left(\frac{2\pi ix}{\lambda_1}\right) + B_1 \exp\left(\frac{-2\pi ix}{\lambda_1}\right)$$

$$\equiv (A_1 + B_1)\cos\left(\frac{2\pi x}{\lambda_1}\right) + i(A_1 - B_1)\sin\left(\frac{2\pi x}{\lambda_1}\right) \quad (3.8)$$

where

$$\lambda_1{}^2 = h^2/2mE; \quad (V = 0).$$

In region 2,

$$\psi_2 = A_2 \exp\left(\frac{2\pi ix}{\lambda_2}\right) + B_2 \exp\left(\frac{-2\pi ix}{\lambda_2}\right) \quad (3.9)$$

and

$$\lambda_2{}^2 = h^2/2m(E - U); \quad (V = U).$$

The wavelength λ_1 is a real quantity, λ_2 can be real or imaginary. The next step, having formulated the problem, is to simplify the expression for the wave functions by making them satisfy the boundary requirements.

At $x = 0$, $\psi_1 = 0$, for the reason discussed in Section 3.1, and consequently $A_1 + B_1 = 0$ and

$$\psi_1 = 2iB_1 \sin\left(\frac{2\pi x}{\lambda_1}\right)$$

Case 1. Consider first the situation when $E < U$ and λ_2 is imaginary. Let $\lambda_2 = i\lambda_2{}^*$, where $\lambda_2{}^*$ is a real number. Then

$$\psi_2 = A_2 \exp\left(\frac{2\pi x}{\lambda_2{}^*}\right) + B_2 \exp\left(\frac{-2\pi x}{\lambda_2{}^*}\right)$$

As $x \to \infty$, $\psi_2 \to 0$, since it would be impossible for the particle to penetrate far into region 2 when $E < U$. For this to be the case

A_2 must be zero and

$$\psi_2 = B_2 \exp \left(- \frac{2\pi x}{\lambda_2{}^*} \right)$$

At the potential barrier, situated where the two regions meet, the values of ψ_1 and ψ_2 must be equal. Were this not the case there would be two values for ψ^2, and two probabilities of finding the particle at this one value of x. This is obviously impossible so that at $x = a$, $\psi_1 = \psi_2$ or

$$2iB_1 \sin \left(\frac{2\pi a}{\lambda_1} \right) = B_2 \exp \left(- \frac{2\pi a}{\lambda_2{}^*} \right) \qquad (3.10)$$

This equation provides a relationship between B_1 and B_2, but in order to determine the wavelengths which are acceptable for this

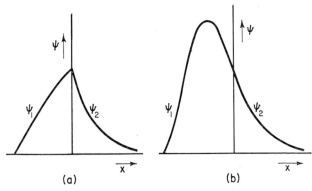

$$(a) \qquad\qquad\qquad (b)$$

FIGURE 3.5 Wave functions at a potential barrier. In (a) $d\psi_1/dx \neq d\psi_2/dx$, and in (b) $d\psi_1/dx = d\psi_2/dx$, at the discontinuity in the potential.

problem yet another restriction has to be placed upon the wave functions near the barrier at $x = a$. The functions ψ_1 and ψ_2 could approach each other at a finite angle, as in Figure 3.5a, or their gradients could be identical, Figure 3.5b. In the first case a graph of the probability of finding the particle at a particular value of x would pass through a discontinuity at $x = a$ whereas in the other case the graph would be smooth. Intuition suggests that the second case is the more likely of these alternatives and this does in fact constitute one of the conditions for an acceptable solution of the wave equation (Chapter 4). At $x = a$ we therefore assume that $d\psi_1/dx = d\psi_2/dx$ or

$$\frac{i4\pi}{\lambda_1} B_1 \cos \left(\frac{2\pi a}{\lambda_1} \right) = - \frac{2\pi}{\lambda_2{}^*} B_2 \exp \left(- \frac{2\pi a}{\lambda_2{}^*} \right) \qquad (3.11)$$

Dividing equation (3.10) by (3.11) we obtain a relation between λ_1 and λ_2*

$$\tan\left(\frac{2\pi a}{\lambda_1}\right) = -\frac{\lambda_2{}^*}{\lambda_1} \tag{3.12}$$

If a quantity λ_0 is defined by the expression $\lambda_0{}^2 = h^2/2mU$ then

$$-\frac{1}{\lambda_2{}^2} \equiv \frac{1}{\lambda_2{}^{*2}} = \frac{1}{\lambda_0{}^2} - \frac{1}{\lambda_1{}^2}$$

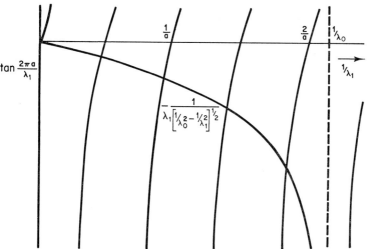

FIGURE 3.6 Graphical solution of equation (3.13) for $m = 10^{-23}$ g, $U = 10^{-13}$ erg, $a = 1$ Å. The solutions are at $1/\lambda_1 = 0.465, 0.929, 1.388,$ and 1.836 Å^{-1}.

and equation (3.12) becomes

$$\tan\left(\frac{2\pi a}{\lambda_1}\right) = -\frac{1}{\lambda_1(1/\lambda_0{}^2 - 1/\lambda_1{}^2)^{1/2}}. \tag{3.13}$$

This equation may be solved numerically to obtain the permitted values of λ_1, and hence of λ_2. Alternatively a graphical method may be employed. In Figure 3.6 both sides of equation (3.13) are separately plotted against $1/\lambda_1$; the curves cross at the values of $1/\lambda_1$ which satisfy the equation.

In the example chosen there are four solutions and the corresponding energies and wave functions are illustrated in Figure 3.7. The greater the value of $1/\lambda_1$ the closer they are together, a limit being reached when $1/\lambda_1 = 1/\lambda_0$, or $E = U$.

The square of the wave function, shown dotted in Figure 3.7, is the probability of finding the particle at the particular value of x. The wave functions must first be normalized to obtain the values of B_1 and B_2 if absolute instead of relative probabilities are required. The interesting feature is the small but finite chance of the particle

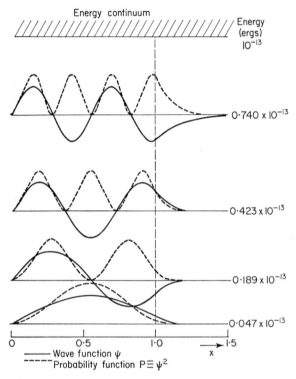

FIGURE 3.7 Energy levels and wave functions for a box with one finite and one infinite potential wall, corresponding to Figure 3.6.

being found in region 2, with its total energy less than its potential energy. This chance decreases rapidly with increasing depth of penetration but, nevertheless, the particle can enter regions which are forbidden to it by classical mechanics.

Case 2. When $E > U$, λ_2 is real and we take

$$\psi_2 = A_2 \exp\left(\frac{2\pi i x}{\lambda_2}\right) + B_2 \exp\left(-\frac{2\pi i x}{\lambda_2}\right)$$

$$\equiv (A_2 + B_2) \cos\left(\frac{2\pi x}{\lambda_2}\right) + i(A_2 - B_2) \sin\left(\frac{2\pi x}{\lambda_2}\right)$$

and

$$\lambda_2{}^2 = \frac{h^2}{2m(E - U)}$$

At $x = a$, $\psi_1 = \psi_2$ as before, or

$$2iB_1 \sin\left(\frac{2\pi a}{\lambda_1}\right) = (A_2 + B_2) \cos\left(\frac{2\pi a}{\lambda_2}\right) + i(A_2 - B_2) \sin\left(\frac{2\pi a}{\lambda_2}\right)$$

Equating the real parts of this equation we find that $A_2 + B_2 = 0$ and from the imaginary parts

$$2B_1 \sin\left(\frac{2\pi a}{\lambda_1}\right) = (A_2 - B_2) \sin\left(\frac{2\pi a}{\lambda_2}\right)$$

$$= 2B_2 \sin\left(\frac{2\pi a}{\lambda_2}\right)$$

This equation provides a relationship between B_1 and B_2 (normalization factors) in terms of the wavelengths in the two regions. It, together with equations (3.8) and (3.9) which relate λ_1 and λ_2 respectively to the total energy E, is satisfied by all values of λ_1 (provided $E > U$). The other boundary condition that $d\psi_1/dx = d\psi_2/dx$ at $x = a$ does not provide a further restriction. The energy therefore is not quantized and can have any value as long as it exceeds the potential energy U.

3.4. The Tunnel Effect

We have discovered that there is a finite probability of a particle being found where its total energy is less than its potential energy. It would therefore seem possible for a particle to pass through a narrow potential barrier. To test this let us consider a potential barrier of the form shown in Figure 3.8. It comprises three regions of constant potential.

Region 1 $-\infty < x < 0$; $V = U_1$

Region 2 $0 < x < a$; $V = U_2$

Region 3 $a < x < \infty$; $V = U_3$

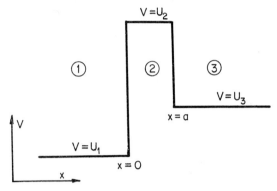

FIGURE 3.8   A one-dimensional potential barrier.

Following the procedure adopted in the previous problem the wave functions in the three regions will be,

Region 1

$$\psi_1 = A_1 \exp\left(\frac{2\pi i x}{\lambda_1}\right) + B_1 \exp\left(-\frac{2\pi i x}{\lambda_1}\right)$$

Region 2

$$\psi_2 = A_2 \exp\left(\frac{2\pi i x}{\lambda_2}\right) + B_2 \exp\left(-\frac{2\pi i x}{\lambda_2}\right)$$

$$= A_2 \exp\left(\frac{2\pi x}{\lambda_2{}^*}\right) + B_2 \exp\left(-\frac{2\pi x}{\lambda_2{}^*}\right)$$

Region 3

$$\psi_3 = A_3 \exp\left(\frac{2\pi i x}{\lambda_3}\right) + B_3 \exp\left(-\frac{2\pi i x}{\lambda_3}\right)$$

In region 2, λ_2 will be an imaginary quantity when $E < U_2$ so it is replaced by $i\lambda_2{}^*$.

Consider the particles with energy between U_1 and U_2 moving up from negative values of x and colliding with the potential barrier. They have the wave function $A_1 \exp(2\pi i x/\lambda_1)$. The majority will be reflected by the potential barrier at $x = 0$ back into region 1— this being described by the term $B_1 \exp(-2\pi i x/\lambda_1)$. Likewise the two terms in the expression for ψ_2 may be considered to represent the motion of particles penetrating into region 2 and returning towards region 1. Any that pass through the barrier into region 3 would have the wave function $A_3 \exp(2\pi i x/\lambda_3)$; the parameter B_3 must be zero since there is no potential barrier to reverse their direction of motion. We now impose four boundary conditions.

At $x = 0$, $\psi_1 = \psi_2$ or $A_1 + B_1 = A_2 + B_2$, and

$$\frac{d\psi_1}{dx} = \frac{d\psi_2}{dx} \quad \text{or} \quad \frac{i}{\lambda_1}(A_1 - B_1) = \frac{1}{\lambda_2^*}(A_2 - B_2)$$

At $x = a$, $\psi_2 = \psi_3$ or

$$A_2 \exp\left(\frac{2\pi a}{\lambda_2^*}\right) + B_2 \exp\left(-\frac{2\pi a}{\lambda_2^*}\right) = A_3 \exp\left(\frac{2\pi i a}{\lambda_3}\right)$$

and

$$\frac{d\psi_2}{dx} = \frac{d\psi_3}{dx}$$

or

$$\frac{1}{\lambda_2^*}\left[A_2 \exp\left(\frac{2\pi a}{\lambda_2^*}\right) - B_2 \exp\left(-\frac{2\pi a}{\lambda_2^*}\right)\right] = \frac{i}{\lambda_3} A_3 \exp\left(\frac{2\pi i a}{\lambda_3}\right)$$

From these four equations the coefficients B_1, A_2, and B_2 may be eliminated (see Appendix 3) giving the equation

$$\frac{A_1}{A_3} = \frac{1}{2}\left[\left(1 + \frac{\lambda_1}{\lambda_3}\right)\cosh\left(\frac{2\pi a}{\lambda_2^*}\right) - \left(\frac{i\lambda_2^*}{\lambda_3} + \frac{\lambda_1}{i\lambda_2^*}\right)\sinh\left(\frac{2\pi a}{\lambda_2^*}\right)\right]$$
$$\times \exp\left(\frac{2\pi i a}{\lambda_3}\right)$$

Hence A_3 is zero only if a/λ_2^* is infinite—i.e. a barrier of infinite thickness. It is consequently possible for particles to pass straight through barriers of finite thickness. This is called the *tunnel effect*. The probability of a particle which collides with the potential barrier tunnelling through into region 3 is given by

$$\frac{A_1 A_1^*}{A_3 A_3^*} = \frac{1}{4}\left[\left(1 + \frac{\lambda_1}{\lambda_3}\right)^2 \cosh^2\left(\frac{2\pi a}{\lambda_2^*}\right) + \left(\frac{\lambda_2^*}{\lambda_3} - \frac{\lambda_1}{\lambda_2^*}\right)^2 \sinh^2\left(\frac{2\pi a}{\lambda_2^*}\right)\right]$$

If the potential barrier is high λ_2^* will be small and $2\pi a/\lambda_2^* \gg 1$. In this case both hyperbolic functions are nearly equal to $\frac{1}{2}\exp(2\pi a/\lambda_2^*)$ and the above equation reduces to $4\exp(-4\pi a/\lambda_2^*)$.

The tunnel effect has several applications in physico-chemical behaviour; one striking example is radioactive decay. The height of the potential barrier keeping the nucleons inside a nucleus, $(U_2 - U_3$ in the box problem), may be estimated by alpha particle bombardment of the nucleus (Rutherford's experiment). The alpha particles which are spontaneously emitted by radioactive atoms have energies appreciably less than this, they can only have escaped by passing through the potential barrier. Gamow,[2] and also Condon and Gurney,[3] have actually utilized the tunnel effect to give a semi-quantitative explanation of the observations summarized in the Geiger–Nuttall law of radioactive decay.

Radioactive decay by beta particle emission normally has a very much greater velocity constant than for alpha particles. This would be expected from its much smaller mass. It might be noted that isomers involving different positions of atomic nuclei are very common but no stable isomers are known with different electron arrangements.

The potential barrier most frequently met with in chemistry is that between reactants and a transition complex (see Chapter 18). Calculations[4-9] show that except for the smallest atoms there is little likelihood of leakage through the barrier.

Two further well-known examples of tunnel phenomena are the inversion of the ammonia molecule (the ammonia clock) and the semiconductor device known as the tunnel diode.

3.5. Particle on a Ring

In this example a particle of mass m and with zero potential energy is confined to movement around the circumference of a circle with radius r. The object of this exercise is twofold, to illustrate the quantization of angular momentum, and to consider a problem in which the eigenfunctions may be expressed in more than one way.

For this problem cartesian coordinates must first be replaced by polar ones. The transformation of coordinates for the Schrödinger equation is given in Appendix 4. In this particular case the angle of rotation ϕ is the only variable, so the appropriate form of the equation is

$$\frac{1}{r^2} \frac{d^2\psi}{d\phi^2} + \frac{8\pi^2 m}{h^2} E\psi = 0 \qquad (V = 0) \tag{3.14}$$

The solutions of this differential equation may be expressed by either of the following equations:

$$\psi = A \sin (M\phi) + B \cos (M\phi) \tag{3.15}$$

$$\psi = C\, e^{iM\phi} + D\, e^{-iM\phi} \tag{3.16}$$

That these can be equivalent is obvious when it is remembered that

$$e^{iM\phi} = \cos (M\phi) + i \sin (M\phi)$$

and

$$e^{-iM\phi} = \cos (M\phi) - i \sin (M\phi).$$

Employing either form for the wave function

$$\frac{d^2\psi}{d\phi^2} = -M^2\psi$$

and substituting this result into equation (3.14) the rotational energy of the particle becomes

$$E = \frac{M^2 h^2}{8\pi^2 m r^2} = \frac{M^2 h^2}{8\pi^2 I} \qquad (3.17)$$

where I is the moment of inertia mr^2.

So far no restriction has been placed upon the value of M. The eigenfunction must however be single valued; at any given value

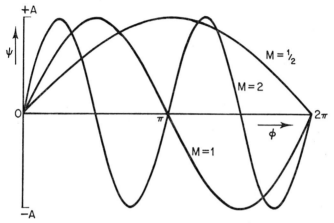

FIGURE 3.9 Graph of $\psi = A \sin M\phi$, for $M = \frac{1}{2}$, 1, and 2.

of ϕ there can only be one value for $|\psi|^2$ and hence for ψ. Further, the actual wave function ψ, as opposed to its modulus $|\psi|$, must be the same whenever ϕ is increased by 2π to $\phi + 2\pi$. Were this not the case, Figure 3.9 demonstrates that for the function $\psi = A \sin (M\phi)$ there would be a discontinuity in the slope of the $\psi - \phi$ graph at $\phi = 0$ (which is the same point on the circle as $\phi + 2\pi$) and is clearly impossible since the potential is uniform round the ring. Hence $\psi_{(\phi)}$ must equal $\psi_{(\phi + 2\pi)}$, and the wave functions are acceptable solutions of the Schrödinger equation only if $M = 0, \pm 1, \pm 2, \pm 3 \ldots$

The solution with $M = 0$, $(E_0 = 0)$, is possible so that there is no zero-point rotational energy. Since E_M depends upon M^2 the other solutions are doubly degenerate having the same energy for $+M$ and $-M$.

Normalizing equation (3.15) we obtain

$$\int_0^{2\pi} [A \sin (M\phi) + B \cos (M\phi)]^2 \, d\phi = 1$$

i.e.

$$A^2 \int_0^{2\pi} \sin^2(M\phi)\,\mathrm{d}\phi + B^2 \int_0^{2\pi} \cos^2(M\phi)\,\mathrm{d}\phi$$
$$+ 2AB \int_0^{2\pi} \sin(M\phi)\cos(M\phi)\,\mathrm{d}\phi = 1$$

or

$$A^2\pi + B^2\pi + 0 = 1 \tag{3.18}$$

This gives the relationship between A and B for equation (3.15) to be normalized. The most convenient method of ensuring that (3.18) holds true is to put A and B equal to $(1/\sqrt{\pi})\cos\theta$ and $(1/\sqrt{\pi})\sin\theta$. The normalized wave function is therefore either

$$\psi_\mathrm{s} = \frac{1}{\sqrt{\pi}}\,[\cos\theta\sin(M\phi) + \sin\theta\cos(M\phi)]$$

$$= \frac{1}{\sqrt{\pi}}\,\sin(M\phi + \theta) \tag{3.19}$$

or

$$\psi_\mathrm{c} = \frac{1}{\sqrt{\pi}}\,[-\sin\theta\sin(M\phi) + \cos\theta\cos(M\phi)]$$

$$= \frac{1}{\sqrt{\pi}}\,\cos(M\phi + \theta) \tag{3.20}$$

These functions can easily be shown to be orthogonal as well as normalized. There are an infinite number of pairs of orthogonal wave functions differing only in the value of the angle θ, which can have any value. The change of the angle from $M\phi$ to $M\phi + \theta$ simply alters the position of the origin.

When $M = 0$ there is only the cosine solution, since $\sin 0$ is zero, and the normalized wave function is a constant ($\psi_0 = 1/\sqrt{(2\pi)}$), but for other values of the quantum number M there are two degenerate solutions given by equations (3.19) and (3.20). These together result in a uniform probability distribution of the particle round the ring, given by $\frac{1}{2}(\psi_\mathrm{s}^2 + \psi_\mathrm{c}^2)$, but either on its own—represented by ψ_s^2 or by ψ_c^2—does not imply a uniform distribution.

The alternative form of the wave function, equation (3.16), corresponds to the two orthonormal solutions

$$\psi_+ = \frac{1}{\sqrt{(2\pi)}}\,\mathrm{e}^{\mathrm{i}M\phi} \quad \text{and} \quad \psi_- = \frac{1}{\sqrt{(2\pi)}}\,\mathrm{e}^{-\mathrm{i}M\phi} \tag{3.21}$$

As in equations (3.19) and (3.20), the origin could be increased by the angle θ if required. The important difference is however that ψ_+^2 and ψ_-^2 each represent, on their own, a uniform probability of finding the particle at any position round the ring. In this respect they are the more satisfactory wave functions.

It is convenient at this point to introduce an equation which will be considered in the next chapter. It is that if

$$\frac{h}{2\pi i}\frac{d\psi}{d\phi} = \text{constant} \times \psi \qquad (3.22)$$

then the *constant* is the angular momentum of the system about an axis perpendicular to the plane of the ring. In other words, if the operator $(h/2\pi i)d/d\phi$ when acting on the wave function gives a result that can be expressed as the product of a number and the original wave function, then this number is the momentum in a particular direction.

Applying this operator to the wave function ψ_s we find that

$$\frac{h}{2\pi i}\frac{d}{d\phi}\left(\frac{1}{\sqrt{\pi}}\sin(M\phi + \theta)\right) = \frac{Mh}{2\pi^{3/2}i}\cos(M\phi + \theta)$$

This is not a constant times the original wave function so the angular momentum is not quantized in a direction perpendicular to the ring. (The square of the angular momentum obtained by utilizing the operator

$$\frac{h}{2\pi i}\frac{d}{d\phi}\left(\frac{h}{2\pi i}\frac{d}{d\phi}\right) \equiv -\frac{h^2}{4\pi^2}\frac{d^2}{d\phi^2},$$

is quantized, its value being $M^2(h/2\pi)^2$.)

If equation (3.22) is applied to ψ_+ or ψ_- however

$$\frac{h}{2\pi i}\frac{d}{d\phi}\left(\frac{1}{\sqrt{(2\pi)}}e^{iM\phi}\right) = M\frac{h}{2\pi}\left(\frac{1}{\sqrt{(2\pi)}}e^{iM\phi}\right)$$

and the angular momentum, $M(h/2\pi)$, is quantized in units of $h/2\pi$. We shall see later that the angular momentum of many systems is quantized in terms of this unit.

To sum up, both equations (3.15) and (3.16) are satisfactory solutions of the wave equation for this problem. The real solutions (ψ_s and ψ_c) can easily be visualized and represented graphically; they do not, however, correspond to well-defined values of the angular momentum or to a uniform probability distribution round the ring. This is because the sine and cosine solutions are standing waves and represent the particle moving round the ring in *both* directions, thus the momentum occurs with both signs and cannot be expected to be a sharp quantity. These solutions are degenerate and their linear combinations $\psi_c \pm i\psi_s$, which are equivalent to

ψ_+ and ψ_-, are also solutions of the wave equation. These new functions represent the particle moving in one direction only, either clockwise or anticlockwise, around the ring. The imaginary solutions indicate therefore that the angular momentum is quantized in a particular direction and result in an equal probability of finding the particle at all values of the angle ϕ. Both solutions indicate the same quantization and degeneracy of energy and that the square of the angular momentum is quantized.

3.6. Analogies to Atomic and Molecular Systems

3.6.1. ELECTRONIC ENERGIES OF ATOMS

In a hydrogen-like atom the potential energy of its single electron, due to the coulombic attraction by the nucleus of charge $+Ze$ and distance r from it, is $V = -Ze^2/r$. As a rough approximation this may be represented by a rectangular potential box with walls of finite height (Figure 3.10).

From the results obtained for the potential box we would expect that in the atom:
1. The electronic energy is quantized.
2. There is a zero-point energy.
3. There are $n - 1$ nodes in the wave function with principal quantum number n.

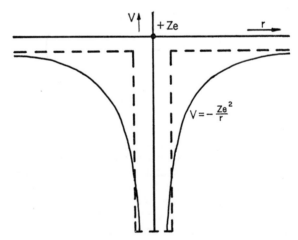

FIGURE 3.10 Variation of the potential energy of an electron in a cross section passing through a hydrogen atom.

4. The probability of finding the electron at a given value of r is independent of the direction taken from the nucleus.

5. The electron can be found at distances from the nucleus such that its total energy is less than its potential energy.

That these predictions are substantially correct will be evident when the hydrogen atom is discussed in Chapter 7.

In the case of a potential box with infinite potential walls the energy levels increase as the square of n (equation (3.5)); in atoms the electronic energies are negative, varying for hydrogen-like atoms as $-1/n^2$ (equation (7.7)). This difference is due to the different potential functions and origin for the potential energy.

3.6.2. ELECTRONIC ENERGIES OF DIATOMIC MOLECULES

The manner in which the potential energy of an electron in a diatomic molecule depends upon distance along the internuclear axis is shown in Figure 3.11. This may be approximated to by the potential box shown with walls of finite heights. From this box we would expect that:

1. The most strongly held (inner) electrons of each atom would be unaffected by the presence of the other atom.

2. Electrons with an energy greater, or only a little less, than that of the potential barrier between the nuclei will be associated with both atoms (valence electrons).

3. There will be an interaction between the valence electrons of comparable energies on each atom.

It is interesting to pursue this last point further, but in order to do so we shall simplify the problem by letting the first and last potential wall rise to infinity, (Figure 3.12).

It may be divided into three regions

$$\text{Region 1} \quad -b < x < -a$$
$$\text{Region 2} \quad -a < x < \quad a$$
$$\text{Region 3} \quad \quad a < x < \quad b$$

with wave functions of the general form

$$\psi_1 \text{ and } \psi_3 = A_1 \exp\left(\frac{2\pi i x}{\lambda_1}\right) + B_1 \exp\left(-\frac{2\pi i x}{\lambda_1}\right)$$
$$\equiv (A_1 + B_1)\cos\left(\frac{2\pi x}{\lambda_1}\right) + i(A_1 - B_1)\sin\left(\frac{2\pi x}{\lambda_1}\right)$$
$$\psi_2 = A_2 \exp\left(\frac{2\pi i x}{\lambda_2}\right) + B_2 \exp\left(-\frac{2\pi i x}{\lambda_2}\right)$$

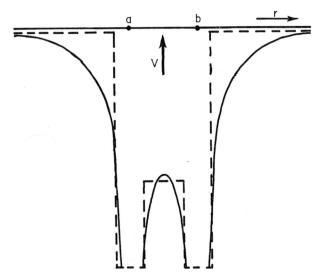

FIGURE 3.11 Variation of the potential energy of an electron in a cross-section passing through a diatomic molecule with nuclei at *a* and *b*.

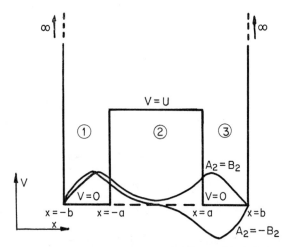

FIGURE 3.12 A one dimensional potential box with infinite potential walls at $x = \pm b$ and finite walls at $x = \pm a$.

For the symmetrical box under consideration the expressions for ψ_1 and ψ_3 are identical. The wavelength λ_2 may be real or imaginary, depending upon whether the energy is respectively greater or less than that of the potential barrier, and the expression for ψ_2 will consequently be left in the exponential form.

Consider the restricting conditions which the wave functions must satisfy at the boundaries.

At $x = \pm b$, $\psi_1 = 0$ (c.f. 3.1). Hence $A_1 + B_1 = 0$ and

$$\psi_1 = \psi_3 = 2iB_1 \sin\left(\frac{2\pi x}{\lambda_1}\right)$$

At $x = -a$, $\psi_1 = \psi_2$, or

$$2iB_1 \sin\left(-\frac{2\pi a}{\lambda_1}\right) = A_2 \exp\left(-\frac{2\pi i a}{\lambda_2}\right) + B_2 \exp\left(\frac{2\pi i a}{\lambda_2}\right) \quad (3.23)$$

and $d\psi_1/dx = d\psi_2/dx$, or

$$-\frac{4\pi i}{\lambda_1} B_1 \cos\left(\frac{2\pi a}{\lambda_1}\right) = -\frac{2\pi i}{\lambda_2} A_2 \exp\left(-\frac{2\pi i a}{\lambda_2}\right)$$
$$+ \frac{2\pi i}{\lambda_2} B_2 \exp\left(\frac{2\pi i a}{\lambda_2}\right) \quad (3.24)$$

At $x = +a$, $\psi_2 = \psi_3$, or

$$2iB_1 \sin\left(\frac{2\pi a}{\lambda_1}\right) = A_2 \exp\left(\frac{2\pi i a}{\lambda_2}\right) + B_2 \exp\left(-\frac{2\pi i a}{\lambda_2}\right) \quad (3.25)$$

and $d\psi_2/dx = d\psi_3/dx$, or

$$\frac{4\pi i}{\lambda_1} B_1 \cos\left(\frac{2\pi a}{\lambda_1}\right) = \frac{2\pi i}{\lambda_2} A_2 \exp\left(\frac{2\pi i a}{\lambda_2}\right)$$
$$- \frac{2\pi i}{\lambda_2} B_2 \exp\left(\frac{-2\pi i a}{\lambda_2}\right) \quad (3.26)$$

Dividing (3.23) by (3.25) and (3.24) by (3.26) we find that

$$\frac{A_2 \exp\left(-2\pi i a/\lambda_2\right) + B_2 \exp\left(2\pi i a/\lambda_2\right)}{A_2 \exp\left(2\pi i a/\lambda_2\right) + B_2 \exp\left(-2\pi i a/\lambda_2\right)}$$
$$= \frac{-A_2 \exp\left(-2\pi i a/\lambda_2\right) + B_2 \exp\left(2\pi i a/\lambda_2\right)}{A_2 \exp\left(2\pi i a/\lambda_2\right) - B_2 \exp\left(-2\pi i a/\lambda_2\right)}$$

Only two relationships between A_2 and B_2 satisfy this last equation. Either $A_2 = B_2$ and the wave function is *symmetrical* about the point $x = 0$, or $A_2 = -B_2$ and the wave function has a node at $x = 0$, the *antisymmetrical* solution (Figure 3.12). For the symmetrical wave function ψ^2 is finite everywhere between the two nuclei and there would be a high probability of finding an electron possessing this wave function between the nuclei where it would be simultaneously attracted, with comparable force, to each nucleus. In other words, it would bond the nuclei together. For the antisymmetrical wave function however ψ^2 is zero mid-way between the nuclei, and the coulombic repulsion between them would only be screened by the electrons to a small extent and the simultaneous attraction of both nuclei for the electron would be small. There would be a net repulsion between the nuclei.

When we consider the covalent chemical bond in Chapter 10 we shall find that suitable wave functions of the individual atoms combine to form bonding (symmetrical), and antibonding (antisymmetrical), wave functions for the molecule. Generally the valence electrons have bonding wave functions and, as far as possible, electrons do not occupy the antibonding levels in ground electronic states.

The energies associated with the wave functions in the box problem and the values of the coefficients A_1, B_1, A_2, and B_2 can be found by a method similar to that adopted in Section 3.3. We shall not pursue this as our object has been to illustrate the formation of symmetrical and antisymmetrical wave functions. The symmetrical solution has a lower energy and the antisymmetrical solution a greater energy than the corresponding level in problem 3.

In addition to the eigenfunctions illustrated in Figure 3.12 there will be symmetrical and antisymmetrical functions of greater energies with additional nodes close to the atomic nuclei.

3.6.3. VIBRATIONAL ENERGY OF A DIATOMIC MOLECULE

When two atoms approach one another to form a diatomic molecule their potential energy decreases at first, passes through a minimum at the equilibrium bond length r_e, and then rises steeply as the internuclear distance is further decreased. This is shown diagrammatically in Figure 3.13 and may be approximated to quite closely by a potential box, shown by broken line, of the form discussed in Section 3.3.

Classical theory predicts that the bonded atoms can undergo vibrations with an energy having any value between zero and the dissociation energy D. The extreme values of the bond length being set by the condition that the total energy cannot be greater than the potential energy of the system, its kinetic energy then being zero.

From an analysis of the potential box problem it would be anticipated that:

1. There would be a zero-point vibrational energy.
2. The energy of the system would be quantized.

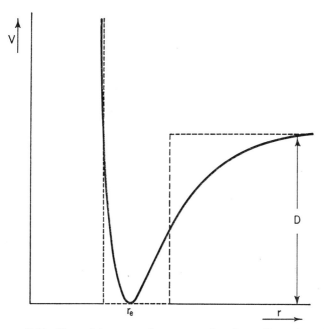

FIGURE 3.13 Potential energy of two atoms forming a diatomic molecule.

3. The lowest energy level would not possess a node between the extremes of the vibration but there would be one node in the second level, two in the third, etc.
4. The probability of finding the system with a particular internuclear distance would depend upon its vibrational energy and resemble the ψ^2 curves in Figure 3.7.
5. The internuclear distance could be such that the potential energy of the system exceeded its total energy, though the chance of this occurring would be small.

The harmonic vibrator, and also the vibrations of the atoms forming an actual chemical bond, are discussed in Chapter 5 where it will be seen that the above predictions are confirmed by a more rigorous mathematical treatment.

3.7. Summary

This chapter has dealt with some simple 'box problems'. The solutions of the differential equations may be expressed either in the form of a sine wave or by an equation involving exponentials.

To be an acceptable solution of the particular problem, however, the wave function must satisfy some extra conditions at the walls of the potential box. This results in a quantization of the total energy, and in the case of vibrational motion in the existence of a zero-point energy. It is also anticipated that the angular momentum will be quantized in a particular direction. These features vanish and the equations reduce to those of classical mechanics if the particles are heavier than atomic systems or the dimensions of the box are large.

The interpretation of the wave amplitude ψ, that ψ^2 is the probability of finding the particle at that particular position in space, gives probability distributions which appear strange to those conversant with classical mechanics. In particular the particle can be found in regions where its kinetic energy is negative.

BIBLIOGRAPHICAL REFERENCES

1. Margenau, H., and Murphy, G., *Mathematics of Physics and Chemistry*, van Nostrand, New York, 1956, p. 267.
2. Gamon, G., *Z. Phys.*, 1928, **51,** 204.
3. Condon, E. U., and Gurney, R. W., *Phys. Rev.*, 1929, **33,** 127.
4. Johnston, H. S., *Advanc. Chem. Phys.*, 1961, **III,** 131.
5. Wigner E. *Phys. Rev.*, 1932, **40,** 749.
6. Bell, R. P., *Trans. Faraday Soc.*, 1959, **55,** 1.
7. Bell, R. P., *Proc. Roy. Soc.*, 1933, A**139,** 466.
8. Bell, R. P., *Proc. Roy. Soc.*, 1935, A**148,** 241.
9. Bawn, C. E. H., and Ogden, G., *Trans. Faraday Soc.*, 1934, **30,** 432.

CHAPTER 4

ACCEPTABLE WAVE FUNCTIONS AND WAVE MECHANICAL OPERATORS

4.1. Acceptable Wave Functions

The 'law' of wave mechanics is the Schrödinger equation; the mathematical problem is to find the wave functions which satisfy this equation for given types of potential functions and to solve it for the corresponding eigenvalues. The interpretation of the wave function is that its square, for a particular value of the coordinates of the system, gives the probability of finding the particles at the specified positions. In the previous chapter we found there were an infinite number of solutions to the wave equations for box problems, but that the interpretation of ψ^2 in terms of the probability P severely restricted the number that could be accepted to those for which:

1. ψ was finite and single valued for all values of the coordinates.
2. ψ was a continuous function of the coordinates.
3. $\partial\psi/\partial x$, $\partial\psi/\partial y$, and $\partial\psi/\partial z$ were continuous functions of x, y, and z respectively.
4. $\int \psi^2 \, d\tau$ was finite, where $d\tau$ is a small volume element and the integration is carried out over the whole of space.

These are fundamental postulates of wave mechanics. Conditions (1) and (2) follow automatically from its statistical character that P is proportional to ψ^2; (3) does not follow so automatically but is a reasonable requirement for ψ. The box problems already considered have demonstrated that it is these restrictions placed upon the expression for ψ that result in a quantization of energy. Condition (4) is necessary if the wave function is to be normalized so as to make ψ^2 equal to, instead of just proportional to, the probability P. The wave equation and these conditions for acceptable solutions have been 'proved' in the sense that they have enabled theoretical values for the energies and other properties of several systems to be obtained which are in agreement with experimental values.

4.2. The Hamiltonian Operator

The Schrödinger equation

$$\frac{\partial^2 \psi}{\partial x^2} + \frac{\partial^2 \psi}{\partial y^2} + \frac{\partial^2 \psi}{\partial z^2} + \frac{8\pi^2 m}{h^2}(E - V)\psi = 0$$

may be written in the form

$$\left[-\frac{h^2}{8\pi^2 m}\left(\frac{\partial^2}{\partial x^2} + \frac{\partial^2}{\partial y^2} + \frac{\partial^2}{\partial z^2}\right) + V \right]\psi = E\psi$$

The first term inside the brackets represents the kinetic energy of the system, but the kinetic energy associated with a mass m moving with a velocity v is

$$T = \tfrac{1}{2}mv^2 = \frac{p^2}{2m} = \frac{1}{2m}(p_{(x)}^2 + p_{(y)}^2 + p_{(z)}^2)$$

where the p's denote the components of linear momentum along the coordinate axes. Comparing these two expressions for kinetic energy it is evident that $p_{(x)}^2$ has been replaced by $(-h^2/4\pi^2)\partial^2/\partial x^2$ or $p_{(x)}$ by $(h/2\pi i)\partial/\partial x$, etc. The energy of the system expressed in terms of potential energy V and momentum p, but with the latter replaced by the operator $(h/2\pi i)\partial/\partial x$, is known as the wave mechanical form of the Hamiltonian function or, more simply, as the Hamiltonian† of the system. It is denoted by **H**. This replacement of the momentum by an operator might seem strange but it forms part of the general theory of quantum mechanics, though this cannot be explained here, i.e.

$$\mathbf{H} = -\frac{h^2}{8\pi^2 m}\left(\frac{\partial^2}{\partial x^2} + \frac{\partial^2}{\partial y^2} + \frac{\partial^2}{\partial z^2}\right) + V$$

$$= -\frac{h^2}{8\pi^2 m}\nabla^2 + V$$

---

† The term Hamiltonian arises through its relation to Hamilton's equations of classical mechanics.

The Hamiltonian form of the wave equation is consequently extremely simple,

$$\mathbf{H}\psi = E\psi.$$

The Hamiltonian $\mathbf{H}$ is an operator, that is it tells one to perform certain operations upon the wave function (the operand). In this particular case it has to be differentiated twice with respect to the coordinates of the system, multiplied by a constant, and then the

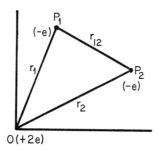

FIGURE 4.1   Coordinates for the helium atom. The nucleus is at 0 and the electrons at P_1 and P_2.

product of the potential energy and ψ added. If as a consequence of performing these operations the result turns out to be the product of a real number E and the original wave function, then the expression for ψ is a satisfactory solution of the wave equation and the number is the corresponding energy of the system. To be an acceptable wave function it must satisfy the conditions listed in the preceding section.

Obviously there is no fundamental difference between the Schrödinger and Hamiltonian forms of the wave equation, but in practice the latter is frequently more convenient to employ. Two simple examples will illustrate how easy it is to formulate the Hamiltonian and the wave equation.

The Helium Atom. This consists of a nucleus of charge $+2e$ and two electrons each with a charge of $-e$ and mass m. Figure 4.1 shows one instantaneous arrangement of these particles and the nomenclature for describing the interparticle distances.

The total kinetic energy for the two electrons is

$$T = T_1 + T_2$$

$$= \frac{1}{2m} [(p_{(x_1)}^2 + p_{(y_1)}^2 + p_{(z_1)}^2) + (p_{(x_2)}^2 + p_{(y_2)}^2 + p_{(z_2)}^2)]$$

The potential energy, arising from the coulombic attractions of the electrons for the nucleus and the repulsions between the electrons is

$$V = -\frac{2e^2}{r_1} - \frac{2e^2}{r_2} + \frac{e^2}{r_{12}}$$

This, of course, depends upon the relative positions of the electrons and nucleus which are changing continuously. The Hamiltonian operator for the electrons will be

$$\mathbf{H} = -\frac{h^2}{8\pi^2 m}\left[\left(\frac{\partial^2}{\partial x_1^2} + \frac{\partial^2}{\partial y_1^2} + \frac{\partial^2}{\partial z_1^2}\right) + \left(\frac{\partial^2}{\partial x_2^2} + \frac{\partial^2}{\partial y_2^2} + \frac{\partial^2}{\partial z_2^2}\right)\right]$$

$$- \frac{2e^2}{r_1} - \frac{2e^2}{r_2} + \frac{e^2}{r_{12}}$$

$$= -\frac{h^2}{8\pi^2 m}(\nabla_1^2 + \nabla_2^2) - e^2\left(\frac{2}{r_1} + \frac{2}{r_2} - \frac{1}{r_{12}}\right).$$

And the Hamiltonian form of the wave equation for a helium atom is consequently

$$\left[-\frac{h^2}{8\pi^2 m}(\nabla_1^2 + \nabla_2^2) - e^2\left(\frac{2}{r_1} + \frac{2}{r_2} - \frac{1}{r_{12}}\right)\right]\psi = E\psi$$

The Hydrogen Molecule. In this case there are two nuclei a and b, each with a charge of $+e$, and two electrons of charge $-e$. The nomenclature for the distances between these particles should be clear from Figure 4.2. The relations corresponding to those given above for the helium atom are

$$T = T_1 + T_2$$

$$= \frac{1}{2m}\left[(p_{(x_1)}^2 + p_{(y_1)}^2 + p_{(z_1)}^2) + (p_{(x_2)}^2 + p_{(y_2)}^2 + p_{(z_2)}^2)\right]$$

$$V = -\frac{e^2}{r_{a1}} - \frac{e^2}{r_{b1}} - \frac{e^2}{r_{a2}} - \frac{e^2}{r_{b2}} + \frac{e^2}{r_{12}} + \frac{e^2}{r_{ab}}$$

$$\mathbf{H} = -\frac{h^2}{8\pi^2 m}(\nabla_1^2 + \nabla_2^2)$$

$$+ e^2\left(-\frac{1}{r_{a1}} - \frac{1}{r_{b1}} - \frac{1}{r_{a2}} - \frac{1}{r_{b2}} + \frac{1}{r_{12}} + \frac{1}{r_{ab}}\right)$$

This expression for **H** is substituted into the wave equation

$$\mathbf{H}\psi = E\psi$$

The next step in the analysis of these systems is to solve these rather complex differential equations in order to obtain suitable

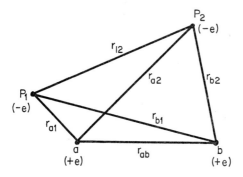

FIGURE 4.2   Coordinates for the hydrogen molecule. The nuclei are at a and b and the electrons at P_1 and P_2.

mathematical expressions for ψ. Only approximate solutions have been obtained (Chapters 9 and 10).

The above equations assume that the electrons move round a stationary nucleus, which is not quite correct as both move round their common centre of gravity. This difficulty can be overcome by employing the reduced mass of electron and nucleus in place of the mass of the electron. The question also arises as to why a term for the kinetic energy of the nucleus, $(-h^2/8\pi^2 M)\,\nabla^2$, has not been included. Born and Oppenheimer[1] showed that because of the much greater mass of the nucleus this term can be separated from the total Hamiltonian and from the wave function (see also Dalgarno and McCarroll[2]). In the case of molecules, nuclear kinetic energy terms should be included in calculations of nuclear vibrations, although their omission only introduces an error of about 0.0075 eV (0.17 kcal) into the calculated energy of the hydrogen molecule.[3,4] The coulombic repulsion between nuclei is frequently omitted from the potential term in the expression for **H** which is then solely concerned with electrons. The nuclear repulsion energy must of course be added to the electronic energy obtained from solving the wave equation to obtain the total energy of the molecule.

4.3. Momentum Operators

The Hamiltonian operator is but one of a series of wave mechanical operators. The wave function must satisfy the relation

$$-\frac{h^2}{8\pi^2 m}\,\nabla^2\psi = (E - V)\psi = T\psi = \frac{p^2}{2m}\,\psi$$

In words, the operator $(-h^2/4\pi^2) \nabla^2$ acting upon ψ gives the square of the momentum multiplied by ψ. Consequently

$$\left(\frac{h}{2\pi i} \nabla\right) \psi = p\psi$$

and $(h/2\pi i) \nabla$ is the *momentum operator*. If this operator when acting upon ψ gives a result in the form of a real number times the original wave function, then the number is the momentum associated with the system.

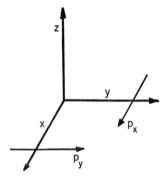

FIGURE 4.3   Angular momentum about the z axis.

In classical mechanics the angular momentum M_z of a particle about the z axis is, from Figure 4.3,

$$M_z = xp_y - yp_x$$

Replacing the linear momenta p_x and p_y by momentum operators, the quantum mechanical *operator for angular momentum about the z axis* is obtained.

$$\mathbf{M}_z = \frac{h}{2\pi i}\left(x \frac{\partial}{\partial y} - y \frac{\partial}{\partial x}\right)$$

If with this operator, $\mathbf{M}_z\psi = m_z\psi$, then the angular momentum has a sharp value of m_z units along the z axis. Analogous operators

$$\mathbf{M}_x = \frac{h}{2\pi i}\left(y \frac{\partial}{\partial z} - z \frac{\partial}{\partial y}\right) \quad \text{and} \quad \mathbf{M}_y = \frac{h}{2\pi i}\left(z \frac{\partial}{\partial x} - x \frac{\partial}{\partial z}\right)$$

perform the same function for angular momentum about the x and y axes respectively.

These operators may be transformed into polar coordinates when they yield (see Appendix 4)

$$\mathbf{M}_x = \frac{h}{2\pi i}\left(-\sin\phi\frac{\partial}{\partial\theta} - \cot\theta\cos\phi\frac{\partial}{\partial\phi}\right)$$

$$\mathbf{M}_y = \frac{h}{2\pi i}\left(\cos\phi\frac{\partial}{\partial\theta} - \cot\theta\sin\phi\frac{\partial}{\partial\phi}\right)$$

$$\mathbf{M}_z = \frac{h}{2\pi i}\left(\frac{\partial}{\partial\phi}\right)$$

and the operator for the square of the total angular momentum becomes

$$\mathbf{M}^2 = \mathbf{M}_x^2 + \mathbf{M}_y^2 + \mathbf{M}_z^2$$

$$= -\frac{h^2}{4\pi^2}\left(\frac{\partial^2}{\partial\theta^2} + \cot\theta\frac{\partial}{\partial\theta} + \frac{1}{\sin^2\theta}\frac{\partial^2}{\partial\phi^2}\right)$$

4.4. Average Value of a Quantity

In general, any observable quantity G has an associated wave mechanical operator $\mathbf{G}$. If when this operator acts upon the wave function

$$\mathbf{G}\psi = g\psi, \tag{4.1}$$

then successive measurements of the quantity G for a given state of the system will always give the value g (normally there are several different quantized values for the given system corresponding to different states). If $\mathbf{G}\psi$ gives a result other than the product of a real number and ψ, then successive measurements give a range of values for the quantity G, even when the system is in identical states. In this case we proceed as follows. Equation (4.1) is multiplied throughout by ψ^* giving

$$\psi^*\mathbf{G}\psi = \psi^* g\psi = g\psi^*\psi$$

or

$$g = \frac{\psi^*\mathbf{G}\psi}{\psi^*\psi}$$

From this equation g would be a function of the coordinates of the system. To eliminate this the expression is integrated over all values of the coordinates thereby giving an average value $\bar{G}$ of the property, i.e.

$$\bar{G} = \frac{\displaystyle\int \psi^*\mathbf{G}\psi\,d\tau}{\displaystyle\int \psi^*\psi\,d\tau} \tag{4.2}$$

3

An alternative approach to this equation may be helpful. Consider one dimension for simplicity. The chance of a particle being found between x and $x + dx$ is proportional to $\psi^*\psi\,dx$. The proportionality constant may be obtained by normalizing the wave function when the absolute chance of the particle lying within this range of x is $\psi^*\psi\,dx/\int\psi^*\psi\,dx$. For N observations the combined chance would be $N\psi^*\psi\,dx/\int\psi^*\psi\,dx$. Now if a property G of the system is directly dependent upon x, then for the N observations $GN\psi^*\psi\,dx/\int\psi^*\psi\,dx$ is the total contribution to this property over the specified range of x. The average contribution per observation would be $G\psi^*\psi\,dx/\int\psi^*\psi\,dx$ and the sum of these average values of G over all values of x, when G is not independent of x, is consequently

$$\bar{G} = \frac{\int G\psi^*\psi\,dx}{\int \psi^*\psi\,dx}$$

For three dimensions, equation (4.2) above is obtained.

In the problems already discussed the energy E has been a sharp quantity, and

$$\mathbf{H}\psi = E\psi$$

where the Hamiltonian $\mathbf{H}$ is the appropriate operator for energy. In Part II problems will be considered which cannot be solved exactly, only approximate expressions for the wave functions are obtained. The correct Hamiltonian operator acting on an approximation to the eigenfunction ψ will not give a number times ψ. An approximation to the energy of the system however can still be obtained by employing equation (4.2) in the form

$$\bar{E} = \frac{\int \psi^*\mathbf{H}\psi\,d\tau}{\int \psi^*\psi\,d\tau}$$

This is an extremely valuable technique known as the *variation principle* and will be discussed in detail in Chapter 8.

Another interesting property is the average distance $\bar{r}$ of an electron from the nucleus of an atom. It is given by

$$\bar{r} = \frac{\int \psi^*r\psi\,d\tau}{\int \psi^*\psi\,d\tau} = \frac{\int r\psi^*\psi\,d\tau}{\int \psi^*\psi\,d\tau} \qquad (4.3)$$

BIBLIOGRAPHICAL REFERENCES

1. Born, M., and Oppenheimer, J. R., *Ann. Phys.*, 1927, **84,** 457.
2. Dalgarno, A., and McCarroll, R., *Proc. Roy. Soc.*, 1956, A**237,** 283.
3. Van Vleck, J. H., *J. Chem. Phys.*, 1936, **4,** 327.
4. Johnson, V. A., *Phys. Rev.*, 1941, **60,** 373.

CHAPTER 5

THE LINEAR HARMONIC OSCILLATOR

The problem of a mass m vibrating under the influence of a restoring force F, directly proportional to its displacement x from an equilibrium position, is not only of fundamental interest in both classical and wave mechanics, but is also important in connexion with the study of chemical bonds and molecular spectra. For small amplitudes of vibration of the atoms forming a chemical bond the system may be treated mathematically as if it was a body of reduced mass μ^1 executing harmonic oscillations; at larger amplitudes this approximation is no longer adequate and the vibrations are then portrayed by an anharmonic oscillator. We will first review the classical problem.

5.1. Classical Theory—Summary

For a particle moving under a Hooke's law restoring force

$$F = -fx \quad \text{and} \quad V = -\int F \, dx = \tfrac{1}{2}fx^2$$

where f is the restoring force constant. The force acting upon the particle can also be expressed as the product of its mass and acceleration. Consequently

$$F = -fx = m\ddot{x} = m \frac{d^2x}{dt^2}$$

The solution of this differential equation is

$$x = a \sin \sqrt{(f/m)}t \quad (t = 0 \text{ when } x = 0)$$

where a is the maximum amplitude of the oscillation. The motion repeats itself whenever the angle $\sqrt{(f/m)}t$ increases by 2π, and if this occurs in a time $t = T$ the frequency of the oscillation ν is

$$\nu = \frac{1}{T} = \frac{1}{2\pi}\sqrt{\frac{f}{m}}$$

and

$$x = a \sin (2\pi\nu t)$$

The total energy $E = T + V$
$$= \tfrac{1}{2}m\dot{x}^2 + \tfrac{1}{2}fx^2$$
$$= \tfrac{1}{2}fa^2$$

and is a constant; the kinetic and potential energies, of course, oscillate. We might also note that at the extremes of the motion $\dot{x}$ is zero $(T = 0, E = V)$, whilst at the centre of the oscillation the particle has its maximum velocity $(V = 0, E = T = \tfrac{1}{2}m\dot{x}^2)$. In other words, there is a maximum probability of finding the particle at the extremes of the oscillation and only a small chance of it being at the centre.

5.2. Wave Mechanical Theory

Inserting the expression for the potential energy of an harmonic oscillator into the one dimensional wave equation (2.9) we obtain

$$\frac{d^2\psi}{dx^2} + \frac{8\pi^2 m}{h^2}(E - \tfrac{1}{2}fx^2)\psi = 0 \tag{5.1}$$

The general solution of this differential equation can only be given in terms of an infinite series. The first step in solving the equation is to find the limiting solution which is valid for large values of x.

Asymptotic Solution

When x becomes very large $E \ll V \simeq T$. The kinetic energy of the particle is an imaginary quantity and the wave function consequently very small. Neglecting E in equation (5.1) the differential equation at large values of x simplifies to

$$\frac{d^2\psi}{dx^2} - \frac{4\pi^2 m}{h^2}fx^2\psi = 0 \tag{5.2}$$

and its asymptotic solutions are of the form $\psi = c \exp(\pm\alpha x^2)$. This may be verified by differentiation and substitution into equation

(5.2), but first note that the solution with the positive sign is unacceptable as it would make ψ very great at large values of x. Let us see if $c \exp(-\alpha x^2)$ is also a solution of equation (5.1) for any value of x.

Now

$$\frac{d\psi}{dx} = \frac{d}{dx}[c \exp(-\alpha x^2)] = -2\alpha x c \exp(-\alpha x^2) = -2\alpha x \psi$$

and

$$\frac{d^2\psi}{dx^2} = \frac{d}{dx}(-2\alpha x\psi) = -2\alpha\psi + 4\alpha^2 x^2\psi$$

Substituting this expression into the equation we obtain

$$(-2\alpha + 4\alpha^2 x^2)\psi + \frac{8\pi^2 m}{h^2}(E - \tfrac{1}{2}fx^2)\psi = 0$$

The energy of the vibrator is a constant and not a function of x however, so this equation may be split into two parts. From the terms involving x^2

$$4\alpha^2 + \frac{8\pi^2 m}{h^2}(-\tfrac{1}{2}f) = 0$$

or

$$\alpha = \frac{\pi}{h}\sqrt{(mf)}$$

and from the terms independent of x

$$-2\alpha + \frac{8\pi^2 m}{h^2}E = 0$$

or

$$E = \frac{h^2}{4\pi^2 m}\alpha$$

$$= \frac{h}{4\pi}\sqrt{\left(\frac{f}{m}\right)}$$

$$= \tfrac{1}{2}h\nu$$

The wave function $\psi = c \exp(-\alpha x^2)$ is consequently an acceptable solution of the wave equation with an eigenvalue of $\tfrac{1}{2}h\nu$. To obtain a general solution of the equation a more elaborate expression for ψ has to be employed.

Complete Solution

Returning to the original wave equation, it is almost certain that its solution will contain $\exp(-\alpha x^2)$ as a factor; the other factors may be obtained by trying, in turn, various likely expressions. If c is dependent upon x the wave function may be amended to

$$\psi = c_{(x)} \exp(-\alpha x^2)$$

Hence

$$\frac{d\psi}{dx} = \left(-2\alpha x c + \frac{dc}{dx}\right) \exp(-\alpha x^2)$$

and

$$\frac{d^2\psi}{dx^2} = \left[\left(4\alpha^2 x^2 c - 2\alpha c - 2\alpha x \frac{dc}{dx}\right) + \left(\frac{d^2c}{dx^2} - 2\alpha x \frac{dc}{dx}\right)\right] \exp(-\alpha x^2)$$

$$= \left[\frac{d^2c}{dx^2} - 4\alpha x \frac{dc}{dx} + (4\alpha^2 x^2 - 2\alpha)c\right] \exp(-\alpha x^2)$$

Substituting this result into equation (5.1) we obtain

$$\left[\frac{d^2c}{dx^2} - 4\alpha x \frac{dc}{dx} + (4\alpha^2 x^2 - 2\alpha)c\right] \exp(-\alpha x^2)$$

$$+ \frac{8\pi^2 m}{h^2}(E - \tfrac{1}{2}fx^2)c \exp(-\alpha x^2) = 0$$

This equation must hold for all values of x but this can only be true if the coefficient of *each power* of x is separately zero. Since most expressions for c will not confer any special terms in c, dc/dx, and d^2c/dx^2 upon x^2, the coefficients of x^2 in the above equation must be zero. Hence in these circumstances

$$4\alpha^2 c \exp(-\alpha x^2) + \frac{8\pi^2 m}{h^2}(-\tfrac{1}{2}f)c \exp(-\alpha x^2) = 0$$

or

$$\alpha = \frac{\pi}{h}\sqrt{(mf)}$$

as already obtained in the asymptotic solution.

Collecting the remaining terms together and dividing throughout by $\exp(-\alpha x^2)$ we obtain

$$\frac{d^2c}{dx^2} - 4\alpha x \frac{dc}{dx} + \left(\frac{8\pi^2 m}{h^2} E - 2\alpha\right)c = 0 \qquad (5.3)$$

The actual form of the factor c must now be decided, and the one which is found to result in acceptable solutions of the Schrödinger equation is a power series in x. Let us try

$$c_{(x)} = k_0 + k_1 x + k_2 x^2 + \ldots + k_n x^n + \ldots = \sum_{n=0}^{\infty} k_n x^n$$

or
$$\psi = \exp(-\alpha x^2) \sum k_n x^n.$$

Considering the coefficient of x^n in the three terms in equation (5.3) we have, since $dc/dx = \sum (nk_n x^{n-1})$,

$$\frac{d^2 c}{dx^2} = \ldots + (n+1)(n+2)k_{n+2}x^n + \ldots$$

$$-4\alpha x \frac{dc}{dx} = \ldots - 4\alpha n k_n x^n - \ldots$$

$$\left(\frac{8\pi^2 m}{h^2} E - 2\alpha\right)c = \ldots + \left(\frac{8\pi^2 m}{h^2} E - 2\alpha\right)k_n x^n + \ldots$$

As already stated the coefficient of each power of x must be zero. Hence for x^n

$$(n+1)(n+2)k_{n+2} + \left(\frac{8\pi^2 m}{h^2} E - 2\alpha - 4\alpha n\right)k_n = 0 \qquad (5.4)$$

This is a *recursion formula*; it permits the calculation of k_{n+2}, the coefficient of x^{n+2}, in terms of k_n. Thus if k_0 is known the formula gives the values of k_2, k_4, k_6, etc., and if k_1 is known the odd coefficients k_3, k_5, k_7, etc. are fixed.

The wave function $\exp(-\alpha x^2) \sum k_n x^n$, with two arbitrary constants k_0 and k_1, is a solution of the Schrödinger differential equation. But is it an acceptable solution? It is evidently single valued and continuous for all values of x, but the series does not converge to a finite value as $x \to \infty$ and in its present form is therefore unacceptable. To show this consider the form of the recursion formula at large values of n. Since $(8\pi^2 m/h^2)E - 2\alpha$ is a constant it becomes

$$n^2 k_{n+2} - 4\alpha n k_n = 0 \qquad (n \gg 1)$$

or

$$k_{n+2} = \frac{4\alpha}{n} k_n \qquad (5.5)$$

The same recursion formula is obtained for the terms in the series expansion of $\exp(4\alpha x^2)$ at high values of n since

$$\exp(4\alpha x^2) = 1 + 4\alpha x^2 + \frac{(4\alpha)^2 x^4}{2!} + \frac{(4\alpha)^3 x^6}{3!} + \ldots + \frac{(4\alpha)^n x^{2n}}{n!}$$

The coefficients for successive terms in this series satisfy the relationship

$$k_{n+2} = \frac{4\alpha}{n+1} k_n$$

At large values of n this reduces to equation (5.5) above, proving that the polynomial $c_{(x)}$ behaves as $\exp(4\alpha x^2)$ at large values of n, and consequently the terms in the expression for the wave function tend to those formed from the expansion of

$$\exp(4\alpha x^2)\exp(-\alpha x^2) = \exp(3\alpha x^2)$$

In other words, as $n \to \infty$, $\psi \to \infty$, which is not possible.

The only way out of this difficulty is to limit the number of terms in the polynomial. Since there are two groups of terms in the polynomial corresponding to even and odd values of n, both series cannot be terminated simultaneously. The only way to get acceptable wave functions for each value of n is to put the second term in equation (5.4) equal to zero, i.e. let

$$\frac{8\pi^2 m}{h^2} E = 2\alpha + 4\alpha n$$

or

$$E = \frac{h^2}{2\pi^2 m}\alpha(n + \tfrac{1}{2})$$

$$= (n + \tfrac{1}{2})h\nu$$

In this case, when n is even, the coefficients $k_{n+2}, k_{n+4} \ldots$ become zero and the even terms in the polynomial terminate at $k_n x^n$; likewise when n is odd, the odd terms terminate. In either case all the coefficients in the non-terminating series must also be zero. Summarizing this result, when n is even,

$$k_1 = k_3 = k_5 = \ldots = 0$$
$$k_{n+2} = k_{n+4} = k_{n+6} = \ldots = 0$$
$$\psi_n = (k_0 + k_2 x^2 + k_4 x^4 + \ldots + k_n x^n)\exp(-\alpha x^2) \qquad (n \text{ even})$$

and when n is odd

$$k_0 = k_2 = k_4 = \ldots = 0$$
$$k_{n+2} = k_{n+4} = k_{n+6} = \ldots = 0$$
$$\psi_n = (k_1 x + k_3 x^3 + k_5 x^5 + \ldots + k_n x^n)\exp(-\alpha x^2) \qquad (n \text{ odd})$$

In either case the parameter $\alpha = (\pi/h)\sqrt{(mf)}$ and the energy of the oscillator is quantized in units of $h\nu$.

$$E_n = (n + \tfrac{1}{2})h\nu \qquad (n = 0, 1, 2, 3 \ldots)$$

The values of the coefficients are given in terms of k_0 or k_1 by the recursion formula, and their absolute magnitude by normalizing the wave functions.† The first four of these normalized wave

† These wave functions may also be written in the general form

$$\psi_n = N_n \exp(-\tfrac{1}{2}q^2)H_n(q)$$

where $q = \sqrt{(2\alpha)}x$, $N_n = [\sqrt{(2\alpha/\pi)}/2^n n!]^{1/2}$ is the normalization factor, and $H_{n(q)}$ represents a Hermite polynomial of degree n

$$H_n = (-1)^n \exp(q^2)\frac{d^n \exp(-q^2)}{dq^n}$$

functions are

$$\psi_0 = \left(\frac{2\alpha}{\pi}\right)^{1/4} \exp(-\alpha x^2)$$

$$\psi_1 = \left(\frac{32\alpha^3}{\pi}\right)^{1/4} x \exp(-\alpha x^2)$$

$$\psi_2 = \left(\frac{\alpha}{2\pi}\right)^{1/4} (1 - 4\alpha x^2) \exp(-\alpha x^2)$$

$$\psi_3 = \left(\frac{72\alpha^3}{\pi}\right)^{1/4} (x - \tfrac{4}{3}\alpha x^3) \exp(-\alpha x^2)$$

These wave functions, together with the probability distributions $P = \psi^2$, are illustrated in Figure 5.1.

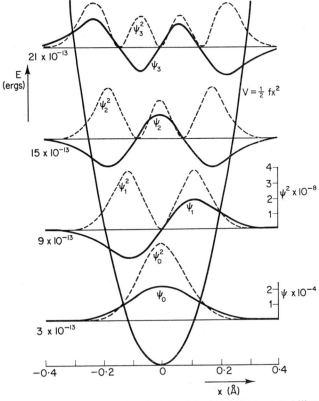

FIGURE 5.1   Energy levels E_n, wave functions ψ_n, and probability functions $P \equiv \psi_n^2$, for the harmonic oscillator with $m = 1\cdot6 \times 10^{-24}$ g, $f = 5 \times 10^5$ dyne/cm, and $\nu = 3{,}000$ cm$^{-1} = 9 \times 10^{13}$ vibrations/sec.

It is evident that there is a zero-point vibrational energy of $\frac{1}{2}h\nu$ which persists even at the absolute zero of temperature. Its existence has been verified by studying the vibrational spectra of molecules. The other permitted solutions have quantized energies equally spaced at intervals of $h\nu$, with n internal nodes of zero probability. In the lowest energy state the system is most likely to be found in its equilibrium position, but with the higher energy levels the probability distribution approaches more closely to that given by classical theory (cf. p. 59).

The vibrations of a diatomic molecule are actually anharmonic and the vibrational potential energy (Figure 3.13) may be expanded in the form of a Taylor series.

$$V = \frac{1}{2}f_1 x^2 - \frac{1}{6}f_2 x^3 + \frac{1}{12}f_3 x^4 - \ldots + \frac{1}{n(n+1)}f_n x^{n+1}$$

or

$$F = -f_1 x + \tfrac{1}{2}f_2 x^2 - \tfrac{1}{3}f_3 x^3 + \ldots$$

where x is the displacement from the equilibrium position during the oscillation. It is generally more convenient to employ the Morse potential function[2]

$$V = D(1 - e^{-ax})^2 \tag{5.6}$$

where D is the maximum vibrational energy of the bonded atoms and a an empirical constant. If the Schrödinger equation is solved using this potential function the eigenvalues are[3]

$$E_n = (n + \tfrac{1}{2})h\nu - \frac{1}{4D}(n + \tfrac{1}{2})^2(h\nu)^2$$

where, for small amplitudes,

$$\nu = \frac{a}{\pi}\sqrt{\left(\frac{D}{2\mu}\right)}$$

in which μ is the reduced mass of the oscillating system.

BIBLIOGRAPHICAL REFERENCES

1. Eyring, H., Walter, J., and Kimball, G. E., *Quantum Chemistry*, John Wiley, New York, 1944, p. 80.
2. Morse, P. M., *Phys. Rev.*, 1929, **34**, 57.
3. Moelwyn-Hughes, E. A., *Physical Chemistry*, Pergamon Press, Oxford, 1957, p. 175.

The Rigid Rotator

The problem of two masses held a fixed distance apart and rotating about their centre of gravity is important for two reasons. Firstly, it is very analogous to a diatomic molecule, though since molecules are vibrating they are not strictly rigid. Nevertheless, the results obtained by solving the Schrödinger equation for this problem are of considerable importance in interpreting molecular spectra and thereby obtaining information about molecular structure and the thermodynamic properties of molecules. Secondly, the mathematical problem is identical with that for the angular part of the wave equation (7.3) for atoms.

If two masses are constrained to remain in one plane, the axis of rotation is in a fixed direction and the system is described as a rigid rotator with fixed axis. In the case of molecular rotation the axis is not generally in a fixed direction and we then have the mathematically more complex problem of a rigid rotator with free axis.

6.1. The Wave Equation for a Rigid Rotator

The kinetic energy of a particle may be written in terms of its component velocities $\dot{x}$, $\dot{y}$, and $\dot{z}$ parallel to the three cartesian axes

$$T = \tfrac{1}{2}mv^2 = \tfrac{1}{2}m(\dot{x}^2 + \dot{y}^2 + \dot{z}^2)$$

If this is expressed in polar coordinates by means of the usual transformations (Appendix 4), it is found that

$$T = \tfrac{1}{2}m(\dot{r}^2 + r^2\dot{\theta}^2 + r^2\dot{\phi}^2 \sin^2 \theta)$$

Since r is a constant the first term, $\dot{r}^2$, is in fact zero. For the two particles constituting a rigid rotator (Figure 6.1), their total kinetic energy is therefore

$$T = \tfrac{1}{2}m_1 r_1^2(\dot\theta^2 + \dot\phi^2 \sin^2\theta) + \tfrac{1}{2}m_2 r_2^2(\dot\theta^2 + \dot\phi^2 \sin^2\theta)$$
$$= \tfrac{1}{2}(m_1 r_1^2 + m_2 r_2^2)(\dot\theta^2 + \dot\phi^2 \sin^2\theta)$$
$$= \tfrac{1}{2}I(\dot\theta^2 + \dot\phi^2 \sin^2\theta)$$

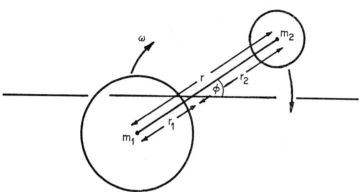

FIGURE 6.1 A rigid rotator comprising masses m_1 and m_2 a distance r apart.

where I is the moment of inertia of this system of two particles.

$$I = m_1 r_1^2 + m_2 r_2^2 = \frac{m_1 m_2}{m_1 + m_2} r^2 = \mu r^2$$

in which μ is termed the reduced mass of the system.

This result shows that a rigid rotator behaves like a single particle of mass I at unit distance from the origin (centre of gravity). Hence in the Schrödinger equation for a rigid rotator the mass m may be replaced by I, and since the potential energy is zero the equation reduces to

$$\nabla^2\psi + \frac{8\pi^2 I}{h^2} E\psi = 0$$

To solve this equation it must first be transformed into polar coordinates and since r is a constant the resulting expression is

$$\frac{1}{\sin\theta}\frac{\partial}{\partial\theta}\left(\sin\theta\frac{\partial\psi}{\partial\theta}\right) + \frac{1}{\sin^2\theta}\frac{\partial^2\psi}{\partial\phi^2} + \frac{8\pi^2 I}{h^2} E\psi = 0 \qquad (6.1)$$

This differential equation has two independent variables, ϕ representing the rotation of the system, and θ the precessional motion of its axis of rotation.

6.2. The Rigid Rotator with Fixed Axis

If the axis of rotation is fixed, θ is a constant and in this case equation (6.1) reduces† to

$$\frac{d^2\psi}{d\phi^2} + \frac{8\pi^2 I}{h^2} E\psi = 0 \qquad (6.2)$$

This equation is identical with that for a particle on a ring discussed in Section 3.5 and has the same mathematical solutions. In particular the eigenvalues are given by

$$E_M = \frac{M^2 h^2}{8\pi^2 I} \qquad (M = 0, \pm 1, \pm 2, \pm 3 \ldots)$$

6.3. The Rigid Rotator with Free Axis

To obtain the more general solution applicable to a rotator with a free axis, equation (6.1) above has to be solved. The first step is to separate the two variables θ and ϕ. We postulate that the wave function may be represented by the product of two factors, each involving just the one variable.

$$\psi_{(\theta,\phi)} = \Theta_{(\theta)}\Phi_{(\phi)}$$

or more simply

$$\psi = \Theta\Phi$$

Since Θ is independent of Φ

$$\frac{\partial\psi}{\partial\theta} = \Phi\frac{\partial\Theta}{\partial\theta} \qquad \text{and} \qquad \frac{\partial^2\psi}{\partial\theta^2} = \Phi\frac{\partial^2\Theta}{\partial\theta^2}$$

† A simpler derivation of this equation is as follows: Since $V = 0$,

$$E = T = \tfrac{1}{2}I\omega^2 = \tfrac{1}{2}I\dot{\phi}^2 = \frac{p^2}{2I}$$

where ω is the angular velocity of rotation and p the angular momentum. Hence the Hamiltonian, obtained by replacing p by the operator $(h/2\pi i)$ d/dϕ, is

$$\mathbf{H} = -\frac{h^2}{8\pi^2 I}\frac{d^2}{d\phi^2}$$

and the wave equation becomes

$$\mathbf{H}\psi = -\frac{h^2}{8\pi^2 I}\frac{d^2\psi}{d\phi^2} = E\psi$$

Likewise

$$\frac{\partial \psi}{\partial \phi} = \Theta \frac{\partial \Phi}{\partial \phi} \quad \text{and} \quad \frac{\partial^2 \psi}{\partial \phi^2} = \Theta \frac{\partial^2 \Phi}{\partial \phi^2}$$

Substitution of these results into equation (6.1) yields

$$\frac{\Phi}{\sin \theta} \frac{\partial}{\partial \theta} \left(\sin \theta \frac{\partial \Theta}{\partial \theta} \right) + \frac{\Theta}{\sin^2 \theta} \frac{\partial^2 \Phi}{\partial \phi^2} + \frac{8\pi^2 I}{h^2} E \Theta \Phi = 0$$

Multiplying this throughout by $\sin^2 \theta / \Theta \Phi$ and rearranging it is seen that

$$\frac{\sin \theta}{\Theta} \frac{\partial}{\partial \theta} \left(\sin \theta \frac{\partial \Theta}{\partial \theta} \right) + \frac{8\pi^2 I}{h^2} E \sin^2 \theta = -\frac{1}{\Phi} \frac{\partial^2 \Phi}{\partial \phi^2} \quad (6.3)$$

The left-hand side of this equation involves the variable θ only, whilst the right-hand side involves ϕ only. Since the equation must hold for all possible values of θ and ϕ, each side must in fact be constant and it is possible to split the equation into two parts

$$-\frac{1}{\Phi} \frac{\partial^2 \Phi}{\partial \phi^2} = m^2 \quad (6.4)$$

and

$$\frac{\sin \theta}{\Theta} \frac{\partial}{\partial \theta} \left(\sin \theta \frac{\partial \Theta}{\partial \theta} \right) + \frac{8\pi^2 I}{h^2} E \sin^2 \theta = m^2 \quad (6.5)$$

Each involves just one variable together with the constant† which for convenience is taken as m^2. That this separation is possible justifies expressing the total wave function ψ as the product of the two factors $\Theta_{(\theta)}$ and $\Phi_{(\phi)}$.

Solution of Equation (6.4)

Equation (6.4) represents the orbital motion of the particles in a fixed plane and mathematically is of the same form as the wave equation for a rigid rotator with fixed axis and for a particle on a ring. Compared to these problems the constant m^2 replaces $(8\pi^2 I/h^2)E$. The solutions can either be expressed in terms of the real functions

$$\psi_s = \frac{1}{\sqrt{\pi}} \sin m\phi \quad \text{and} \quad \psi_c = \frac{1}{\sqrt{\pi}} \cos m\phi$$

or in terms of the complex functions

$$\psi_+ = \frac{1}{\sqrt{(2\pi)}} e^{im\phi} \quad \text{and} \quad \psi_- = \frac{1}{\sqrt{(2\pi)}} e^{-im\phi}$$

† It is customary to employ the symbol m^2 for this constant but care must be taken not to confuse it with a mass.

These are only single valued if m is an integer; when this integer is zero there is just the one solution in which ψ is a constant, otherwise there are two degenerate solutions.

Solution of Equation (6.5)

Equation (6.5) represents the precessional motion of the axis of rotation. Mathematically the most difficult part of the rotator problem is to solve this equation and only an indication of the procedure employed will be given.

Multiplying (6.5) through by $\Theta/\sin^2 \theta$ and writing K in place of $(8\pi^2 I/h^2)E$ we obtain

$$\frac{1}{\sin \theta} \frac{\partial}{\partial \theta}\left(\sin \theta \frac{\partial \Theta}{\partial \theta}\right) + \left(K - \frac{m^2}{\sin^2 \theta}\right) \Theta = 0 \qquad (6.6)$$

If a new variable s is now defined by $s = \cos \theta$ this equation may be transformed into a differential equation which is familiar to mathematicians and known as Legendre's equation. It is solved in most books on differential equations[1-3] but the arguments will not be reproduced. The wave functions which are obtained may be expressed in the general form

$$\Theta = (\sin \theta)^{|m|} \sum (k_n \cos^n \theta)$$

This is substituted into equation (6.5) and a similar procedure to that adopted in solving equation (5.3) for a linear harmonic oscillator followed. When this is done, the recursion formula corresponding to (5.4) is

$$(n + 2)(n + 1)k_{n+2} = [(n + |m| + 1)(n + |m|) - K]k_n \qquad (6.7)$$

As with the harmonic oscillator problem, the series factor $\sum (k_n \cos^n \theta)$ in the expression for the wave function must be terminated at a particular value of n. This is done by putting the factor enclosed in square brackets in equation (6.7) equal to zero, i.e.

$$K \equiv \frac{8\pi^2 I}{h^2} E = (n + |m| + 1)(n + |m|)$$

$$= (J + 1)J \qquad (6.8)$$

where J is written in place of $(n + |m|)$ and is known as the rotational quantum number. In solving equation (6.4) the quantum number m was found to be zero or an integer and the same holds true for n; their sum J is consequently also zero or an integer. From the relationship above the energy is restricted to the eigenvalues

$$E_J = \frac{h^2}{8\pi^2 I} J(J + 1) \qquad (J = 0, 1, 2, 3 \ldots) \qquad (6.9)$$

Only the even or the odd series of terms is terminated by the above restriction, the other series must be terminated by putting either k_0 or k_1 equal to zero. Hence when n is even, the functions Θ are given by

$$\Theta = (k_0 + k_2 \cos^2 \theta + \ldots + k_n \cos^n \theta) \sin^{|m|} \theta$$

and when n is odd†

$$\Theta = (k_1 \cos \theta + k_3 \cos^3 \theta + \ldots + k_n \cos^n \theta) \sin^{|m|} \theta$$

The complete solution of the wave equation for a rigid rotator is the product of the solutions to equations (6.4) and (6.5). Some of the eigenfunctions are collected in Table 6.1, their corresponding eigenvalues being given by equation (6.9). The pictorial representation of these is not of great significance in the present context and will be left until the same problem is considered later as part of the solution for the hydrogen atom.

TABLE 6.1. WAVE FUNCTIONS FOR A RIGID ROTATOR

J	m	$\psi \equiv \Theta\Phi$
0	0	$(1/4\pi)^{1/2}$
1	0	$(3/4\pi)^{1/2} \cos \theta$
1	±1	$(3/8\pi)^{1/2} \sin \theta \, e^{\pm i\phi}$
2	0	$(5/16\pi)^{1/2} (3 \cos^2 \theta - 1)$
2	±1	$(15/8\pi)^{1/2} \sin \theta \cos \theta \, e^{\pm i\phi}$
2	±2	$(15/32\pi)^{1/2} \sin^2 \theta \, e^{\pm 2i\phi}$

The solution of equation (6.4) for the function Φ shows that there are actually two eigenfunctions for each value of m (ψ_s and ψ_c, or ψ_+ and ψ_- above), except that when $m = 0$ only the single solution ($\psi = 1/\sqrt{2\pi}$) is possible. $\psi = \Theta\Phi$ has $2J + 1$ solutions for each value of J, and since the rotational energy is determined by the value of this quantum number there is a $(2J + 1)$-fold degeneracy for each eigenvalue.

6.4. Angular Momentum of a Rigid Rotator with Free Axis

Another important property of a rotator which is of great interest is its angular momentum. With a particle on a ring problem the

† These results may be expressed in a more elegant mathematical manner as

$$\Theta = \left(\frac{(2J + 1)}{2} \frac{(J - |m|)!}{(J + |m|)!}\right)^{1/2} P_{(\cos \theta)} (\sin \theta)^{|m|}$$

where $P_{(\cos \theta)}$ is the associated Legendre function of $\cos \theta$ with degree J and order m.

angular momentum was found to be quantized in a particular direction and the same result would be anticipated for a rigid rotator. There is a very important consequence of this if the rotating body is electrically charged or possesses an electric moment. A rotating charge constitutes a magnetic moment which may readily be shown to be directly proportional to its angular momentum. Hence a quantized angular momentum in a particular direction implies a quantization of magnetic moment. This is of fundamental importance in understanding and interpreting the phenomenon of paramagnetism and the interaction of magnetic and electric fields with atoms and molecules (Zeeman and Stark splitting of spectral lines, nuclear magnetic resonance and electron-spin resonance spectra).

Momentum operators $\mathbf{M}$ were considered in Chapter 4 and in Appendix 4; if when they act upon the wave function they regenerate the original function and multiply it by a number, then this number p is the momentum of the system.

$$\mathbf{M}\psi = p\psi$$

Otherwise, the momentum varies from one observation to the next and does not have a sharp value. The angular momentum operators for rotation about the x and y axes when acting upon the wave functions listed in Table 6.1 show that (except when $J = 0$) the momenta are not sharp quantities; their average values could be computed by equation (4.2) but are of little interest. The operator, in polar coordinates, for rotation about the z axis is

$$\mathbf{M}_z = \frac{h}{2\pi i} \frac{\partial}{\partial \phi}$$

It is therefore concerned with the rotation of the system and not with the precessional motion of the rotation axis. In other words, it depends upon the quantum number m (often called the magnetic quantum number).

If $m = 0$, $p_z = 0$ and the system has no angular momentum about the z axis. (If $J = 0$, p_x and p_y are also zero.)

If $m = \pm 1$, $\psi = \Theta\Phi = \Theta\, e^{\pm i\phi}$. Hence

$$\mathbf{M}_z \psi = \frac{h}{2\pi i} \frac{\partial}{\partial \phi} (\Theta\, e^{\pm i\phi})$$

$$= \pm \frac{h}{2\pi} \Theta\, e^{\pm i\phi}$$

$$= \pm \frac{h}{2\pi} \Theta\Phi$$

From this we see that when $m = 1$ the angular momentum of the system about the z axis has sharp values of either $+h/2\pi$ or $-h/2\pi$ units.

Likewise when $m = \pm 2$, $\psi = \Theta\, e^{\pm 2i\theta}$ and

$$\mathbf{M}_z \psi = \frac{h}{2\pi i}\frac{\partial}{\partial \phi}(\Theta\, e^{\pm 2i\phi})$$

$$= \pm \frac{h}{\pi}\,\Theta\Phi$$

Summarizing these results. When $J = 0$ the angular momentum is zero, for other values of J the angular momentum about the x or y axes is not a sharp quantity, but about the z axis it has a sharp quantized value of $m(h/2\pi)$ units.

We may wonder why the z axis plays a role so different from the other two axes. It is due entirely to the method arbitrarily chosen to relate cartesian to polar coordinates—z was related to the angle ϕ whereas x and y were related to both angles θ and ϕ. We could equally well have used a different combination when the x or the y axis would then have had this special significance. The particular direction in which the angular momentum and magnetic moment have sharp values can be chosen arbitrarily. An atom or molecule does not possess any 'built-in' axes, particular directions can only be specified by some external agency such as by the direction of an external electric or magnetic field.

6.5. A Non-rigid Rotator

It is concluded from the analysis and interpretation of molecular spectra that the greater the rotational energy of a molecule the longer are its bonds—centrifugal stretching. Allowing for this increase in the moment of inertia with increased rotational energy, it is possible to show that equation (6.9) for the eigenvalues has to be replaced by

$$E_J = \frac{h^2}{8\pi^2 I}\,J(J+1) - DJ^2(J+1)^2$$

The constant D is approximately equal to $h^4/128\pi^6 I^3\omega^2$ in which ω is the angular velocity. The correction factor is small except at large values of the rotational quantum number. A further correction may be made for the change in the average moment of inertia of the molecule in excited vibrational states. It is of the form[4] $-C(n + \frac{1}{2})J(J+1)$ where n is the vibrational quantum number and C another constant.

BIBLIOGRAPHICAL REFERENCES

1. Margenau, H., and Murphy, G., *Mathematics of Physics and Chemistry*, van Nostrand, New York, 1956, p. 68.
2. Glasstone, S., *Theoretical Chemistry*, van Nostrand, New York, 1944, p. 40.
3. Eyring, H., Walter, J., and Kimball, G. E., *Quantum Chemistry*, John Wiley, New York, 1944, p. 52.
4. Herzberg, G., *Molecular Spectra and Molecular Structure, I Diatomic Molecules*, van Nostrand, New York, 1950, chap. 3.

CHAPTER 7

THE HYDROGEN ATOM

The hydrogen atom and hydrogen-like atoms and ions, D, He$^+$, Li^{++}, etc. are the simplest of the atomic systems as they consist of just one electron with charge $-e$ and a nucleus of charge $+Ze$, where Z is the atomic number. These are also the only atomic species for which the Schrödinger equation has been solved exactly—in all other cases there are two or more electrons and the repulsion between them so complicates the mathematics that only approximate solutions have been obtained. These will be considered in Chapter 9. The hydrogen atom is therefore unique in the wave theory of atoms and its solution is of tremendous importance. Nearly all general approaches to a theoretical treatment of atoms and molecules depends upon the exact solutions obtained for hydrogen.

The mathematics entailed in the complete solution is not easy and only an outline of the procedure will be attempted in this book. The potential energy of attraction between the nucleus and electron (Figure 7.1), $V = -Ze^2/r$, is spherically symmetrical. Consequently *some* of the solutions of the wave equation will also be spherically symmetrical. These will be considered in detail. Solutions of lower symmetry will then be discussed, followed by an outline of the complete solution. The results obtained are presented in the final section of this chapter and their full appreciation is vital if many of the arguments advanced in subsequent parts of this book are to be fully understood.

The wave equation for the hydrogen atom is easily formulated. Writing $-Ze^2/r$ in place of V in the Schrödinger equation we obtain

$$\nabla^2\psi + \frac{8\pi^2 m}{h^2}\left(E + \frac{Ze^2}{r}\right)\psi = 0 \tag{7.1}$$

Or in the Hamiltonian form

$$\mathbf{H}\psi = \left[-\frac{h^2}{8\pi^2 m}\nabla^2 - \frac{Ze^2}{r}\right]\psi = E\psi \tag{7.2}$$

The zero of potential energy has been taken to be that of the nucleus and electron an infinite distance apart. Consequently E will be negative when the electron is bound to the nucleus.

In these equations m is the mass of the electron. In fact the electron does not rotate round the nucleus—instead both the electron and the nucleus rotate round their centre of gravity. This can easily be corrected by replacing m with the reduced mass μ of the electron and nucleus. To solve the equation it must first be expressed in polar coordinates, that is in terms of the distance r

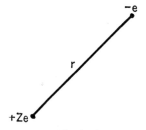

FIGURE 7.1   The hydrogen atom.

between the electron and nucleus and two angular coordinates θ and ϕ. Utilizing the transformations developed in Appendix 4 equation (7.1) becomes

$$\frac{\partial^2 \psi}{\partial r^2} + \frac{2}{r}\frac{\partial \psi}{\partial r} + \frac{1}{r^2 \sin \theta}\frac{\partial}{\partial \theta}\left(\sin \theta \frac{\partial \psi}{\partial \theta}\right) + \frac{1}{r^2 \sin^2 \theta}\frac{\partial^2 \psi}{\partial \phi^2}$$

$$+ \frac{8\pi^2 \mu}{h^2}\left(E + \frac{Ze^2}{r}\right)\psi = 0 \quad (7.3)$$

7.1. Spherically Symmetrical Solutions

As already mentioned, since V is spherically symmetrical *some* solutions of the wave equation must also be of this symmetry. When the wave function does not depend upon the angles θ and ϕ the wave equation is considerably simplified.

$$\frac{\mathrm{d}^2 \psi}{\mathrm{d}r^2} + \frac{2}{r}\frac{\mathrm{d}\psi}{\mathrm{d}r} + \frac{8\pi^2 \mu}{h^2}\left(E + \frac{Ze^2}{r}\right)\psi = 0 \quad\quad (7.4)$$

This equation will now be solved by a technique similar to that employed for the harmonic vibrator.

Asymptotic Solution

An indication of the form of the wave function is obtained by considering what happens as $r \to \infty$. Equation (7.4) reduces to

$$\frac{d^2\psi}{dr^2} + \frac{8\pi^2\mu}{h^2} E\psi = 0$$

and this simple differential solution has the general solutions

$$\psi = c\, e^{\alpha r} \qquad \text{or} \qquad \psi = c\, e^{-\alpha r}$$

where c and α are constants. The first of these is unacceptable as ψ would increase to infinity at large values of r. Let us see if the second function is a satisfactory solution of (7.4) *at all values* of r.

Differentiating this trial wave function

$$\frac{d\psi}{dr} = -\alpha c\, e^{-\alpha r} = -\alpha\psi$$

and

$$\frac{d^2\psi}{dr^2} = \alpha^2\psi$$

If these expressions are now substituted into equation (7.4) we find that

$$\alpha^2\psi + \frac{2}{r}(-\alpha\psi) + \frac{8\pi^2\mu}{h^2}\left(E + \frac{Ze^2}{r}\right)\psi = 0$$

The energy is not a function of r however and since the equation must hold at all values of r it may be separated into two parts, one involving the terms independent of r, and the other those dependent upon r. From the coefficients of $1/r$

$$-2\alpha + \frac{8\pi^2\mu}{h^2} Ze^2 = 0$$

or

$$\alpha = \frac{4\pi^2\mu Ze^2}{h^2}$$

And from the terms independent of r

$$\alpha^2 + \frac{8\pi^2\mu}{h^2} E = 0$$

or

$$E = -\frac{h^2}{8\pi^2\mu}\alpha^2$$

$$= -\frac{2\pi^2\mu Z^2 e^4}{h^2}$$

This wave function is therefore an acceptable solution of the wave equation, provided the constant α has the value given above. It is interesting to note that α has the dimensions of (length)$^{-1}$ and is actually the reciprocal of the Bohr radius of the hydrogen atom; so called because it first occurred in Bohr's theory of the hydrogen atom in which the electron was thought to describe a circle of this radius around the nucleus.

Complete Solution

The complete solution of equation (7.4) for wave functions possessing spherical symmetry will almost certainly contain $e^{-\alpha r}$ as a factor. Let us consider the situation which arises if this is multiplied by a function of r, which modifies the whole wave function at small values of r but allows it to behave as $e^{-\alpha r}$ when r is large. Let

$$\psi = R\,e^{-\alpha r}$$

Then

$$\frac{d\psi}{dr} = -\alpha R\,e^{-\alpha r} + \frac{dR}{dr}\,e^{-\alpha r}$$

and

$$\frac{d^2\psi}{dr^2} = \left(\alpha^2 R - \alpha\frac{dR}{dr}\right)e^{-\alpha r} + \left(-\alpha\frac{dR}{dr} + \frac{d^2R}{dr^2}\right)e^{-\alpha r}$$

Substituting these expressions into the wave equation we obtain

$$\left(\alpha^2 R - 2\alpha\frac{dR}{dr} + \frac{d^2R}{dr^2}\right)e^{-\alpha r} + \frac{2}{r}\left(\frac{dR}{dr} - \alpha R\right)e^{-\alpha r}$$
$$+ \frac{8\pi^2\mu}{h^2}\left(E + \frac{Ze^2}{r}\right)Re^{-\alpha r} = 0$$

This equation must hold for all values of r and this is only possible if the coefficient of each power of r is separately equal to zero. Now with all the likely expressions for the function R it will contain a term in r with a power not present in its derivatives, dR/dr and d^2R/dr^2, or in the terms $(2/r)\,dR/dr$ and $(Ze^2/r)R$. Consequently the coefficient of $R\,e^{-\alpha r}$ in the above equation must be zero, i.e.

$$\alpha^2 + \frac{8\pi^2\mu}{h^2}E = 0$$

As expected, this is the same result as was obtained for the asymptotic solution. Cancelling these terms in the equation, dividing throughout by $e^{-\alpha r}$, and writing 2β in place of $(8\pi^2\mu/h^2)Ze^2$, the equation reduces to

$$\frac{d^2R}{dr^2} + \left(\frac{2}{r} - 2\alpha\right)\frac{dR}{dr} + \left(\frac{2\beta}{r} - \frac{2\alpha}{r}\right)R = 0 \qquad (7.5)$$

To proceed further with the mathematical solution an expression for R is required which satisfies equation (7.5) and results in the wave function being an acceptable one. A power series seems to be indicated. Let

$$R = k_0 + k_1 r + k_2 r^2 + \ldots + k_s r^s + \ldots = \sum_{j=0}^{\infty} (k_j r^j).$$

Then

$$\frac{\mathrm{d}R}{\mathrm{d}r} = \sum (jk_j r^{j-1})$$

and

$$\frac{\mathrm{d}^2 R}{\mathrm{d}r^2} = \sum ((j-1)jk_j r^{j-2})$$

The coefficient of r^{s-1} in equation (7.5) is therefore

$$s(s+1)k_{s+1} + 2(s+1)k_{s+1} - 2\alpha s k_s + 2(\beta - \alpha)k_s$$

and since each coefficient must be zero

$$[s(s+1) + 2(s+1)]k_{s+1} + [2(\beta - \alpha) - 2\alpha s]k_s = 0 \quad (7.6)$$

This recursion formula permits the calculation of k_{s+1} in terms of the coefficient k_s, so that once k_0 is known, the power series R is completely defined.

The wave function $\psi = \mathrm{e}^{-\alpha r} \sum_{j=0}^{\infty} (k_j r^j)$ is a solution of the Schrödinger equation but it is not acceptable since it does not converge to a finite value as $r \to \infty$. This may be demonstrated by considering the form of the recursion formula (7.6) at large values of s. It becomes

$$s^2 k_{s+1} - 2\alpha s k_s = 0$$

or

$$k_{s+1} = \frac{2\alpha}{s} k_s$$

This is also the recursion formula for the terms in the series expansion of $\mathrm{e}^{2\alpha r}$.

$$\mathrm{e}^{2\alpha r} = 1 + 2\alpha r + \frac{(2\alpha)^2 r^2}{2!} + \frac{(2\alpha)^3 r^3}{3!} + \ldots$$

Remembering that the difference between $s+1$ and s is insignificant when s is large, the coefficients of successive terms in this expansion satisfy the formula

$$k_{s+1} = \frac{2\alpha}{s+1} k_s = \frac{2\alpha}{s} k_s$$

Hence when the power s is large the polynomial R behaves as $\mathrm{e}^{2\alpha r}$ and the complete wave function as

$$\mathrm{e}^{2\alpha r} \, \mathrm{e}^{-\alpha r} = \mathrm{e}^{\alpha r}$$

This tends to infinity as $r \to \infty$ which is not acceptable.

The difficulty may be avoided if the polynomial is terminated after a finite number of terms so that it does not contain high powers of r. From an examination of equation (7.6) it is evident that if $\beta - \alpha = \alpha s$ for a particular value of s, then k_{s+1} and all the succeeding coefficients will be zero. The behaviour of the wave function at large values of r will then be controlled by the factor $e^{-\alpha r}$ and will be completely acceptable. Hence,

$$\psi = e^{-\alpha r} \sum_{j=0}^{s} (k_j r^j)$$

with $\alpha = \beta/(s + 1)$.

Or, substituting back the expressions for α and β,

$$-\frac{8\pi^2\mu}{h^2} E = \left(\frac{4\pi^2\mu}{h^2} Ze^2\right)^2 \frac{1}{(s + 1)^2}$$

and

$$E = -\frac{2\pi^2\mu Z^2 e^4}{(s + 1)^2 h^2} \quad (s = 0, 1, 2 \ldots)$$

$$= -\frac{2\pi^2\mu Z^2 e^4}{n^2 h^2} \quad (n = s + 1 = 1, 2, 3 \ldots) \quad (7.7)$$

The energy of the hydrogen atom is quantized, the greatest energy of attraction between the electron and nucleus being $2\pi^2\mu Z^2 e^4/h^2$ and the other eigenvalues $\frac{1}{4}, \frac{1}{9}, \frac{1}{16} \ldots$ of this value. The maximum binding energy is equivalent to the ionization potential of the atom and in Table 7.1 the theoretical values of this quantity are compared with those determined spectroscopically.

TABLE 7.1. IONIZATION POTENTIALS OF
HYDROGEN-LIKE ATOMS

Atom	Z	$2\pi^2\mu Z^2 e^4/h^2$ (eV)	Ionization Potential (eV)
H	1	13·596	13·596
He$^+$	2	54·16	54·16
Li^{2+}	3	121·8	121·84
Be^{3+}	4	216·6	216·63

The wave functions, known as s-type wave functions, are discussed later. Finally we may note that since

$$\alpha^2 = -\frac{8\pi^2\mu}{h^2} E$$

$$\alpha = \frac{4\pi^2\mu Ze^2}{nh^2} = \frac{1}{na}$$

where a is the Bohr radius of the hydrogen atom (0·529 Å).

7.2. Solutions of Lower Symmetry

So far only solutions in which the wave function is solely dependent upon the distance r have been considered, we will now show that there are also solutions of the form

$$\psi_{(x)} = x f_{(r)} \tag{7.8}$$

These possess some specific feature in the x direction but since there is no distinction possible between the x, y, and z directions there must also be the solutions

$$\psi_{(y)} = y f_{(r)} \quad \text{and} \quad \psi_{(z)} = z f_{(r)}$$

having the same energy for the same function of r.

Differentiating the above equation we obtain

$$\frac{\partial \psi}{\partial x} = f + x \frac{\partial f}{\partial r} \frac{\partial r}{\partial x} = f + \frac{x^2}{r} \frac{\partial f}{\partial r}$$

This follows since $r = (x^2 + y^2 + z^2)^{1/2}$ and $\partial r / \partial x = x/r$. Hence,

$$\frac{\partial^2 \psi}{\partial x^2} = \frac{\partial f}{\partial r} \frac{\partial r}{\partial x} + \frac{2x}{r} \frac{\partial f}{\partial r} - \frac{x^2}{r^2} \frac{\partial f}{\partial r} \frac{\partial r}{\partial x} + \frac{x^2}{r} \frac{\partial^2 f}{\partial r^2} \frac{\partial r}{\partial x}$$

$$= \frac{x}{r} \frac{\partial f}{\partial r} + \frac{2x}{r} \frac{\partial f}{\partial r} - \frac{x^3}{r^3} \frac{\partial f}{\partial r} + \frac{x^3}{r^2} \frac{\partial^2 f}{\partial r^2}$$

Also

$$\frac{\partial \psi}{\partial y} = x \frac{\partial f}{\partial r} \frac{\partial r}{\partial y} = \frac{xy}{r} \frac{\partial f}{\partial r}$$

and

$$\frac{\partial^2 \psi}{\partial y^2} = \frac{x}{r} \frac{\partial f}{\partial r} - \frac{xy}{r^2} \frac{\partial f}{\partial r} \frac{\partial r}{\partial y} + \frac{xy}{r} \frac{\partial^2 f}{\partial r^2} \frac{\partial r}{\partial y}$$

$$= \frac{x}{r} \frac{\partial f}{\partial r} - \frac{xy^2}{r^3} \frac{\partial f}{\partial r} + \frac{xy^2}{r^2} \frac{\partial^2 f}{\partial r^2}$$

$\partial \psi / \partial z$ and $\partial^2 \psi / \partial z^2$ will be similar to the derivatives with respect to y. Hence, adding the three second differentials,

$$\nabla^2 \psi = \frac{\partial^2 \psi}{\partial x^2} + \frac{\partial^2 \psi}{\partial y^2} + \frac{\partial^2 \psi}{\partial z^2}$$

$$= \frac{4x}{r} \frac{\partial f}{\partial r} + x \frac{\partial^2 f}{\partial r^2}$$

The wave equation with this form for $\nabla^2\psi$ is consequently

$$\left(\frac{4x}{r}\frac{\partial f}{\partial r} + x\frac{\partial^2 f}{\partial r^2}\right) + \frac{8\pi^2\mu}{h^2}\left(E + \frac{Ze^2}{r}\right)xf = 0$$

or

$$\frac{\partial^2 f}{\partial r^2} + \frac{4}{r}\frac{\partial f}{\partial r} + \frac{8\pi^2\mu}{h^2}\left(E + \frac{Ze^2}{r}\right)f = 0$$

This equation is of the same form as equation (7.4), with f replacing ψ and the number 4 in place of the 2 in the second term. It can therefore be solved for f showing that equation (7.8) is an acceptable eigenfunction and, because of the different numerical factor, will have the eigenvalues

$$E = -\frac{2\pi^2\mu Z^2e^4}{(n+1)^2h^2} \qquad (n = 1, 2, 3 \ldots)$$

$$= -\frac{2\pi^2\mu Z^2e^4}{n^2h^2} \qquad (n = 2, 3, 4 \ldots)$$

Eigenfunctions of this type are known as p wave functions, the three degenerate ones being referred to as p_x, p_y, and p_z. Combined, they possess spherical symmetry, as they must since the electron is moving under a potential with this symmetry.

Degenerate wave functions can always be expressed in alternative forms. This was found to be the case for a particle on a ring and it can easily be shown that if ψ_1 and ψ_2 are any two degenerate wave functions then their linear combination

$$\psi = a\psi_1 + b\psi_2$$

is also a solution of the same Schrödinger equation and has the same energy. This is so because with this wave function

$$(a\nabla^2\psi_1 + b\nabla^2\psi_2) + \frac{8\pi^2 m}{h^2}(E - V)(a\nabla^2\psi_1 + b\nabla^2\psi_2) = 0$$

The first and third terms together are zero since ψ_1 is an eigenfunction, and likewise for the other terms involving ψ_2. This has been mentioned here because it is sometimes desirable to replace the three p wave functions by

$$\psi_{+1} = p_x + ip_y = (x + iy)f$$
$$\psi_{-1} = p_x - ip_y = (x - iy)f$$
$$\psi_0 = p_z = zf$$

Solutions of yet other symmetries are possible, by the method just employed it may be shown that

$$xyf, \quad yzf, \quad zxf, \quad (x^2 - y^2)f, \quad (y^2 - x^2)f, \quad \text{and} \quad (z^2 - x^2)f$$

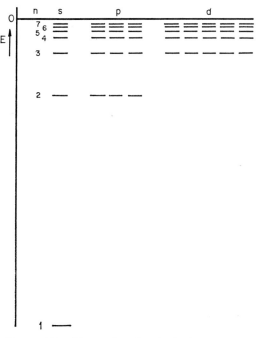

FIGURE 7.2 Eigenvalues for the hydrogen atom.

form a degenerate set of eigenfunctions with

$$E = -\frac{2\pi^2\mu Z^2 e^4}{n^2 h^2} \qquad (n = 3, 4, 5 \ldots)$$

These solutions, d-type wave functions, are actually only five-fold degenerate; the last function listed above may be expressed as the sum of the two preceding functions so is not an independent function. There are also seven degenerate f-type wave functions with eigenvalues

$$E = -\frac{2\pi^2\mu Z^2 e^4}{n^2 h^2} \qquad (n = 4, 5, 6 \ldots)$$

nine g-type† functions, etc.

The eigenvalues of the hydrogen atom are summarized diagrammatically in Figure 7.2.

---

† The nomenclature s, p, d, f, arises from the historical description of spectroscopic lines in the atomic spectra of alkali metals.

7.3. Complete Solution

A rigorous mathematical solution of the wave equation for the hydrogen atom entails the complete solution of equation (7.3). Only an outline of the procedure will be attempted.

The first step is to see if the wave function can be written as the product of three factors, each involving just one of the three polar coordinates r, θ, and ϕ. Let

$$\psi = R(r)\Theta(\theta)\Phi(\phi)$$

Then

$$\frac{\partial \psi}{\partial r} = \Theta\Phi \frac{\partial R}{\partial r}$$

$$\frac{\partial^2 \psi}{\partial r^2} = \Theta\Phi \frac{\partial^2 R}{\partial r^2} \text{, etc.}$$

Making use of these relationships equation (7.3) may be written in the form

$$\Theta\Phi \frac{\partial^2 R}{\partial r^2} + \frac{2}{r} \Theta\Phi \frac{\partial R}{\partial r} + \frac{1}{r^2 \sin\theta} \frac{\partial}{\partial \theta}\left(\sin\theta R\Phi \frac{\partial \Theta}{\partial \theta}\right)$$

$$+ \frac{1}{r^2 \sin^2\theta} R\Theta \frac{\partial^2 \Phi}{\partial \phi^2} + \frac{8\pi^2\mu}{h^2}\left(E + \frac{Ze^2}{r}\right)R\Theta\Phi = 0$$

If this is now multiplied through by $r^2/R\Theta\Phi$ and the terms rearranged it can be converted into

$$\frac{r^2}{R} \frac{\partial^2 R}{\partial r^2} + \frac{2r}{R} \frac{\partial R}{\partial r} + \frac{8\pi^2\mu r^2}{h^2}\left(E + \frac{Ze^2}{r}\right)$$

$$= -\frac{1}{\Theta \sin\theta} \frac{\partial}{\partial \theta}\left(\sin\theta \frac{\partial \Theta}{\partial \theta}\right) - \frac{1}{\Phi \sin^2\theta} \frac{\partial^2 \Phi}{\partial \phi^2}$$

The left-hand side of this equation is solely a function of the parameter r and the right-hand side of θ and ϕ. If the whole expression is to hold for all possible values of r, irrespective of the values of θ and ϕ, this part of the equation must be a constant K, i.e.

$$\frac{r^2}{R} \frac{\partial^2 R}{\partial r^2} + \frac{2r}{R} \frac{\partial R}{\partial r} + \frac{8\pi^2\mu r^2}{h^2}\left(E + \frac{Ze^2}{r}\right) = K \qquad (7.9)$$

The right-hand side must be equal to the same constant and multiplying it by $\sin^2\theta$ we find that

$$\frac{\sin\theta}{\Theta} \frac{\partial}{\partial \theta}\left(\sin\theta \frac{\partial \Theta}{\partial \theta}\right) + K\sin^2\theta = -\frac{1}{\Phi} \frac{\partial^2 \Phi}{\partial \phi^2}$$

This has exactly the same form as equation (6.3) for a rigid rotator and may be split into the two parts corresponding to equations (6.4) and (6.5).

$$\frac{\sin \theta}{\Theta} \frac{\partial}{\partial \theta}\left(\sin \theta \frac{\partial \Theta}{\partial \theta}\right) + K \sin^2 \theta = m^2 \qquad (7.10)$$

and

$$-\frac{1}{\Phi}\frac{\partial^2 \Phi}{\partial \phi^2} = m^2 \qquad (7.11)$$

The original wave equation has therefore been split into three parts, equations (7.9), (7.10), and (7.11), each containing only one of the polar coordinates; that this is possible justifies the postulate that $\psi = R\Theta\Phi$. These equations are now solved to obtain the independent functions, R, Θ, and Φ.

The function R describes how the wave function of the electron depends upon its radial distance from the nucleus. It is consequently known as the *radial factor*. The other functions Θ and Φ together describe how the wave function depends upon the direction taken from the nucleus and their product $\Theta\Phi$ is called the *angular factor*.

Solution of Equation (7.11)

This equation is identical with equation (6.4) for a rigid rotator and will not be considered further.

Solution of Equation (7.10)

This equation is identical with equation (6.5). Hence from equation (6.8) the constant K is restricted to the values given by the expression $J(J + 1)$, where J is an integer. For the electronic energy of atoms however the symbol J is replaced by l and known as the *azimuthal quantum number*, i.e.

$$K = l(l + 1) \qquad (l = 0, 1, 2, 3 \ldots)$$

The mathematical expressions for some of the angular factors $\Theta\Phi$ have been given already in Table 6.1 if l is read in place of J, and will be discussed again in the following section.

Solution of Equation (7.9)

Equation (7.9) can be solved to obtain the radial factor R and, at the same time, it gives the eigenvalues for the system as it is the only equation to contain the energy E. From what has just been said the constant K in equation (7.9) can only have the values

$l(l + 1)$. It is of the same form as equation (7.4) for the spherically symmetrical solutions of the hydrogen atom, except that the right-hand side of the equation is $[l(l + 1)/r^2]R$ instead of zero. If the analysis of equation (7.4) is studied it will be appreciated that this extra term will alter the first factor in the recursion formula (7.6), and consequently the eigenfunctions, but will not affect the eigen-values which remain

$$E = -\frac{2\pi^2\mu Z^2 e^4}{n^2 h^2} \qquad (n = 1, 2, 3 \ldots) \qquad (7.7)$$

The altered recursion formula means that the eigenfunctions now depend upon l as well as upon n. Some of them are reproduced in Table 7.2. The detailed treatment of the radial equation also shows that $l \leqslant n$.

TABLE 7.2. THE RADIAL FUNCTION R FOR HYDROGEN-LIKE ATOMS

n	l	State	R (r in a.u.)
1	0	$1s$	$2Z^{3/2}\,e^{-Zr}$
2	0	$2s$	$(Z/2)^{3/2}(2 - Zr)\,e^{-Zr/2}$
2	1	$2p$	$(Z^5/24)^{1/2}r\,e^{-Zr/2}$
3	0	$3s$	$2(Z/27)^{3/2}(27 - 18Zr + 2Z^2r^2)\,e^{-Zr/3}$
3	1	$3p$	$\frac{1}{81}(8Z^5/3)^{1/2}(6 - Zr)r\,e^{-Zr/3}$
3	2	$3d$	$\frac{1}{81}(8Z^7/15)^{1/2}r^2\,e^{-Zr/3}$

The mathematical results for the complete solution of the hydrogen atom may be summarized as follows:

1. The wave functions are expressed as the product of a radial factor R and an angular factor $\Theta\Phi$.
2. The radial factor depends upon the values of two quantum numbers—the principal quantum number n and the azimuthal, or subsidiary, quantum number l.

$$n = 1, 2, 3 \ldots$$
$$l = 0, 1, 2 \ldots (n - 1)$$

3. The factor Θ depends upon the value of l and upon the magnetic quantum number m. From what was said at the end of Section 6.3 there are $2l + 1$ possible values for m

$$m = l, l - 1, l - 2 \ldots 0, \ldots -(l - 1), -l$$

4. The factor Φ depends upon the value of m alone.
5. The eigenvalues depend upon $1/n^2$ (equation (7.7)). These eigenvalues have been illustrated in Figure 7.2.

Some of the complete wave functions are given in Table 7.3.

TABLE 7.3. THE WAVE FUNCTIONS $\Psi \equiv R\Theta\Phi$ FOR HYDROGEN-LIKE ATOMS

n	l	m	State	$\psi = R\Theta\Phi$ (r in a.u.)
1	0	0	$1s$	$(Z^3/\pi)^{1/2}\,e^{-Zr}$
2	0	0	$2s$	$\frac{1}{4}(Z^3/2\pi)^{1/2}(2 - Zr)\,e^{-Zr/2}$
2	1	0	$2p_0$	$\frac{1}{4}(Z^5/2\pi)^{1/2}r\cos\theta\,e^{-Zr/2}$
			or	
			$2p_z$	$\frac{1}{4}(Z^5/2\pi)^{1/2}z\,e^{-Zr/2}$
2	1	± 1	$2p_{\pm 1}$	$\frac{1}{8}(Z^5/\pi)^{1/2}\,e^{-Zr/2}r\sin\theta\,e^{\pm i\phi}$
			or	
			$2p_x$	$\frac{1}{4}(Z^5/2\pi)^{1/2}\,e^{-Zr/2}r\sin\theta\cos\phi$ $\equiv \frac{1}{4}(Z^5/2\pi)^{1/2}x\,e^{-Zr/2}$
			and	
			$2p_y$	$\frac{1}{4}(Z^5/2\pi)^{1/2}\,e^{-Zr/2}r\sin\theta\sin\phi$ $\equiv \frac{1}{4}(Z^5/2\pi)^{1/2}y\,e^{-Zr/2}$
3	0	0	$3s$	$\frac{1}{81}(Z^3/3\pi)^{1/2}(27 - 18Zr + 2Z^2r^2)\,e^{-Zr/3}$
3	1	0	$3p_0$	$\frac{1}{81}(2Z^3/\pi)^{1/2}(6Zr - Z^2r^2)\,e^{-Zr/3}\cos\theta$
			or	
			$3p_z$	$\frac{1}{81}(2Z^5/\pi)^{1/2}(6 - Zr)z\,e^{-Zr/3}$
3	1	± 1	$3p_{\pm 1}$	$\frac{1}{81}(Z^3/\pi)^{1/2}(6Zr - Z^2r^2)\,e^{-Zr/3}\sin\theta\,e^{\pm i\phi}$
			or	
			$3p_x$	$\frac{1}{81}(2Z^5/\pi)^{1/2}(6 - Zr)\,e^{-Zr/3}r\sin\theta\cos\phi$ $\equiv \frac{1}{81}(2Z^5/\pi)^{1/2}(6 - Zr)x\,e^{-Zr/3}$
			and	
			$3p_y$	$\frac{1}{81}(2Z^5/\pi)^{1/2}(6 - Zr)\,e^{-Zr/3}r\sin\theta\sin\phi$ $\equiv \frac{1}{81}(2Z^5/\pi)^{1/2}(6 - Zr)y\,e^{-Zr/3}$
3	2	0	$3d_0$	$\frac{1}{81}(Z^7/6\pi)^{1/2}\,e^{-Zr/3}r^2(3\cos^2\theta - 1)$
			or	
			$3d_{z^2}$	$\frac{1}{81}(Z^7/6\pi)^{1/2}(3z^2 - r^2)\,e^{-Zr/3}$
3	2	± 1	$3d_{\pm 1}$	$\frac{1}{81}(Z^7/\pi)^{1/2}\,e^{-Zr/3}r^2\sin\theta\cos\theta\,e^{\pm i\phi}$
			or	
			$3d_{xz}$	$\frac{1}{81}(2Z^7/\pi)^{1/2}\,e^{-Zr/3}r^2\sin\theta\cos\theta\cos\phi$ $\equiv \frac{1}{81}(2Z^7/\pi)^{1/2}xz\,e^{-Zr/3}$
			and	
			$3d_{yz}$	$\frac{1}{81}(2Z^7/\pi)^{1/2}\,e^{-Zr/3}r^2\sin\theta\cos\theta\sin\phi$ $\equiv \frac{1}{81}(2Z^7/\pi)^{1/2}yz\,e^{-Zr/3}$
3	2	± 2	$3d_{\pm 2}$	$\frac{1}{162}(Z^7/\pi)^{1/2}\,e^{-Zr/3}r^2\sin^2\theta\,e^{\pm 2i\phi}$
			or	
			$3d_{x^2-y^2}$	$\frac{1}{81}(Z^7/2\pi)^{1/2}\,e^{-Zr/3}r^2\sin^2\theta\cos 2\phi$ $\equiv \frac{1}{81}(Z^7/2\pi)^{1/2}(x^2 - y^2)\,e^{-Zr/3}$
			and	
			$3d_{xy}$	$\frac{1}{81}(Z^7/2\pi)^{1/2}\,e^{-Zr/3}r^2\sin^2\theta\sin 2\phi$ $\equiv \frac{1}{81}(Z^7/2\pi)^{1/2}xy\,e^{-Zr/3}$

4

The square of the wave function is the probability of finding the electron at the particular point in space, or alternatively, it represents the electron density at that point. To distinguish this three dimensional distribution from the older Bohr-Sommerfeld concept of an electron moving in a circular or elliptical orbit, these distributions are called *orbitals*. To designate an atomic orbital it is customary to specify the numerical value of its principal quantum number

$$n = 1, 2, 3 \ldots,$$

followed by a letter signifying the value of the azimuthal quantum number. The letters employed are,

$$1 = 0, 1, 2, 3, 4, \ldots$$
$$s, p, d, f, g, \ldots$$

Hence the $1s$ orbital has $n = 1$, $l = 0$ and represents the lowest energy level, maximum binding energy, of the hydrogen atom. Note that the following levels *cannot* exist because l must be less than n.

$$1p \qquad 1d \qquad 1f \ldots$$
$$2d \qquad 2f \ldots$$
$$3f \ldots$$

Two schemes are in common use to distinguish between the degenerate states—both are given as subscripts to the main symbol. In the one scheme the value of m is quoted and the function Φ left in the form $e^{mi\phi}$ so that the angular momentum is quantized about the z axis. In the other method, the angular factor $\Theta\Phi$ is expressed in cartesian coordinates and these are given as the subscript, with the exception that d_{z^2} is generally written in place of $d_{(3z^2-r^2)}$. This nomenclature emphasizes the orientation of the orbital with respect to the cartesian axes and the position and number of the nonspherical nodes.

7.4. Wave Functions for the Hydrogen Atom

In this section, the mathematical expressions for the wave functions of the hydrogen atom are represented pictorially. Since they are three-dimensional functions involving the product of radial and angular factors they cannot be represented completely in two-dimensional pictures. Nevertheless, a full appreciation of these results is vital for a physical concept of the electron distribution in atoms and molecules and for understanding directed valence.

The Radial Factor R

The radial factors, describing how the wave function depends upon distance from the nucleus, were given in Table 7.2 for various combinations of n and l, that is for various orbitals. Figure 7.3

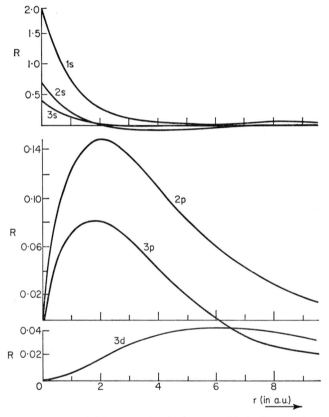

FIGURE 7.3   The radial factor R for hydrogen orbitals (in atomic units).

shows a plot of R against the distance from the nucleus for six orbitals. This distance is most conveniently given in terms of atomic units (a.u.), that is in terms of the Bohr radius a as unity (Appendix 1).

It will be noted that between $r = 0$ and $r = \infty$ there are $n - l - 1$ spherical nodes where R is zero. There is no chance of finding the electron at these distances from the nucleus. The radial probability curves may be obtained from Figure 7.3 by squaring the value of R and this probability obviously falls away rapidly as r increases.

The variation of $R^2 \, dr$ with r does not give a picture of the probability of finding the electron in the volume element $d\tau$ at a particular distance since it only refers to one particular direction from the nucleus. As r increases the number of volume elements in all directions at this distance increases rapidly. The radial distribution function $4\pi r^2 R^2$ gives the probability of finding the electron somewhere at a distance r, no mention being made of the direction. This function is plotted in Figure 7.4.

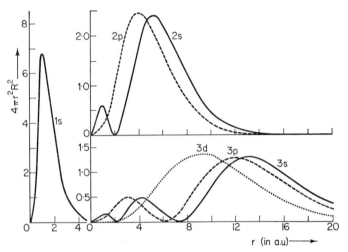

FIGURE 7.4   The radial distribution function $4\pi r^2 R^2$ for hydrogen orbitals (in atomic units).

The curves for $1s, 2p, 3d, 4f \ldots$ orbitals have one maximum only and it is interesting to note that these are at distances equal to the radius of the corresponding Bohr orbit ($r = n^2 a$). In theory an electron in these orbitals could be anywhere between $r = 0$ and $r = \infty$ but the chance of finding it at large distances from the nucleus is obviously extremely small.

The other curves in Figure 7.4 have more than one maximum, with nodes of zero probability between them, but it is evident that the electron spends most of its time in the outermost zone. It will also be noticed that, for a given principal quantum number the maximum in the outermost zone is somewhat closer to the nucleus the greater the value of the azimuthal quantum number l.

The Angular Factor $\Theta\Phi$

The angular factor is of great importance in understanding the geometrical and other physical properties of molecules and consequently in interpreting their general chemistry. The function $\Theta\Phi$ portrays how the wave function varies with its direction from the nucleus, measured with reference to two arbitrary planes (see the diagram in Appendix 4). The function is a three-dimensional one and only a cross-section of it can conveniently be given on paper.

The expressions for $\Theta\Phi$ were given in Table 6.1, but for some purposes it is desirable to make the angular eigenfunction for an s orbital equal to unity, as it is a constant independent of θ and ϕ.

TABLE 7.4. THE ANGULAR WAVE FUNC-
TIONS $\Theta\Phi$ NORMALIZED TO 4π

l	m	State	$\Theta\Phi$
0	0	s	1
1	0	p_0 or p_z	$\sqrt{3}\cos\theta$
1	± 1	$p_{\pm 1}$	$\sqrt{(3/2)}\sin\theta\,e^{\pm i\phi}$
		or	
		p_x	$\sqrt{3}\sin\theta\cos\phi$
		and	
		p_y	$\sqrt{3}\sin\theta\sin\phi$
2	0	d_0 or d_{z^2}	$\sqrt{(5/4)}(3\cos^2\theta - 1)$
2	± 1	$d_{\pm 1}$	$\sqrt{(15/2)}\sin\theta\cos\theta\,e^{\pm i\phi}$
		or	
		d_{xz}	$\sqrt{15}\sin\theta\cos\theta\cos\phi$
		and	
		d_{yz}	$\sqrt{15}\sin\theta\cos\theta\sin\phi$
2	± 2	$d_{\pm 2}$	$\sqrt{(15/8)}\sin^2\theta\,e^{\pm 2i\phi}$
		or	
		$d_{x^2-y^2}$	$\frac{1}{2}\sqrt{15}\sin^2\theta\cos 2\phi$
		and	
		d_{xy}	$\frac{1}{2}\sqrt{15}\sin^2\theta\sin 2\phi$

This is done by normalizing the functions to 4π and these are reproduced in Table 7.4. On this scale the maximum values of $\Theta\Phi$ for s, p, and d orbitals are 1, $\sqrt{3}$, and $\sqrt{5}$ respectively.

s-orbitals. For an s-type wave function $\Theta\Phi$ is a constant and the wave function is spherically symmetrical. This may be represented by the surface of a sphere, or in two dimensions by its cross-section which is a circle, (Figure 7.5). The interpretation of this is that since the distance from the nucleus to this surface is independent of the direction taken, the wave function is also independent of the direction.

p-orbitals. For a p wave function, $\Theta\Phi$ consists of two spheres in contact, rather like a dumbell, (Figure 7.5). Separating the spheres is a nodal plane so that the wave function is of different sign, or phase, in its two parts. Its maximum value is $\sqrt{3}$ times that of an s wave function. (It must be emphasized that the absolute scale of these diagrams is of no significance whatever—the angular solution describes how the complete wave function depends upon *direction* from the nucleus, the effect of distance being given by the radial factor.) The broken line in the diagram is the plot of $|\Theta\Phi|^2$. The complete figures may be obtained by rotating these cross-sections about their symmetry axis. The probability of finding an s electron is the same in all directions round the nucleus, but with a p electron there is a pronounced tendency to find it in certain directions, and there is a plane perpendicular to this direction in which it can never be found.

There are actually three degenerate p wave functions, distinguished by their m values. They all have the same orbital shape but their symmetry axes are mutually at right angles to each other—hence their designation p_x, p_y, and p_z according to whether their lobes are symmetrical about the x, y, or z reference axis. There are only three linearly independent p-type orbitals—any similar orbital, pointing in a different direction, may be regarded as the superposition of certain amounts of p_x, p_y, and p_z. This is done vectorially so that we may write

$$p = ap_x + bp_y + cp_z \qquad (7.12)$$

where a, b, and c are the direction cosines of the angles between p_x, p_y, and p_z respectively and the new orbital p.

d-orbitals. There are five independent d-type orbitals. In Section 7.2 we mentioned that six wave functions could be formulated, but that one of these could be expressed in terms of two of the remainder. One consequence of this is that the shape, but not the energy, of one of the d orbitals differs from that of the other four. This orbital (d_{z^2}) has two large lobes along one axis, by convention the z axis, and a small 'smoke-ring' about the x–y plane. The other orbitals each have four equivalent lobes with two nodal planes separating them—somewhat like two of the p orbitals considered together (Figure 7.5). They have their lobes in different directions. The d_{xz} orbital for example is illustrated in Figure 7.5; the d_{yz} and d_{zx} orbitals are identical but have the y–z and z–x planes as symmetry planes. The last of the d orbitals $d_{(x^2-y^2)}$ differs from d_{xy} in that its lobes lie along the cartesian axes x and y, instead of making a 45° angle to them.

f-orbitals. These orbitals are of less importance and will not be considered in detail. In general they possess eight lobes with three nodal planes separating them.

Before concluding this discussion of the angular factor we might remind ourselves that it is ϕ which determines the angular momentum and magnetic moment associated with the electron in a given direction (cf. Section 6.4). The total angular momentum is

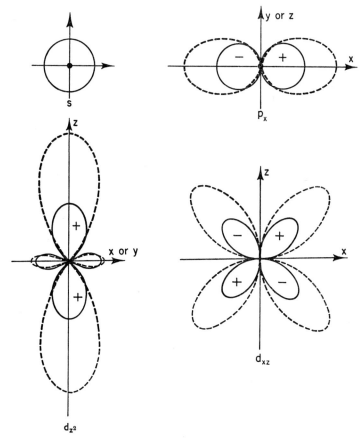

FIGURE 7.5 The angular factor for s, p_x, d_{z^2}, and d_{xz} orbitals.

$\sqrt{(l(l+1))}h/2\pi$, i.e. 0, $\sqrt{2}$, and $\sqrt{6}$, $h/2\pi$ for s, p, and d electrons respectively. This can only have a quantized component in one particular direction—conventionally taken to be along the z axis—and has the value $mh/2\pi$ units. For an electron in the various orbitals the quantized component of angular momentum along the z axis in these units is therefore

$$\begin{cases} s & p_0 & p_{+1} & p_{-1} & d_0 & d_{+1} \\ & p_z & p_x + ip_y & p_x - ip_y & d_{z^2} & d_{zx} + id_{yz} \end{cases}$$
$$0 \quad 0 \qquad 1 \qquad\quad -1 \qquad 0 \qquad 1$$

$$\begin{cases} d_{-1} & d_{+2} & d_{-2} \\ d_{zx} - id_{yz} & d_{(x^2-y^2)} + id_{xy} & d_{(x^2-y^2)} - id_{xy} \end{cases}$$
$$-1 \qquad\qquad 2 \qquad\qquad\qquad -2$$

The Complete Wave Function

The complete wave functions for hydrogen are the product of the corresponding radial and angular factors. With a little thought and imagination these may be visualized, but are virtually impossible to depict adequately on paper. The shape of an orbital is determined entirely by its angular factor, the size by its radial factor. The angular factor has l non-spherical nodal surfaces which, with the $n - l - 1$ spherical nodes arising from the radial factor, gives a total of $n - 1$ nodes. As with a particle in a box, the greater the number of nodes the greater is the kinetic energy of the electron. Spherical nodes are not of importance chemically.

What do we mean by 'orbital size' since the wave function extends to infinity? Some possible measures of it are:

1. The distance of the main maximum in the radial distribution function from the nucleus.
2. The average distance of the electron from the nucleus, given by equation (4.3).
3. The distance, averaged over all angles, within which the electron spends say 95% of its time.

The size increases approximately with n^2 as the principal quantum number increases but for a given value of n the electron is slightly closer to the nucleus the greater the value of l.

PART II

APPROXIMATE SOLUTIONS OF
THE SCHRÖDINGER EQUATION

CHAPTER 8

WAVE MECHANICAL TECHNIQUES

In Part I the wave equation was applied to problems in which it was possible to obtain exact solutions. We must now consider more complicated atoms and also molecules. The Hamiltonian for one of the electrons in a polyelectronic atom is

$$\mathbf{H}_1 = -\frac{h^2}{8\pi^2 m} \nabla_1^2 - \frac{Ze^2}{r_1} + \sum_{i>1}^{Z} \frac{e^2}{r_i}$$

where the last term represents the coulombic repulsion between all the other electrons in the atom and the one under consideration. The Hamiltonian for each electron therefore requires a knowledge of the probability distribution of all the other electrons in the atom and this mutual dependence so complicates the mathematics that the wave equation cannot be solved exactly. The same situation arises with molecules. Even with the simplest, the hydrogen molecule ion H_2^+, the Schrödinger equation has not been solved exactly. Fortunately it is possible to get approximate solutions in these cases and although the numerical results may not be in good quantitative agreement with experiment, the semi-quantitative values and the description of the electron distribution in the systems is of the utmost value in understanding their chemical behaviour and other properties. The discrepancy between the theoretical and experimental results depends very largely upon the time and effort devoted to the calculations.

There are two problems in obtaining approximate solutions to a wave equation. Firstly, an expression for the wave function ψ has to be formulated and secondly, the equation has to be solved with this wave function. Some of the techniques employed are described in this chapter and applied to the problem of the helium atom.

8.1. The Perturbation Method

This is a mathematical technique used to compute the energy of a system with given expressions for $\mathbf{H}$ and ψ. It is suitable for problems which differ only by a comparatively small extent from one which has been solved already, and is particularly valuable when the Hamiltonian of the system differs from that of the similar system by the addition of an extra potential energy term. For example, as a first approximation, the helium atom may be considered in terms of the exact solutions for He$^+$ (Chapter 7), but with the addition of a perturbing potential due to the repulsion between the two electrons.

For the exact solution of the simpler unperturbed problem

$$\mathbf{H}\psi = E\psi$$

where $\mathbf{H}$ is the appropriate Hamiltonian. The perturbed system will have an extra potential term V in its Hamiltonian function $\mathbf{H}'$, i.e.

$$\mathbf{H}' = \mathbf{H} + V$$

Consequently the wave equation for the perturbed system is

$$\mathbf{H}'\psi' = E'\psi' \tag{8.1}$$

but if the perturbation is small it is reasonable to expect that the wave function ψ' does not differ greatly from ψ. There is however one important difference between these wave functions; whereas ψ' is an exact solution of equation (8.1) ψ is not, and the energy obtained from this approximate wave function would depend upon the coordinates of the system. For any one configuration the instantaneous energy would be $\mathbf{H}'\psi/\psi$. A weighted mean must now be taken by multiplying this by the probability of getting this configuration $\psi^2/\int\psi^2 \, d\tau$ and integrating over the whole of space thus giving

$$\bar{E} = \frac{\int \psi \mathbf{H}'\psi \, d\tau}{\int \psi^2 \, d\tau} = \frac{\int \psi(\mathbf{H} + V)\psi \, d\tau}{\int \psi^2 \, d\tau}$$

$$= \frac{\int \psi \mathbf{H}\psi \, d\tau}{\int \psi^2 \, d\tau} + \frac{\int \psi V \psi \, d\tau}{\int \psi^2 \, d\tau} = E + \frac{\int V \psi^2 \, d\tau}{\int \psi^2 \, d\tau} \tag{8.2}$$

The energy is increased by the last factor in this equation which is therefore known as the perturbation energy. Naturally, the smaller the perturbation energy the greater will be the accuracy of the procedure.

The above description is essentially that of first-order perturbation theory. In some cases the perturbation energy turns out to be zero and it is then necessary to consider second-order perturbation. One situation where this arises is for the effect of an external electric field on an atom, but this will not be pursued further.

The Ground State of the Helium Atom

The Hamiltonian for the helium atom was formulated in Chapter 4 and is

$$\mathbf{H} = -\frac{h^2}{8\pi^2 m}(\nabla_1{}^2 + \nabla_2{}^2) - \frac{2e^2}{r_1} - \frac{2e^2}{r_2} + \frac{e^2}{r_{12}}$$

where r_1 and r_2 are the distances of the two electrons respectively from the nucleus and r_{12} that between the two electrons (Figure 4.1). If the repulsion energy $+e^2/r_{12}$ between the electrons is ignored then each electron in the ground state of the helium atom would have the energy of a $1s$ electron in the hydrogen-like ion He$^+$. The energy of the unperturbed state is therefore $-2E_{\text{He}^+}$ or -108.32 eV where E_{He^+} is given by equation (7.7). The corresponding eigenfunction would be

$$\psi = \psi_1\psi_2 = \left(\frac{8}{\pi}\right)^{1/2} \exp\left(-2r_1\right)\left(\frac{8}{\pi}\right)^{1/2}\exp\left(-2r_2\right)$$

$$= \frac{8}{\pi}\exp\left[-2(r_1 + r_2)\right] \tag{8.3}$$

where ψ_1 and ψ_2 are $1s$ wave functions for the two electrons (Table 7.3).

This is an important general result which may be proved as follows. Let the wave equations for two unconnected systems be

$$\mathbf{H}_1\psi_1 = E_1\psi_1 \quad \text{and} \quad \mathbf{H}_2\psi_2 = E_2\psi_2$$

Since there is no interaction between them in the unperturbed state the Hamiltonian of the combined system is

$$\mathbf{H} = \mathbf{H}_1 + \mathbf{H}_2$$

and the corresponding wave equation

$$\mathbf{H}\psi = E\psi$$

We can see that $\psi = \psi_1\psi_2$ since

$$\mathbf{H}_1\psi_1\psi_2 = \psi_2\mathbf{H}_1\psi_1 = \psi_2 E_1\psi_1 = E_1\psi_1\psi_2$$

and

$$\mathbf{H_2}\psi_1\psi_2 = \psi_1\mathbf{H_2}\psi_2 = \psi_1E_2\psi_2 = E_2\psi_1\psi_2$$

so that

$$\mathbf{H}\psi \equiv (\mathbf{H_1} + \mathbf{H_2})\psi_1\psi_2 = (E_1 + E_2)\psi_1\psi_2 = E\psi$$

i.e. $\psi = \psi_1\psi_2$ is a satisfactory solution of the wave equation for the non-interacting systems with an eigenvalue of $E = E_1 + E_2$.

Returning to the helium atom, the perturbation energy arising from the repulsion between the electrons would be

$$\frac{\iint \psi_1\psi_2(e^2/r_{12})\psi_1\psi_2 \, d\tau_1 \, d\tau_2}{\iint (\psi_1\psi_2)^2 \, d\tau_1 \, d\tau_2} = \frac{\iint (e^2/r_{12}) \exp\left[-4(r_1 + r_2)\right] d\tau_1 \, d\tau_2}{\iint \exp\left[-4(r_1 + r_2)\right] d\tau_1 \, d\tau_2}$$

These integrals are not particularly difficult to evaluate and give the perturbation energy as $\tfrac{5}{8}E_{\mathrm{He}^+}$. The total energy calculated for the helium atom is therefore $(-2 + \tfrac{5}{8})E_{\mathrm{He}^+} = -1.375\,E_{\mathrm{He}^+}$. The experimental value of $-1.45\,E_{\mathrm{He}^+}$ is about 5% greater.

8.2. The Variation Principle

This is a method for obtaining an upper limit to the energy of a system and for improving approximate expressions for the wave function. The wave equation is

$$\mathbf{H}\psi = E\psi$$

but if only an approximate expression for the wave function ψ, or for the Hamiltonian $\mathbf{H}$ is used, then when $\mathbf{H}$ operates upon ψ the result will not be of the form $E\psi$. A system that possessed these approximate expressions for $\mathbf{H}$ or ψ would not have a quantized energy and only an average value for E could be obtained. This may be done by employing equation (4.2) for the average value of any property which can be associated with a wave mechanical operator. In this case it takes the form

$$\xi = \frac{\int \psi\mathbf{H}\psi \, d\tau}{\int \psi\psi^* \, d\tau} \tag{8.4}$$

where ξ is the average energy associated with these particular values of $\mathbf{H}$ and ψ. If $\mathbf{H}$ is the correct Hamiltonian for the system but ψ only an approximate wave function, then the *variation theorem* states that the mean energy ξ is greater than the true energy E. This very important result is derived in Appendix 6. If we try a series of expressions for the wave function they will be associated with different values of ξ; the lowest will be the nearest to the true energy. Further, we would expect the corresponding expression for the wave function to be the closest to the correct eigenfunction for the system.

The power of the variation method can be extended by including variable parameters in the expression for ψ. Let

$$\psi = f(c_1, c_2 \ldots)$$

Then from equation (8.4)

$$\xi = f(c_1, c_2 \ldots)$$

and the values of the parameters $c_1, c_2 \ldots$ may be found which minimize the value of ξ. In this way the best set of values for these constants may be determined and this in turn gives the best expression for ψ with the general form that has been adopted. Naturally the more parameters which are introduced the better will be the final result. *Whatever extra parameter or term is introduced into the trial wave function the closer must ξ be to the true energy.* Unfortunately there is no way of deciding how much greater. In principle, therefore, the only thing which prevents us from calculating the true energy of the system is the labour and mathematical difficulties involved in handling a wave function that has many unknown parameters.†

The Ground State of Helium

As an example of the use of the variation method to evaluate the best value for a parameter in a trial wave function let us again consider the ground state of the helium atom. The repulsion between the two electrons will produce an expansion of their charge clouds. One way to take account of this is by employing an effective nuclear change $Z'e$, in place of the real value Ze, in the wave function considered above (equation (8.3)). Let

$$\psi = N \exp\left[-Z'(r_1 + r_2)\right]$$

where $Z' < Z = 2$ and N is the normalization factor. Another way to look at this is to say that the one electron screens the nuclear charge from the other electron so that it is under the influence of a charge rather less than Ze.

† As a simple example of the application of the variation principle the reader might like to find ξ for a particle in a box with infinite potential walls (p. 21), using the approximate wave function $\psi = x(a - x)$, and compare it with the exact solution.

If this wave function is now employed in equation (8.4) with the appropriate Hamiltonian, ξ is obtained as a function of Z'. The energy will be minimized when $d\xi/dZ' = 0$ and this leads to the result that $Z' = \frac{27}{16}$, ($\equiv 2 - \frac{5}{16}$). This screening constant of $-\frac{5}{16}$ is obtained for all helium-like atoms (H$^-$, He, Li$^+$ ...). The corresponding value of ξ is $-1.42\ E_{He^+}$ which is only 1.7% greater than the experimental value. The agreement is good but can be further improved by adding additional terms to the wave function. Hylleraas[1] tried many other expressions and found that the next most important modification was to allow for the mutual repulsion between the electrons; their positions are correlated in the sense that the probability of finding them on opposite sides of the nucleus is somewhat greater than that of finding them close together. With the wave function

$$\psi = N(1 + cr_{12}) \exp\left[-Z'(r_1 + r_2)\right]$$

which makes some allowance for this radial correlation, Hylleraas obtained an energy within 0.4% of the true value. This wave function with just two variable parameters, Z' and c, gives a remarkably good result, but in his final treatment, Hylleraas employed a wave function which contained fourteen terms and fifteen adjustable parameters. When the energy was minimized with respect to each of these it was indistinguishable from the experimental value. The advent of high speed computing machines has revolutionized the handling of these complicated functions and Kinoshita[2] was able to employ a function which contained thirty-nine terms (see also Pekeris and Roothaan and Weiss[3,4]).

The simpler functions provide information about the importance of various correction factors to the 'basic expression' for the wave function, given by equation (8.3). The merit of the more complex functions is to show that, even though the wave equation for polyelectronic atoms cannot be solved exactly, nevertheless the technique for obtaining an approximate solution can be so refined by extensive calculation that the theoretical and experimental results are indistinguishable. We may therefore have confidence in the technique even when it is not taken to the limit. There are many papers in the scientific literature[5,6] which consider the problem of the helium atom in terms of a limited number of adjustable parameters. The main objective is to find a form for the wave function which is reasonably accurate, but not too complex to be applied to larger atoms.

Normally the variation method is employed for the ground states of atoms and molecules. If the system is spherically symmetrical then each term in the trial wave function must have this symmetry. If it is also possible to have solutions which possess a nodal plane then each term of these solutions must have the same nodal plane and there could be no contribution from spherically symmetrical functions. In other words, each symmetry type of wave function is independent of the other functions, and so the lowest energy of each symmetry type may be determined by the variation method. For an atom, this means that the energies of the lowest $s, p, d \ldots$ states may be found.

8.3. Symmetrical and Antisymmetrical Wave Functions

We have been careful to consider only the ground state of the helium atom where both electrons are in the $1s$ orbital. In considering an excited helium atom in which the electrons occupy different energy levels† we meet a new and very important wave mechanical principle.

Let the two orbitals which are occupied be labelled ψ_a and ψ_b and the electrons numbered 1 and 2. Then if electron 1 is in orbital a and electron 2 in b, the wave function of the unperturbed atom (i.e. ignoring the repulsion between the electrons) may be written in the form

$$\psi_{(1,2)} = \psi_{a1}\psi_{b2} \tag{8.5}$$

Since the electrons are considered to behave independently of each other their combined energy would be the sum of the energies of He^+ with electrons in these same orbitals, (see also the previous discussion of the ground state on p. 99), i.e.

$$E = E_a + E_b$$

The corresponding wave function in which the electrons have been interchanged

$$\psi_{(2,1)} = \psi_{a2}\psi_{b1} \tag{8.6}$$

obviously satisfies the same equation and has the same eigenvalue. The solutions are degenerate and their linear combination

$$\psi = c_1\psi_{a1}\psi_{b2} + c_2\psi_{a2}\psi_{b1} \tag{8.7}$$

gives other solutions with the same energy. In fact there are an infinite number of solutions which are orthogonal in pairs, (cf. p. 40).

† The orbitals occupied by electrons in polyelectronic atoms are discussed in the next chapter. Their form is not revelant to the present argument but we might note that their shape and designation are the same as for the hydrogen atom.

In the above wave functions it has been assumed that it is possible to distinguish between electrons. There is no experimental method by which this can be done for two electrons in the same atom, and the uncertainty principle implies that there is no possible theoretical distinction either, as the trajectories of electrons in atoms cannot be calculated. We must accept the fundamental principle that *electrons are indistinguishable*, and consequently the wave functions which describe them must not distinguish between electrons. The probability of finding electron 1 at a particular point in orbital *a* and simultaneously of finding electron 2 at a certain position in orbital *b* is given by $\psi^2_{(1,2)}$. If the electrons are interchanged the probability is $\psi^2_{(2,1)}$, but as the electrons are indistinguishable these probabilities must be the same, i.e.

$$\psi^2_{(1,2)} = \psi^2_{(2,1)}$$

Instead of an infinite number of wave functions only two combinations of c_1 and c_2 in equation (8.7) satisfy this requirement. Either $c_1 = c_2$, in which case

$$\psi_+ = N_+(\psi_{a1}\psi_{b2} + \psi_{a2}\psi_{b1}) \tag{8.8}$$

or $c_1 = -c_2$ and

$$\psi_- = N_-(\psi_{a1}\psi_{b2} - \psi_{a2}\psi_{b1}) \tag{8.9}$$

In these equations N_+ and N_- are normalization factors.

If electrons 1 and 2 in equation (8.8) are interchanged the wave function ψ is unaltered—it is said to be symmetrical to the electron exchange. In equation (8.9), ψ_- changes sign when the electrons are interchanged and it is referred to as the antisymmetrical solution. In the unperturbed state these two solutions are degenerate. (When both electrons are in the same orbital there is only the single eigenfunction $\psi_{a1}\psi_{a2}$.)

Perturbation Energy

Let us now consider what happens when the potential energy of repulsion between the electrons is included in the calculation. The perturbation energy ΔE will be given by the last factor in equation (8.2),

$$\Delta E = \frac{\int N_\pm(\psi_{a1}\psi_{b2} \pm \psi_{a2}\psi_{b1})^2(e^2/r_{12})\,d\tau}{\int N_\pm(\psi_{a1}\psi_{b2} \pm \psi_{a2}\psi_{b1})^2\,d\tau}$$

$$= \frac{\int (\psi_{a1}^2\psi_{b2}^2 + \psi_{a2}^2\psi_{b1}^2 \pm 2\psi_{a1}\psi_{b2}\psi_{a2}\psi_{b1})(e^2/r_{12})\,d\tau}{\int (\psi_{a1}^2\psi_{b2}^2 + \psi_{a2}^2\psi_{b1}^2 \pm 2\psi_{a1}\psi_{b2}\psi_{a2}\psi_{b1})\,d\tau}$$

The first two terms make equal contributions to ΔE so this equation may be simplified

$$\Delta E = \frac{\int (\psi_{a1}{}^2\psi_{b2}{}^2 \pm \psi_{a1}\psi_{b2}\psi_{a2}\psi_{b1})(e^2/r_{12})\,d\tau}{\int (\psi_{a1}{}^2\psi_{b2}{}^2 \pm \psi_{a1}\psi_{b2}\psi_{a2}\psi_{b1})\,d\tau} \qquad (8.10)$$

Consider the first integral in the numerator

$$\int \frac{\psi_{a1}{}^2\psi_{b2}{}^2 e^2}{r_{12}}\,d\tau = Q$$

$\psi_{a1}{}^2e$ and $\psi_{b2}{}^2e$ are the charge densities of two electrons at particular points in their respective orbitals and $\psi_{a1}{}^2e\psi_{b2}{}^2e/r_{12}$ is the corresponding coulombic repulsion between these points. When this is integrated over all possible positions of the two electrons the result is the coulombic repulsion Q between the charge clouds representing each electron. The second integral

$$\pm \int \frac{\psi_{a1}\psi_{b2}\psi_{a2}\psi_{b1}e^2}{r_{12}}\,d\tau = \pm J$$

could be considered as a coulombic energy between a charge cloud $\psi_{a1}\psi_{b1}e$, in which the electron is distributed over both orbitals, with the corresponding charge cloud for electron 2, but this is not a very happy description. The integral arises through not being able to distinguish between the electrons when they interchange places and it is consequently called the *exchange integral J*. This may also be called the *spin correlation energy*, because as we shall see in the next chapter, $+J$ is associated with paired electron spins and $-J$ with parallel spins. The calculated probability distribution for the two electrons shows that this term also results in some correlation of the positions of the electrons.[7] When the spins are paired there is a slight tendency for them to be drawn together but when they are parallel the tendency is for them to move apart. This effect is independent of the *charge correlation* resulting from the coulombic repulsion between electrons. For atoms, J is a positive quantity and normally numerically greater than Q.

Now consider the denominator in equation (8.10). If the individual wave functions are normalized

$$\int \psi_{a1}{}^2\,d\tau = \int \psi_{b2}{}^2\,d\tau = 1$$

and since they must be orthogonal (see Appendix 5)

$$\int \psi_{a1}\psi_{b1}\,d\tau_1 = \int \psi_{a2}\psi_{b2}\,d\tau_2 = 0$$

Hence the denominator is unity and the perturbation energy

$$\Delta E = Q \pm J$$

In the perturbed state the degeneracy of ψ_+ and ψ_- is removed. If both electrons are in the same orbital the wave functions represented by equations (8.5), (8.6), and (8.7) become identical and the perturbation energy is simply Q, the coulombic repulsion energy. These results are shown diagrammatically in Figure 8.1.

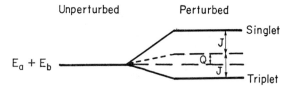

FIGURE 8.1   The perturbation energy of helium (ground and excited states).

The expressions for the wave function may be modified to allow for screening, electron correlation, etc. as discussed previously for the ground state. The existence of symmetrical and antisymmetrical wave functions of different energies is a characteristic feature of wave mechanical treatments of both atoms and molecules (cf. Section 3.6).

8.4. One-electron Wave Functions

In an atomic or molecular system containing several electrons the Hamiltonian for one of the electrons may be written in the form

$$\mathbf{H} = -\frac{8\pi^2 m}{h^2}\,\nabla_1^2 - \sum \frac{Ze^2}{r_a} + \sum \frac{e^2}{r_i} \tag{8.11}$$

where the first summation covers the coulombic attraction of the electron for each nucleus and the second the repulsion between electron 1 and each of the other electrons. The eigenfunctions of this electron would satisfy the equation

$$\mathbf{H}\psi_1 = E_1\psi_1$$

Unfortunately to solve this equation and obtain the *one-electron wave function* ψ_1, and hence the charge cloud due to the electron, the wave functions and charge cloud distributions must be known for each of the other electrons so that the last term in equation (8.11) can be evaluated. The wave functions for each electron are mutually dependent.

The first two terms in equation (8.11) depend only upon electron 1 and the nuclei, and are sometimes termed the 'core Hamiltonian' $\mathbf{H}_1$. It is the third term ($V_1 = \Sigma(e^2/r_i)$) representing the electronic repulsions which causes the trouble mathematically, and normally only an approximate analysis is possible.

Slater Wave Functions for Atoms

Only the outermost electrons in atoms are involved in valence problems and so an approximate, but simple, expression for their wave functions would be of great value. Slater[8] suggested that as an approximation to the radial part of the wave function the effect of all the inner electrons could be allowed for by considering the valence electron to move in a central field of charge $+Z'e$. The effective nuclear charge Z' differs from the nuclear charge by the screening effect of the inner electrons. When this is done, only the core Hamiltonian remains and the mathematics is considerably simplified. In these circumstances the wave equation for each electron becomes

$$\mathbf{H}_1\psi_1 = \left(-\frac{8\pi^2 m}{h^2} \nabla_1^2 + \frac{Z'e^2}{r_1} \right)\psi_1 = E_1\psi_1$$

and the solutions resemble those for the hydrogen atom. Slater actually further simplified the wave functions so that their inner spherical nodes are missing (see Appendix 7). These functions, because of their simplicity and comparative accuracy, have been employed extensively for calculations on atoms and molecules. It is because of the great use which is made of these functions that they have been mentioned in this chapter on 'techniques'.

BIBLIOGRAPHICAL REFERENCES

1. Hylleraas, E. A., *Z. Phys.*, 1929, **54**, 347.
2. Kinoshita, T., *Phys. Rev.*, 1957, **105**, 1490.

108   SOLUTIONS OF THE SCHRÖDINGER EQUATION

3. Pekeris, C. L., *Phys. Rev.*, 1958, **112,** 1649.
4. Roothaan, C. C. J., Weiss, A., *Rev. Mod. Phys.*, 1960, **32,** 194.
5. Lennard-Jones, J. E., and Pople, J. A., *Phil. Mag.*, 1952, **43,** 581.
6. Taylor, G. R., and Parr, R. G., *Proc. Nat. Acad. Sci., U.S.A.*, 1952, **38,** 154.
7. Dickens, P. G., and Linnett, J. W., *Quart. Rev.*, 1957, **11,** 291.
8. Slater, J. C., *Phys. Rev.*, 1930, **36,** 57.

CHAPTER 9

POLYELECTRONIC ATOMS

We have seen that the wave equation for an atom which contains more than one electron cannot be solved in the exact manner possible for hydrogen. The helium atom with two electrons was considered in the previous chapter and this treatment must now be extended and generalized.

In the first place the wave function for each electron will be the product of radial and angular factors. When hydrogen was discussed it was found that the angular factor $\Theta\Phi$ did not involve the potential energy of the electron. Hence we would anticipate that the angular factors in polyelectronic atoms would be independent of the number and nature of the electrons present, particularly when the potential field is spherically symmetrical. The radial factor, however, does involve the potential energy, and will depend upon the probability distribution of each of the other electrons. The energy naturally also depends upon the coulombic repulsions in the atom.

9.1. Space Wave Functions

Two space, or orbital, wave functions were found to exist in the two-electron problem, namely

$$\psi_+ = N_+(\psi_{a1}\psi_{b2} + \psi_{a2}\psi_{b1}) \tag{8.8}$$

and

$$\psi_- = N_-(\psi_{a1}\psi_{b2} - \psi_{a2}\psi_{b1}) \tag{8.9}$$

The symbols ψ_{a1}, ψ_{b2}, etc. are the wave functions of electrons 1 and 2 in orbitals a and b respectively and will be very similar to the one-electron wave functions found for hydrogen-like atoms. The functions ψ_+ and ψ_- have the above forms because electrons are indistinguishable, and all theoretical expressions must treat them as such.

If there are three electrons and three orbitals many more terms have to be included in the expression for the total orbital wave function of the atom. For example,

$$\psi = N(\psi_{a1}\psi_{b2}\psi_{c3} + \psi_{a1}\psi_{b3}\psi_{c2} + \psi_{a2}\psi_{b1}\psi_{c3}$$
$$+ \psi_{a2}\psi_{b3}\psi_{c1} + \psi_{a3}\psi_{b1}\psi_{c2} + \psi_{a3}\psi_{b2}\psi_{c1})$$

and

$$\psi' = N'(\psi_{a1}\psi_{b2}\psi_{c3} - \psi_{a1}\psi_{b3}\psi_{c2} - \psi_{a2}\psi_{b1}\psi_{c3}$$
$$+ \psi_{a2}\psi_{b3}\psi_{c1} + \psi_{c3}\psi_{b1}\psi_{a2} - \psi_{a3}\psi_{b2}\psi_{c1})$$

These are considerably simplified if two electrons occupy the same atomic orbital, as may be seen by writing a in place of b in the above equations.

9.2. Spin Wave Functions

The components of angular momentum and magnetic moment associated with the orbital momentum of an electron can only have $2l + 1$ quantized values in any reference direction, such as that provided by an external magnetic field (Sections 6.4 and 7.4). They are designated by the quantum number m_l. In the presence of a magnetic field $2l + 1$ different energies of interaction between the field and electron are possible. This splitting of the energy level results in a corresponding splitting of the lines in the atomic spectrum of the atom (Zeeman effect). Since l is an integer, $2l + 1$ must be an odd number and, from studying the Zeeman effect, cases have indeed been found where an energy level splits into an odd number of components. There are many cases however where the splitting is into an even number. This problem was solved by Uhlenbeck and Goudsmit[1,2] in 1925. They suggested that in addition to its orbital motion, characterized by the quantum numbers l and m_l, an electron is also capable of a spinning motion with an angular momentum of $\sqrt{[s(s + 1)]}$ in units of $h/2\pi$, and a component of this in a particular direction of m_s units. To fit the experimental facts, the spin quantum number s of a single electron can only have the value of $\frac{1}{2}$, and the spin magnetic quantum number m_s is consequently restricted to $+\frac{1}{2}$ or $-\frac{1}{2}$; these will be designated α or $\uparrow$ and β or $\downarrow$ respectively. It does not necessarily follow that this spin represents an actual motion of the electron. The concept of 'spin' was introduced to explain certain experimental observations, but Dirac[3,4] demonstrated that spin, or rather the phenomenon of spin momentum and its associated magnetic moment, appear automatically when the Schrödinger equation is made consistent with relativity theory.

If an electron is in an s state the orbital angular momentum is zero ($m_l = 0$) but it will still possess a spin angular momentum. When l is greater than zero the electron has a finite quantized angular momentum. In this case the orbital and spin magnetic moments interact, and since each is quantized in a particular direction their resultant will also be quantized. In terms of quantum numbers this may be represented by their vectorial sum, as follows:

$$j = l \pm s = l + \tfrac{1}{2}$$

$$m_j = m_l \pm m_s = m_l \pm \tfrac{1}{2}$$

where j designates the total angular momentum. Because of this magnetic interaction, states with $j = l + \tfrac{1}{2}$ and $j = l - \tfrac{1}{2}$ have different energies, provided $l \neq 0$, but the difference is usually sufficiently small for it to be neglected in theoretical calculations. Each level will split into $2j + 1$ components in a magnetic field and since j is half integral this can be an odd or an even number.

The existence of electron spin has important consequences for the formulation and symmetry of wave functions. Conventionally, the spin of an electron is represented by multiplying the space wave function of an electron by α or by β. Total electronic wave functions are therefore of the form $\psi_{a1}\alpha$, $\psi_{b2}\beta$, etc. For two electrons their combined spin wave functions could be $\alpha_1\alpha_2$, $\beta_1\beta_2$, $\alpha_1\beta_2$, or $\beta_1\alpha_2$. The first two of these are symmetrical to an exchange of electrons, but the last two are neither symmetrical or antisymmetrical. In fact they resemble the space wave functions (8.5) and (8.6), and have to be replaced by linear combinations which are either symmetrical or antisymmetrical. The four possible spin functions which do not distinguish between two electrons are therefore

	Angular momentum along the z axis
$\psi_1 = \alpha_1\alpha_2$	$h/2\pi$
$\psi_2 = \dfrac{1}{\sqrt{2}}(\alpha_1\beta_2 + \alpha_2\beta_1)$	0
$\psi_3 = \beta_1\beta_2$	$-h/2\pi$
$\psi_4 = \dfrac{1}{\sqrt{2}}(\alpha_1\beta_2 - \alpha_2\beta_1)$	0

Of these four functions the first three represent parallel spins† ($\uparrow\uparrow$ or $\downarrow\downarrow$) and are symmetrical to an exchange of electrons, whilst the last, ψ_4, is antisymmetrical and corresponds to paired spins ($\uparrow\downarrow$).

† ψ_2 may be considered to have parallel spins but in a direction such that there is no resultant angular momentum along the reference z axis.

9.3. The Pauli Exclusion Principle

If the interaction between the spin and orbital motions is negligible, the complete wave function for a two-electron problem is given by the products of the space and the spin functions. There are eight possibilities.

$$
\left.
\begin{aligned}
\psi_{\mathrm{I}} &= \psi_+\psi_1 \\
\psi_{\mathrm{II}} &= \psi_+\psi_2 \\
\psi_{\mathrm{III}} &= \psi_+\psi_3 \\
\psi_{\mathrm{IV}}^* &= \psi_+\psi_4
\end{aligned}
\right\}
= N(\psi_{a1}\psi_{b2} + \psi_{a2}\psi_{b1})
\left\{
\begin{aligned}
&\alpha_1\alpha_2 \\
&\alpha_1\beta_2 + \alpha_2\beta_1 \\
&\beta_1\beta_2 \\
&\alpha_1\beta_2 - \alpha_2\beta_1
\end{aligned}
\right.
$$

$$
\left.
\begin{aligned}
\psi_{\mathrm{V}}^* &= \psi_-\psi_1 \\
\psi_{\mathrm{VI}}^* &= \psi_-\psi_2 \\
\psi_{\mathrm{VII}}^* &= \psi_-\psi_3 \\
\psi_{\mathrm{VIII}} &= \psi_-\psi_4
\end{aligned}
\right\}
= N(\psi_{a1}\psi_{b2} - \psi_{a2}\psi_{b1})
\left\{
\begin{aligned}
&\alpha_1\alpha_2 \\
&\alpha_1\beta_2 + \alpha_2\beta_1 \\
&\beta_1\beta_2 \\
&\alpha_1\beta_2 - \alpha_2\beta_1
\end{aligned}
\right. \qquad (9.1)
$$

Of these total wave functions four, ψ_{I}, ψ_{II}, ψ_{III}, and ψ_{VIII}, are symmetrical to an exchange of electrons and the other four, which are starred in the above list, are antisymmetrical. The existence of eight wave functions is not in agreement with experimental findings however. From an examination of the spectra of atoms and molecules and the effect of an external magnetic field upon them, it is found that the only energy levels which exist are those whose complete wave functions are antisymmetrical to an exchange of electrons. This fundamental postulate of wave mechanics was proposed by Pauli[5]† and has become known as his *exclusion principle*. In the above list only the wave functions which are starred can represent the actual state of an atom.

If the space part of the wave function is symmetrical to an exchange of electrons (ψ_{IV}) then the spin factor must be antisymmetrical and the spins paired. This is a singlet level and is not split into components by an external magnetic field. Conversely, when the space part is antisymmetrical (ψ_{V}, ψ_{VI}, and ψ_{VII}) then the spin factor must be symmetrical and the electron spins parallel. It is a triplet state, and because of the magnetic interaction between orbital and spin motions the three states may not have exactly the same energies; this becomes more apparent in an external

† For particles with an integral spin, in units of $h/2\pi$, only the symmetrical functions are found, (e.g. photons and alpha particles).

magnetic field. If both electrons occupy the same orbital, as in the ground state of helium, the energy level must be a singlet and the spins paired; otherwise the spins can be either paired or parallel, and both singlet and triplet states exist with slightly different energies. According to a rule due to Hund, the triplet state possesses the lower energy (cf. Figure 8.1).

Suppose there are a number of orbitals in which both the space and the spin parts are defined (e.g. $1s\alpha$, $2p\beta$, $3d\beta$, etc.); these are sometimes called *spin orbitals*. Then the total wave function for the atom may be expressed as the sum of the products of these spin orbitals. For three electrons and three spin orbitals A, B, and C, the wave function is

$$\psi = A_1B_2C_3 - A_1B_3C_2 + A_2B_3C_1 - A_2B_1C_3 + A_3B_1C_2 - A_3B_2C_1$$

$$= \sum_p (-1)^p P(A_1B_2C_3) \qquad (9.2)$$

where P stands for the permutation of 1, 2, and 3, and p the number of interchanges of electrons necessary to get from the generating function $A_1B_2C_3$ to one of the other terms. If this requires an odd number of changes, $(-1)^p$ is negative (e.g. 1, 2, 3 → 1, 3, 2), but for an even number of changes $(-1)^p$ is positive, (e.g. 1, 2, 3 → 2, 3, 1). This is a general procedure and the summation form is particularly suitable if many spin orbitals are involved; for six orbitals there are no less than 720 terms in the wave function. Another way of representing the wave function is as a determinant

$$\psi = \begin{vmatrix} A_1 & A_2 & A_3 \\ B_1 & B_2 & B_3 \\ C_1 & C_2 & C_3 \end{vmatrix} \qquad (9.3)$$

This form is due to Slater and may be abbreviated by writing just the leading diagonal in the form

$$\psi = \det \{A_1 \quad B_2 \quad C_3\} \qquad (9.4)$$

The important feature of each of these formulations is that they are consistent with the Pauli exclusion principle —the wave functions are antisymmetrical. It is obvious from these expressions that if any two spin orbitals were identical, say A and B, then two rows in the determinant would be the same and ψ zero. In other words, two electrons cannot be in the same spin orbital or their values of the four quantum numbers n, l, m_l, and m_s cannot be the same.

Suppose the three space orbitals are all different. In this case the resultant spin could either be 3/2, in which case the wave function is given by (9.1), (9.2), or (9.3), or it could be 1/2, say two electrons with spin α and one with spin β. Now any of the three orbitals could have the β spin and there is no means of deciding which. Hence the wave functions should be written as a combination of three determinants,

$$\psi = \det \{(\psi_a\alpha)_1, (\psi_b\alpha)_2, (\psi_c\beta)_3\}$$
$$\pm \det \{(\psi_a\alpha)_1, (\psi_b\beta)_2, (\psi_c\alpha)_3\}$$
$$\pm \det \{(\psi_a\beta)_1, (\psi_b\alpha)_2, (\psi_c\alpha)_3\}$$

For two spin orbitals we can see immediately that this leads to the wave functions ψ_{IV}, ψ_V, ψ_{VI}, and ψ_{VII} formulated in equations (9.1).

9.4. The Electronic Structure of Atoms

By the combination of experiment and theory outlined in the previous pages we have arrived at the following conclusions about the electronic structure of atoms.

1. The electrons will occupy orbitals, the size of which will be mainly governed by the effective nuclear charge and by the value of the principal quantum number n, and whose shape is fixed by the azimuthal quantum number l. There are $2l + 1$ degenerate energy levels designated by their magnetic quantum number m_l.

2. Each electron has also a spin quantum number $s = \frac{1}{2}$, and there are two spin states designated by the values of m_s.

3. The total wave function must be antisymmetrical for the exchange of any two electrons (Pauli exclusion principle). This means that they cannot exist in the same orbital with parallel spins, or in terms of quantum numbers, no two electrons in an atom can possess the same values for the four quantum numbers n, l, m_l, and m_s.

4. The energy of an electron is primarily determined by the value of n and the effective nuclear charge $Z'e$. The interaction energy with the other electrons does depend to some extent upon the shape of the orbital, so that electrons in orbitals which differ in their value of l also have somewhat different energies.

We might consider atoms to be built up in sequence, starting with hydrogen and generating the next atom by the addition of one proton, plus neutrons, to the nucleus and one electron to the valence shell. The approximate sequence of orbitals into which the additional electron enters as the atomic number of the element is increased by one is shown diagrammatically in Figure 9.1. The electronic energy of an atom strives to attain a minimum value, subject to the restrictions of the Pauli principle. Hence the additional electron

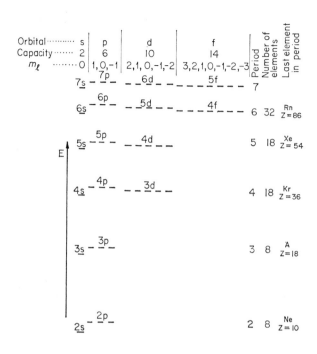

FIGURE 9.1 The relative energies of the valence orbitals of atoms.

normally enters an orbital of the same energy as the previous electron, but if this is not possible it enters the orbital of next greatest energy.

5. The spin of an electron has comparatively little effect upon its energy and is generally ignored in theoretical calculations.

6. If electrons can occupy degenerate orbitals then the lowest energy state is determined by Hund's rules which are:

   a. Electrons avoid occupying the same space orbital in order to lessen the coulombic repulsion between them, and so that,

   b. The electrons have parallel spins. This tends to keep the electrons even further apart (spin correlation) and further lowers the energy through electron exchange or resonance.

From Figure 9.1 it is evident that lithium, for example, with three electrons would have two in the $1s$ shell and one in the orbital $(2s)$ of next higher energy. This is written as

$$Li, 1s^2 2s^1 \quad or \quad 1s^2 2s$$

Some other structures are:

$$C, 1s^2\ 2s^2\ 2p_x\ 2p_y$$

(Hund's rules show that in the ground state two electrons in the $2p$ orbitals will occupy any two of the degenerate p_x, p_y, and p_z orbitals and have parallel spins.)

$$K, 1s^2\ 2s^2\ 2p^6\ 3s^2\ 3p^6\ 4s$$

$$V, 1s^2\ 2s^2\ 2p^6\ 3s^2\ 3p^6\ 3d^3\ 4s^2$$

(Note that the $4s$ level is occupied before the $3d$.)

$$Cr, 1s^2\ 2s^2\ 2p^6\ 3s^2\ 3p^6\ 3d^5\ 4s$$

(This has a slightly lower energy than the configuration . . . $3d^4\ 4s^2$ because of an additional stability, which results through having one electron in each of the five $3d$ orbitals.)

The electronic structures of all atoms are recorded in Appendix 9.

Figure 9.1 has its limitations. It would lead one to predict a slightly incorrect structure for chromium (see above), and for some other atoms. This is not of great importance but there are two more serious inaccuracies. It implies that $3d$ electrons, for example, always have energies much greater than the $3p$ electrons, greater even than the $4s$ electrons. That this is not the case for the *inner electrons* of heavy atoms is demonstrated by their X-ray spectra. The other point may be illustrated by reference to scandium. Since the additional electron it possesses, compared with calcium, is in the $3d$ orbital one would expect it to be the first to be lost upon ionization to give Sc^+. This is contrary to spectroscopic evidence which indicates that the 19th electron added to a scandium nucleus, to give Sc^{2+}, is a $3d$ electron whilst the 20th and 21st, enter the $4s$ orbital.

When electrons are 'added' to an ion they occupy energy levels which confer the greatest stability upon the whole system. In the case of scandium, $Sc^{2+}(. . . 3d^1)$ has a lower energy than $Sc^{2+}(. . . 4s^1)$, and $Sc^+(. . . 3d^1\ 4s^1)$ is more stable than either $Sc^+(. . . 3d^2)$ or $Sc^+(. . . 4s^2)$. Another way of looking at this is to imagine that calcium can be converted into scandium in two steps. First add a proton. This will cause a rearrangement of the valence electrons

$$Ca(. . . 3d^0\ 4s^2) \rightarrow Sc^+(. . . 3d^1\ 4s^1)$$

Now add the electron which will enter the 4s level. Likewise,

$$Sc(\ldots 3d^1\, 4s^2) \rightarrow Ti^+(\ldots 3d^2\, 4s^1)$$

so that the last electron to be put round a titanium nucleus is also a 4s electron.

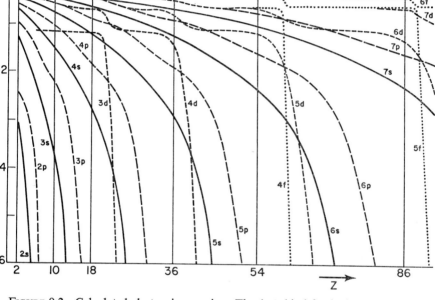

FIGURE 9.2   Calculated electronic energies. The 1s orbital for hydrogen has unit energy on the scale employed.

The only way to find the precise ground state electronic configuration of atoms and ions is by experiment—spectroscopic data[6] and ionization potentials. The information can also be presented in the form of a chart.[7,8] Finally in Figure 9.2 *calculated* electronic energies[9] are shown as a function of atomic number. This shows very clearly the lowering of all energy levels as the nuclear charge increases, and the grouping of the inner electrons into shells determined by the principal quantum number. A detailed examination of this diagram unfortunately shows that the calculated curves do not cross one another at the points corresponding to the start and end of the d- and f-transition series of elements, and so is not completely reliable.

The full significance of atomic structures with respect to the periodic classification of the elements is discussed in books of inorganic chemistry. It is the unpaired electrons which can form covalent bonds by interacting with similar electrons of other atoms. Two mutually paired electrons in the outermost shell, or valency shell, which do not contribute to the valency of the atom are called *lone-pair* electrons.

9.5. Self-consistent Field Methods

Hartree Wave Functions

In 1927 Hartree[10,11] suggested what is now known as the self-consistent field method for dealing with many electron atoms. With one improvement, it remains the most satisfactory general method for atoms. Suppose we have k electrons in spin orbitals $A, B, C, \ldots K$. Hartree took the total atomic wave function to be the product

$$\psi = A_1 B_2 C_3 \ldots K_k \qquad (9.5)$$

This makes two main assumptions; (1) it does not allow explicitly for the distance r_{ij} between two electrons, but to incorporate this electron correlation would introduce tremendous complications, and (2) it does not recognize that electrons are indistinguishable. Provided each single-electron wave function $A, B \ldots$, is normalized, the best wave function of the above type will be the one for which

$$\xi = \int \psi \mathbf{H} \psi \, d\tau \qquad (9.6)$$

is a minimum (from the variation principle). The Hamiltonian $\mathbf{H}$ for the atom is

$$\mathbf{H} = \sum_{i=1}^{k} \left(-\frac{h^2}{8\pi^2 m} \nabla_i^2 - \frac{Ze^2}{r_i} \right) + \frac{1}{2} \sum_i \sum_{j \neq i} \frac{e^2}{r_{ij}}$$

$$= \sum \mathbf{H}_i + \text{Coulombic repulsions between the electrons} \quad (9.7)$$

where $\mathbf{H}_i$ represents the one-electron 'core' Hamiltonians. The second summation in equation (9.7) represents the potential energy of repulsion between the electrons, which is taken as the interaction of each electron with the time average distribution, or charge cloud, of all the other electrons. For electron 1 at any instant this would be

$$V_1 = e \int \frac{B_2^2 e}{r_2} \, d\tau_2 + e \int \frac{C_3^2 e}{r_3} \, d\tau_3 + \ldots \qquad (9.8)$$

This neglects any correlation between the positions of the electrons and a further approximation is made by averaging this expression over all angles so that it becomes spherically symmetrical. For each electron the Hamiltonian is

$$\mathscr{H}_i = \mathbf{H}_i + V_i$$

and the solution of equation (9.6) shows that the best possible expression for ψ is obtained by solving the k simultaneous equations of the form

$$\mathscr{H}_1 A_1 = \xi_1 A_1 \qquad (9.9)$$

The procedure is therefore as follows

1. Guess at expressions for the spin orbital functions $A_1, B_2 \ldots$ (the choice being guided by the functions found for similar atoms).
2. From these, calculate the average charge cloud distribution and hence V_i.
3. Equation (9.9) is now solved for each electron to obtain a more accurate set of functions. This can always be done numerically when the potential field is spherically symmetrical and is best accomplished with an electronic computer.
4. The above steps are repeated as many times as is necessary for the wave functions to be unchanged by further repetition.

Each electron may be represented by a charge cloud obtained by solving equation (9.9) in which the potential terms are due to the nucleus and the charge clouds of the other electrons—they are self consistent. The total energy of the atom is

$$\xi = \sum \xi_i - \sum V_i$$

(The potential term $\sum V_i$ has to be subtracted as it is already included in the calculation of each ξ_i value and would otherwise be counted twice.) The energy so obtained is in error by about $0{\cdot}5$ eV per electron.

These calculations give a theoretical value for the ionization potential of each electron in the atom, and the wave functions are used to obtain the 'scattering factors' for X-ray and electron diffraction studies and also to provide an estimate of the size of atoms.

Hartree–Fock Wave Functions

A big objection to the Hartree method is that the atomic wave function (9.5) does not admit that electrons are indistinguishable and so does not satisfy the exclusion principle. Fock[12,13] overcame this by employing a determinental function (cf. equations (9.3) and (9.4)) in place of (9.5).

$$\psi = \det \{A_1 \, B_2 \, C_3 \ldots K_k\} \qquad (9.10)$$

This is subject to the additional restriction that the individual spin orbitals are orthogonal. It introduces further potential terms into the expression for $\mathscr{H}$ in equation (9.9), corresponding to the possibility of electron exchange between orbitals with the same spins. The calculations are naturally more accurate, but the results for the wave functions and energies do not differ very greatly from those of the simpler Hartree procedure.

BIBLIOGRAPHICAL REFERENCES

1. Uhlenbeck, G. E., and Goudsmit, S., *Naturwiss.*, 1925, **13**, 953.
2. Uhlenbeck, G. E., and Goudsmit, S., *Nature*, 1926, **117**, 264.
3. Dirac, P. A. M., *Proc. Roy. Soc.*, 1928, A**117**, 610.
4. Dirac, P. A. M., *Proc. Roy. Soc.*, 1928, A**118**, 351.
5. Pauli, W., *Z. Phys.*, 1925, **31**, 765.
6. Moore, C. E., Atomic Energy Levels, *Circular Nat. Bur. Stand No. 467*, Vol. I, 1949; Vol. II, 1952; Vol. III, 1958.
7. De Vault, D., *J. Chem. Educ.*, 1944, **21**, 575.
8. Keller, R. N., *J. Chem. Educ.*, 1962, **39**, 289.
9. Latter, R., *Phys. Rev.*, 1955, **99**, 510.
10. Hartree, D. R., *Proc. Camb. Phil. Soc.*, 1927, **24**, 89, 111, 426.
11. Hartree, D. R., *The Calculation of Atomic Structures*, John Wiley, New York, 1957.
12. Fock, V., *Z. Phys.*, 1930, **61**, 126.
13. Fock, V., *Z. Phys.*, 1930, **62**, 795.

CHAPTER 10

DIATOMIC MOLECULES

In this chapter a wave mechanical approach to molecular structure will be developed. The wave equations for molecules cannot be solved exactly, so the first problem is how to formulate molecular wave functions. We can only hope to obtain approximate expressions to start with, but by means of the variation procedure these could be improved, in principle, to give eigenvalues with considerable accuracy. In practice, extensive refinements are usually very laborious and intricate mathematically so that, apart from the simplest diatomic molecules, the hydrogen molecule ion H_2^+ and the hydrogen molecule H_2, they have not been carried very far. Nevertheless, even the very approximate treatments provide valuable insights into the nature of chemical bonds. Also, the estimated values for their energies and the calculated electron distribution in the molecules are extremely important for the appreciation of many physico-chemical aspects of molecules.

The starting point in formulating the expressions for molecular wave functions is, not unnaturally, the solutions obtained for the isolated atoms forming the molecule. These have been combined in two main ways. In the older theory, the method of *molecular orbitals* (M.O.), one attempts to construct orbitals resembling atomic orbitals but centred round more than one nucleus. This theory was first applied to metals by Bloch,[1] and it was not until a later date that Hund, Mulliken, Lennard-Jones, and many others, used it for molecules. In the meanwhile the *valence bond* (V.B.) theory, which Heitler and London employed to explain the stability of the hydrogen molecule, had been extensively developed by Pauling. In this approximation, bonds are considered to be formed by pairing the spins of particular electrons from each atom. Since both approaches are approximations the energies and charge distributions which each gives for the same molecule differ somewhat, but the more each theory is refined the closer together become the two sets of results and the greater is our confidence in them.

10.1. Space Wave Functions

Valence Bond Approximation

Let us consider the original approach of Heitler and London[2] to the problem of the hydrogen molecule. Consider first of all two hydrogen atoms, (nucleus a with electron 1 and nucleus b with electron 2), sufficiently far apart for the coulombic interactions between them to be negligible. Each atom will be in its ground state and if we denote their $1s$ atomic wave functions by ψ_{a1} and ψ_{b2} respectively, their individual wave equations are

$$\mathbf{H}_1 \psi_{a1} = E_a \psi_{a1} \qquad \mathbf{H}_1 = -\frac{h^2}{8\pi^2 m} \nabla_1^2 - \frac{e^2}{r_{a1}}$$

$$\mathbf{H}_2 \psi_{b2} = E_b \psi_{b2} \qquad \mathbf{H}_2 = -\frac{h^2}{8\pi^2 m} \nabla_2^2 - \frac{e^2}{r_{b2}}$$

The energy of the two atoms together is obviously

$$E = E_a + E_b = 2E_{\mathrm{H}}$$

where E_{H} is the energy of a hydrogen atom (equation (7.7)). Since there is no interaction between the systems their combined Hamiltonian is

$$\mathbf{H} = \mathbf{H}_1 + \mathbf{H}_2$$

$$= -\frac{h^2}{8\pi^2 m} (\nabla_1^2 + \nabla_2^2) - \frac{e^2}{r_{a1}} - \frac{e^2}{r_{b2}} \qquad (10.1)$$

and, as we saw on page 99, the combined wave function will be

$$\psi = \psi_{a1} \psi_{b2}$$

$$= \frac{1}{\pi} \exp \left[-(r_{a1} + r_{b2}) \right] \qquad (10.2)$$

These relationships are all exact. Now let us consider what happens if the two atoms are brought closer together (Figure 10.1).

There will be an interaction between the two atoms and the Hamiltonian of the system will now include four additional potential terms.

$$\mathbf{H} = -\frac{h^2}{8\pi^2 m} (\nabla_1^2 + \nabla_2^2) - \frac{e^2}{r_{a1}} - \frac{e^2}{r_{b2}} - \frac{e^2}{r_{a2}} - \frac{e^2}{r_{b1}} + \frac{e^2}{r_{12}} + \frac{e^2}{r_{ab}}$$

$$(10.3)$$

The usual equation

$$\mathbf{H}\psi = E\psi$$

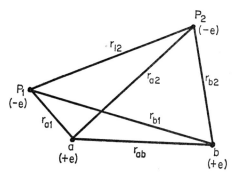

FIGURE 10.1 Coordinates for the hydrogen molecule. The nuclei are at
a and b and the electrons at P_1 and P_2.

has to be solved with this expression for **H**. As a first approximation,
assume that the eigenfunction applicable at large internuclear
distances, equation (10.2), is still adequate. The energy will not
have a sharp value and a mean energy ξ has to be obtained from
equation (8.4).

$$\xi = \frac{\int \psi \mathbf{H} \psi \, d\tau}{\int \psi^2 \, d\tau}$$

In other words we have to evaluate

$$\xi = \frac{\int \psi_{a1}\psi_{b2}\left[-\dfrac{h^2}{8\pi^2 m}(\nabla_1{}^2 + \nabla_2{}^2) - \dfrac{e^2}{r_{a1}} - \dfrac{e^2}{r_{b2}} - \dfrac{e^2}{r_{a2}} - \dfrac{e^2}{r_{b1}} + \dfrac{e^2}{r_{12}} + \dfrac{e^2}{r_{ab}}\right]\psi_{a1}\psi_{b2} \, d\tau}{\int \psi_{a1}{}^2\psi_{b2}{}^2 \, d\tau} \quad (10.4)$$

If the individual atomic wave functions are normalized the denominator is unity. Now consider the numerator. The first four terms
in the Hamiltonian are those of equation (10.1) and give rise to the
energy of the two isolated hydrogen atoms $2E_H$. The next term in
equation (10.4) is $-\int \psi_{a1}\psi_{b2}(e^2/r_{a2})\psi_{a1}\psi_{b2} \, d\tau$, which may be written
in the form $-\int [(\psi_{b2}{}^2 e)e/r_{a2}] \, d\tau_2$, since the potential term does not
involve electron 1 and $\int \psi_{a1}{}^2 \, d\tau_1 = 1$. But $\psi_{b2}{}^2 e$ is the fractional
charge due to electron 2 at a particular point in orbital ψ_b and so
the integral is simply the coulombic attraction Q_{a2} between nucleus
a and the charge cloud which represents electron 2. The next term
is likewise the coulombic attraction of nucleus b for electron 1.

The penultimate term may be written as $[\int (\psi_{a1}{}^2 e)(\psi_{b2}{}^2 e)/r_{12}]\,d\tau$ and is the coulombic repulsion Q_{12} between the two electrons considered as charge clouds. The final term does not involve the electrons at all and is just the coulombic repulsion Q_{ab} between the two nuclei. Hence equation (10.4) may be reduced to the form

$$\xi = 2E_H - \int \frac{(\psi_{b2}{}^2 e)e}{r_{a2}}\,d\tau_2 - \int \frac{(\psi_{a1}{}^2 e)e}{r_{b1}}\,d\tau_1$$

$$+ \int \frac{(\psi_{a1}{}^2 e)(\psi_{b2}{}^2 e)}{r_{12}}\,d\tau + \frac{e^2}{r_{ab}}$$

$$= 2E_H - Q_{a2} - Q_{b1} + Q_{12} + Q_{ab}$$

$$= 2E_H + Q \tag{10.5}$$

where Q represents the total coulombic interaction energy between the two atoms. Each term contributing to Q depends upon the internuclear distance r_{ab}. The various integrals may be evaluated without too much trouble and the calculated energy ξ, as a function of r_{ab}, has the form shown in Figure 10.2. It has a minimum energy at $r_{ab} = 0.9$ Å when it is about $\frac{1}{4}$ eV less than that of the separated atoms. Although this provides an explanation of the existence of the hydrogen molecule, the numerical values are in poor agreement with experiment.

Heitler and London pointed out a major error in the above treatment, and when they made the necessary correction the agreement with the experimental results was greatly improved. The wave function employed above

$$\psi_I = \psi_{a1}\psi_{b2}$$

assumes that electron 1 is always associated with nucleus a and 2 with b. Heitler and London pointed out that the wave function

$$\psi_{II} = \psi_{a2}\psi_{b1}$$

is equally likely, and since it is a fundamental principle of wave mechanics that electrons are indistinguishable, ψ_I and ψ_{II} have to be replaced by their linear combination

$$\psi = c_1\psi_I \pm c_2\psi_{II}$$

The coefficients c_1 and c_2 are chosen so that ξ is a minimum, but in the case of a homonuclear molecule its symmetry requires that ψ_I and ψ_{II} make equal contributions† to the electron distribution. It follows that

$$c_1{}^2\psi_I{}^2 = c_2{}^2\psi_{II}{}^2$$

† For a formal proof of this statement see page 135.

and
$$c_1 = \pm c_2$$

Consequently there are only two wave functions of the above form which do not distinguish between the electrons. Either,

$$\psi_+ = N(\psi_I + \psi_{II}) = \sqrt{\tfrac{1}{2}}(\psi_{a1}\psi_{b2} + \psi_{a2}\psi_{b1}) \qquad (10.6)$$

or,

$$\psi_- = N(\psi_I - \psi_{II}) = \sqrt{\tfrac{1}{2}}(\psi_{a1}\psi_{b2} - \psi_{a2}\psi_{b1}) \qquad (10.7)$$

Of these, ψ_+ is symmetrical and ψ_- antisymmetrical to the exchange of electrons, but $\psi_+{}^2$ and $\psi_-{}^2$ which are the only quantities with physical significance, are unchanged by electron exchange.

Consider the symmetrical wave function. Then

$$\xi_+ = \frac{\displaystyle\int (\psi_I + \psi_{II})\mathbf{H}(\psi_I + \psi_{II})\,d\tau}{\displaystyle\int (\psi_I + \psi_{II})^2\,d\tau} \qquad (10.8)$$

with the Hamiltonian given by equation (10.3) as before. In this expression the numerator is

$$\int \psi_+\mathbf{H}\psi_+\,d\tau = \int \sqrt{\tfrac{1}{2}}(\psi_I + \psi_{II})\mathbf{H}\sqrt{\tfrac{1}{2}}(\psi_I + \psi_{II})\,d\tau$$

$$= \frac{1}{2}\left[\int \psi_I\mathbf{H}\psi_I\,d\tau + \int \psi_{II}\mathbf{H}\psi_{II}\,d\tau\right.$$

$$\left. + \int \psi_I\mathbf{H}\psi_{II}\,d\tau + \int \psi_{II}\mathbf{H}\psi_I\,d\tau\right]$$

$$= \tfrac{1}{2}[(2E_H + Q) + (2E_H + Q) + J' + J']$$

$$= 2E_H + Q + J' \qquad (10.9)$$

If the expressions for ψ_I and ψ_{II} are considered it will be appreciated that the last two integrals are equivalent, and we shall denote them by J'. The denominator in equation (10.8) is

$$\int \tfrac{1}{2}(\psi_I + \psi_{II})^2\,d\tau = \frac{1}{2}\left[\int \psi_I{}^2\,d\tau + \int \psi_{II}{}^2\,d\tau + 2\int \psi_I\psi_{II}\,d\tau\right]$$

$$= \tfrac{1}{2}[1 + 1 + 2S^2] \qquad (10.10)$$

where $\quad S^2 = \displaystyle\int \psi_I\psi_{II}\,d\tau = \int \psi_{a1}\psi_{b2}\psi_{a2}\psi_{b1}\,d\tau$

$$= \int \psi_{a1}\psi_{b1}\,d\tau_1 \int \psi_{a2}\psi_{b2}\,d\tau_2$$

and where $S = \int \psi_a \psi_b \, d\tau$ is known as the *overlap or non-orthogonality integral*. It is so called because it is only when ψ_a and ψ_b are simultaneously large and of the same phase that there is a significant contribution to S; that is, from those regions of space where the wave functions overlap to an appreciable extent.

Hence the energy associated with the symmetrical wave function is

$$\xi_+ = \frac{2E_H + Q + J'}{1 + S^2} = 2E_H + \frac{Q + (J' - 2E_H S^2)}{1 + S^2}$$

$$= 2E_H + \frac{Q + J}{1 + S^2} \tag{10.11}$$

and similarly

$$\xi_- = \frac{2E_H + Q - J'}{1 - S^2} = 2E_H + \frac{Q - (J' - 2E_H S^2)}{1 - S^2}$$

$$= 2E_H + \frac{Q - J}{1 - S^2} \tag{10.12}$$

In these equations J is known as the exchange integral because it arises through making the wave function symmetrical, or anti-symmetrical, to electron exchange.

$$J = J' - 2E_H S^2 = \int \psi_I H \psi_{II} \, d\tau - 2E_H \int \psi_I \psi_{II} \, d\tau$$

$$= \int \psi_I H \psi_{II} \, d\tau - \int \psi_I (2E_H) \psi_{II} \, d\tau$$

$$= \int \psi_I (H - 2E_H) \psi_{II} \, d\tau$$

$$= \int \psi_{a1} \psi_{b2} \frac{e^2}{r_{12}} \psi_{a2} \psi_{b1} \, d\tau$$

$$- 2S \int \psi_{a1} \frac{e^2}{r_{b1}} \psi_{b1} \, d\tau_1 + \frac{e^2 S^2}{r_{ab}} \tag{10.13}$$

N.B.

$$Q = \int \psi_I (H - 2E_H) \psi_I \, d\tau$$

$$= \int \psi_{a1} \psi_{b2} \frac{e^2}{r_{12}} \psi_{a1} \psi_{b2} \, d\tau - 2 \int \psi_{a1} \frac{e^2}{r_{b1}} \psi_{a1} \, d\tau + \frac{e^2}{r_{ab}} \tag{10.14}$$

Numerically J is negative but of a greater value than Q so that ξ_+ is always less than ξ_-.

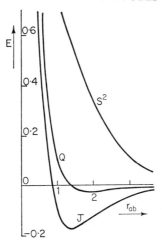

FIGURE 10.2   The integrals Q, J, and S^2 as a function of the internuclear distance r_{ab} for the hydrogen molecule, (in atomic units).

The individual quantities Q, J, and S^2, are shown as a function of r_{ab} in Figure 10.2, and the energy functions ξ_+ and ξ_- in Figure 10.3. It is immediately obvious that the symmetrical wave function ψ_+ has a much more pronounced minimum in its energy curve than was obtained for ψ_I or ψ_{II}. The maximum binding energy calculated for ψ_+ is 3·14 eV (at $r_{ab} = 0·869$ Å) which is to be compared with the experimental value of 4·747 eV (at $r_{ab} = 0·7412$ Å). The energy associated with the antisymmetrical wave function ξ_-

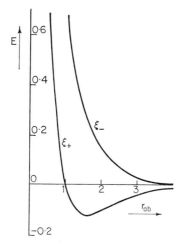

FIGURE 10.3   The energy functions ξ_+ and ξ_- for the hydrogen molecule.

increases continuously as the nuclei are brought closer together, and represents an unstable repulsive state of the hydrogen molecule.

Molecular Orbital Approximation

This differs radically from the valence bond approach by considering just one electron at a time and associating it with both nuclei. In fact orbitals are first constructed for the molecule and the electrons are then placed in them after the manner employed in building up the electronic structure of atoms.

When the electron is close to nucleus a the effective part of the Hamiltonian, and hence of the molecular wave function, must resemble that of one of the atomic orbitals of the isolated atom, say ψ_a. Likewise when it is close to nucleus b the charge cloud will be similar to that from ψ_b. It is therefore natural to take as an approximation to the molecular wave function a *linear combination of atomic orbitals* ψ_a and ψ_b, (the L.C.A.O. approximation).

$$\psi = c_1\psi_a + c_2\psi_b$$

In the case of a homonuclear molecule the electron is equally likely to be found near either nucleus, and so,

$$c_1{}^2 = c_2{}^2 \quad \text{or} \quad c_1 = \pm c_2$$

There are therefore two forms for the wave function. Either

$$\psi_+ = N_+(\psi_a + \psi_b); \quad N^{-2} = 2(1 + S)$$

or

$$\psi_- = N_-(\psi_a - \psi_b); \quad N^{-2} = 2(1 - S)$$

(10.15)

The normalization factors N_+ and N_- are obtained by the usual procedure (cf. equation (10.10)). The expression for obtaining the average value of the energy associated with these wave functions

$$\xi_\pm = \frac{\int \psi_\pm \mathbf{H}\psi_\pm \, d\tau}{\int \psi_\pm{}^2 \, d\tau} = \frac{\int (\psi_a \pm \psi_b)\mathbf{H}(\psi_a \pm \psi_b) \, d\tau}{\int (\psi_a \pm \psi_b)^2 \, d\tau}$$

is formally similar to equation (10.8), and so

$$\xi_\pm = \frac{E_H \pm \beta}{1 \pm S} = E_H \pm \frac{\beta - E_H S}{1 \pm S}$$

(10.16)

In this equation $S = \int \psi_a\psi_b \, d\tau$ is the overlap integral as before and $\beta = \int \psi_a \mathbf{H}\psi_b \, d\tau$ takes the place of J'. This integral cannot strictly be called an exchange integral as it refers to only one electron, so it is known as a resonance integral; resonance, because of analogies which can be drawn with mechanical vibrations. It is an unfortunate term as it might imply that the electron is resonating, or vibrating, from one atom to the other. It has already been stressed that wave theory cannot consider the motion of an electron in an atom or molecule so the implication of a resonating system is unjustified. Since β is negative the lowest energy is associated with the $+$ sign in the above equations, and because of the factor $(1 \pm S)$ in the denominator, the antibonding ξ_- level exceeds E_H by a greater amount than the energy ξ_+ lies below E_H.

In the ground state of the hydrogen molecule both electrons reside in the orbital with space wave function ψ_+, so their combined eigenfunction will be

$$\psi = N(\psi_a + \psi_b)_1(\psi_a + \psi_b)_2$$
$$= N(\psi_{a1}\psi_{b2} + \psi_{a2}\psi_{b1} + \psi_{a1}\psi_{a2} + \psi_{b1}\psi_{b2}) \quad (10.17)$$

The maximum binding energy calculated with this expression is 2·70 eV at $r_{ab} = 0·85$ Å, which is not quite as good as that obtained by the alternative valence bond method.

The first two terms in equation (10.17) correspond to the complete wave function adopted in the valence bond approximation, but in addition and with equal weighting there are two factors representing a situation in which both electrons are associated with the same atom. Or, in other words, the first two terms cater for a purely covalent bond, H—H, with one electron associated with each atom, and the last two terms represent equal contributions from the ionic forms H⁻H⁺ and H⁺H⁻. Another important point to note is that the valence bond formulation implies complete electron correlation, if electron 1 is associated with nucleus a, then 2 is coupled with nucleus b, or *vice versa*. In the molecular orbital theory there is no electron correlation. This is the reason why the energy of the system at large internuclear distances is greater than $2E_H$; at large values of r_{ab} there is an equal chance of the molecule separating into two atoms ($E = 2E_H$), or into two ions ($E = 2E_H + 12·88$ eV).

It is a characteristic feature of these approximate formulations of molecular wave functions that the valence bond method over-emphasizes electron correlation and underestimates the ionic character of a bond, whilst the molecular orbital method does the reverse. These defects remain in more refined calculations based upon these two basic methods.

10.2. Spin Wave Functions

Nothing has so far been said about the spin of the electrons. The actual energy of interaction between the spin and orbital motions is marginal and almost always ignored in calculations. Four possible spin wave functions for the two electrons in a helium atom were discussed in the previous chapter. The same expressions apply to the two electrons in a hydrogen molecule, and so the complete wave functions for hydrogen are

Valence bond

$$\psi = N(\psi_{a1}\psi_{b2} + \psi_{a2}\psi_{b1}) \times (\alpha\beta - \beta\alpha)$$

or

$$\psi = N(\psi_{a1}\psi_{b2} - \psi_{a2}\psi_{b1}) \times \begin{Bmatrix} \alpha & \alpha \\ (\alpha\beta + \beta\alpha) \\ \beta & \beta \end{Bmatrix} \quad (10.18)$$

Molecular orbital

$$\psi = N(\psi_a + \psi_b)_1(\psi_a + \psi_b)_2 \times (\alpha\beta - \beta\alpha)$$

or

$$\psi = N(\psi_a - \psi_b)_1(\psi_a - \psi_b)_2 \times \begin{Bmatrix} \alpha & \alpha \\ (\alpha\beta + \beta\alpha) \\ \beta & \beta \end{Bmatrix} \quad (10.19)$$

Only the antisymmetrical wave functions have been formulated in accordance with the Pauli exclusion principle. In both methods the bonding wave function is associated with paired spins, whilst the repulsive space wave function can be coupled with any one of three spin functions representing parallel spins. If two hydrogen atoms approach one another there is only one chance in four that the spins will be paired and that a stable combination can be formed by the dissipation of surplus energy.

When atoms were being discussed on page 105 it was pointed out that spin correlation between two electrons with parallel spins tended to keep them apart, and this resulted in a lower energy than when the spins were paired. The converse holds for bonds between atoms as, when the spins are paired, the tendency of the electronic charge cloud to concentrate between the nuclei stabilizes the system. Numerically the exchange integral is normally positive for atoms and negative for diatomic molecules.

10.3. Improved Wave Functions

The molecular wave functions developed above may be improved in two ways. The actual formulation of the function can be altered and so can the mathematical expressions for the factors ψ_{a1}, ψ_{a2}, ψ_{b1}, and ψ_{b2}.

Improvements in the Atomic Functions

When atoms approach one another to form a chemical bond, the electrons are attracted by both nuclei and the charge cloud contracts. This is a similar situation to the one considered for the helium atom, and the simple remedy[3] is the same—namely to employ an effective nuclear charge $Z'e$ in place of Ze in the atomic wave function and then to minimize the energy with respect to Z'.

Another effect of the interaction between atoms is that the atomic orbitals are distorted from their normal spherical symmetry. Rosen[4] allowed for this polarization by replacing the factor $e^{-Z'r}$ by $e^{-Z'r}(1 + \lambda x)$, where x is the distance measured from the nucleus towards the other atom. In effect it amounts to mixing a small fraction of an orbital possessing p-type symmetry with the $1s$ wave function.

The screening factor increases the binding energy obtained with the Heitler–London wave function by 0·64 eV, to 3·78 eV, and if the polarization is also included this becomes 4·04 eV.

Improvements in Formulating the Wave Functions

Valence bond. From the two atomic orbitals ψ_a and ψ_b and the two electrons 1 and 2 two Heitler–London-type wave functions were constructed, (equations (10.6) and (10.7)). It is actually possible to form four space wave functions which do not distinguish between the electrons. These are

$$\psi_{I} = \psi_{a1}\psi_{a2} \qquad \text{(representing } H^-H^+\text{)}$$

$$\psi_{II} = \psi_{b1}\psi_{b2} \qquad \text{(representing } H^+H^-\text{)}$$

$$\psi_{III} = \sqrt{\tfrac{1}{2}}\,(\psi_{a1}\psi_{b2} + \psi_{a2}\psi_{b1}) \text{ (representing } H\text{—}H \text{ (bonding))}$$

$$\psi_{IV} = \sqrt{\tfrac{1}{2}}\,(\psi_{a1}\psi_{b2} - \psi_{a2}\psi_{b1}) \text{ (representing } H\text{—}H \text{ (antibonding))}$$

The first three of these are symmetrical to an exchange of the electrons, so that a better space wave function would result from their linear combination.

$$\psi = c_1\psi_{I} + c_2\psi_{II} + c_3\psi_{III} \qquad (10.20)$$

This final wave function is a combination of expressions which represent two ionic forms and one covalent form, or *canonical structures*, weighted so as to minimize the energy of the molecule. Obviously, since a homonuclear diatomic molecule is not polar $|c_1| = |c_2|$. This construction of the wave function is often referred to as a resonance method, and the molecule stated to be a resonance hybrid of the individual canonical structures. This can be misleading. The various structures do not exist and never can exist as real molecules;

hence there can be no resonance between them and in fact there is no form of oscillation taking place. What we are attempting to do is to find the true wave function of the molecule; that is to find a *mathematical expression* whose square gives the charge cloud distribution in the molecule. Of the functions ψ_I, ψ_{II}, and ψ_{III}, the last approaches most closely to the true function, but a better approximation to the electron distribution may be obtained by taking c_3^2 of the charge cloud given by ψ_{III} and adding to it c_1^2 ($=c_2^2$) of the charge clouds resulting from the ionic forms ψ_I and ψ_{II}. The electron density is a little greater near the nuclei than is given by ψ_{III} alone. It is sometimes stated that the molecule has $2c_1^2 \times 100/(2c_1^2 + c_3^2)\%$ ionic character (cf. Chapter 14). These are valuable ideas but are not quite accurate since they neglect cross-products of the type $\psi_I\psi_{II}$, etc. Calculation gives $c_1 \simeq (1/\sqrt{32})c_3$, or 6% ionic character, when the energy is minimized ($\xi = 4\cdot12$ eV if the modified expressions for the atomic wave functions discussed above are utilized).

The energy associated with this composite wave function must be lower and closer to the true energy of the molecule than the energy of any of the individual canonical forms. This follows from the variation theorem. It is possible to estimate the energies of these non-existent canonical forms from tables of bond energies (see Chapter 14) and the energy difference between that of the most stable single structure and the experimental energy is a measure of the extra stability resulting from resonance. It is therefore known as the *resonance energy*.

The symmetrical space wave function will be associated with the antisymmetrical spin function, whilst ψ_{IV} is the space part of the triply degenerate state being associated with any of the three symmetrical spin functions.

Molecular orbital. From the atomic orbitals ψ_a and ψ_b we have constructed two molecular orbitals (equations (10.15)).

$$\theta = \psi_a + \psi_b \quad \text{(bonding)}$$
$$\phi = \psi_a - \psi_b \quad \text{(antibonding)}$$

These, with two electrons, can give rise to four molecular wave functions

$$\psi_I = \theta_1\theta_2 \qquad = \psi_{a1}\psi_{a2} + \psi_{b1}\psi_{b2} + (\psi_{a1}\psi_{b2} + \psi_{a2}\psi_{b1})$$
$$\psi_{II} = \phi_1\phi_2 \qquad = \psi_{a1}\psi_{a2} + \psi_{b1}\psi_{b2} - (\psi_{a1}\psi_{b2} + \psi_{a2}\psi_{b1})$$
$$\psi_{III} = \theta_1\phi_2 + \theta_2\phi_1 = \psi_{a1}\psi_{a2} - \psi_{b1}\psi_{b2}$$
$$\psi_{IV} = \theta_1\phi_2 - \theta_2\phi_1 = -\psi_{a1}\psi_{b2} + \psi_{a2}\psi_{b1}$$

Only ψ_I and ψ_{II} are symmetrical to an exchange of electrons *and* of nuclei so these are the only two which may be combined, giving

$$\psi' = c_1\psi_I + c_2\psi_{II} \quad \text{(antibonding)}$$

and

$$\psi'' = c_1\psi_I - c_2\psi_{II} \quad \text{(bonding)}$$

At large values of r_{ab}, $c_1 = c_2$ and

$$\psi'' = \psi_{a1}\psi_{b2} + \psi_{a2}\psi_{b1}$$

There is, then, complete electron correlation and the molecule would break into atoms, not ions; the energy would consequently become $2E_H$. This combination of a bonding and an antibonding function is associated with the antisymmetrical spin function. ψ_{IV} is the space part of the triplet state.

These improved molecular wave functions lessen the outstanding defects of the two approximations which were mentioned previously, viz. that the valence bond approach overemphasizes electron correlation and underestimates ionic character, whilst the reverse is the case for the molecular orbital theory. Unfortunately they are more difficult to handle than the simple functions.

10.4. The Secular Equations

Wave functions of the general form

$$\psi = c_1\psi_1 + c_2\psi_2 + \ldots$$

have now been encountered in both the valence bond and the molecular orbital methods. It has been stated that c_1 and c_2 are chosen so that the energy is minimized. This problem arises so frequently that we must consider how it is accomplished. The variation principle comes to our aid.

Consider, for simplicity, the linear combination of just two functions. The mean value of the energy associated with this approximation to the true wave function will be

$$\xi = \frac{\int \psi H \psi \, d\tau}{\int \psi^2 \, d\tau} = \frac{\int (c_1\psi_1 + c_2\psi_2) H (c_1\psi_1 + c_2\psi_2) \, d\tau}{\int (c_1\psi_1 + c_2\psi_2)^2 \, d\tau}$$

$$= \frac{c_1^2 \int \psi_1 H \psi_1 \, d\tau + 2c_1c_2 \int \psi_1 H \psi_2 \, d\tau + c_2^2 \int \psi_2 H \psi_2 \, d\tau}{c_1^2 \int \psi_1^2 \, d\tau + 2c_1c_2 \int \psi_1 \psi_2 \, d\tau + c_2^2 \int \psi_2^2 \, d\tau}$$

In this last expression we have utilized the fact† that $\int \psi_1 H \psi_2 \, d\tau = \int \psi_2 H \psi_1 \, d\tau$. As a shorthand notation it is customary to use the following symbols for the integrals

$$H_{ij} = \int \psi_i H \psi_j \, d\tau$$

$$S_{ij} = \int \psi_i \psi_j \, d\tau$$

H_{ij} is known as the matrix component of H with respect to ψ_i and ψ_j. Adopting this nomenclature the above equation becomes

$$\xi = \frac{c_1{}^2 H_{11} + 2c_1 c_2 H_{12} + c_2{}^2 H_{22}}{c_1{}^2 S_{11} + 2c_1 c_2 S_{12} + c_2{}^2 S_{22}}$$

The coefficients c_1 and c_2 are the only variable parameters and their values which minimize the energy can be obtained by putting

$$\frac{\partial \xi}{\partial c_1} = \frac{\partial \xi}{\partial c_2} = 0$$

Differentiating with respect to c_1

$$\frac{\partial \xi}{\partial c_1} (c_1{}^2 S_{11} + 2c_1 c_2 S_{12} + c_2{}^2 S_{22}) + 2(c_1 S_{11} + c_2 S_{12})\xi$$
$$= 2(c_1 H_{11} + c_2 H_{12})$$

Therefore, when $\partial \xi / \partial c_1 = 0$,

$$c_1(H_{11} - \xi S_{11}) + c_2(H_{12} - \xi S_{12}) = 0 \qquad (10.21)$$

Likewise, when $\partial \xi / \partial c_2 = 0$ the corresponding equation is

$$c_1(H_{21} - \xi S_{21}) + c_2(H_{22} - \xi S_{22}) = 0$$

These two equations are termed the *secular equations* and if they are to have solutions other than the trivial one, that $c_1 = c_2 = 0$,

---

† This is obviously the case for the potential terms in H, but the proof is not quite so straight forward for the kinetic terms. Consider just the one element $\partial^2/\partial x^2$; integrating by parts

$$\int \psi_1 \frac{\partial^2}{\partial x^2} \psi_2 \, dx = \left[\psi_1 \frac{\partial \psi_2}{\partial x} \right]_0^x - \int \frac{\partial \psi_1}{\partial x} \frac{\partial \psi_2}{\partial x} \, dx$$

$$= \left[\psi_1 \frac{\partial \psi_2}{\partial x} \right]_0^x - \left[\psi_2 \frac{\partial \psi_1}{\partial x} \right]_0^x + \int \psi_2 \frac{\partial^2 \psi_1}{\partial x^2} \, dx$$

$$= \int \psi_2 \frac{\partial^2 \psi_1}{\partial x^2} \, dx$$

This follows because both ψ_1 and ψ_2 are acceptable wave functions and so are zero at large values of x. The same is true for all the elements in the kinetic terms and consequently, $\int \psi_1 H \psi_2 \, d\tau = \int \psi_2 H \psi_1 \, d\tau$.

the determinant formed from the terms enclosed by brackets, the *secular determinant*, must be zero

$$\begin{vmatrix} H_{11} - \xi S_{11} & H_{12} - \xi S_{12} \\ H_{21} - \xi S_{21} & H_{22} - \xi S_{22} \end{vmatrix} = 0 \qquad (10.22)$$

If the wave functions ψ_1 and ψ_2 are normalized $S_{11} = S_{22} = 1$, and the two energy values satisfying this determinant will be given by the roots of the equation

$$(H_{11} - \xi)(H_{22} - \xi) - (H_{12} - \xi S_{12})^2 = 0 \qquad (10.23)$$

$$\text{(N.B.} \quad H_{12} = \int \psi_1 H \psi_2 \, d\tau \equiv \int \psi_2 H \psi_1 \, d\tau = H_{21})$$

If the expressions for ψ_1 and ψ_2 are the same $H_{11} = H_{22}$ and

$$(H_{11} - \xi) = \pm(H_{12} - \xi S_{12})$$

Hence,

$$\xi_+ = \frac{H_{11} + H_{12}}{1 + S_{12}} \quad \text{and} \quad c_1 = c_2$$

or

$$\xi_- = \frac{H_{11} - H_{12}}{1 - S_{12}} \quad \text{and} \quad c_1 = -c_2$$

The integral $H_{11} = \int \psi_1 H \psi_1 \, d\tau$ is the energy which would be associated with the wave function ψ_1; it is essentially a coulombic integral and is frequently denoted by the symbol α_1. This is to distinguish it from $H_{12} = \int \psi_1 H \psi_2 \, d\tau = \beta_{12}$ which involves both ψ_1 and ψ_2 and is an exchange, or resonance integral. S_{12} is the overlap integral. In terms of these quantities

$$(\alpha_1 - \xi)(\alpha_2 - \xi) - (\beta_{12} - \xi S_{12})^2 = 0$$

and when $\alpha_1 = \alpha_2$,

$$\xi_\pm = \frac{\alpha_1 + \beta_{12}}{1 \pm S_{12}}$$

Once the value of ξ is known the ratio c_1/c_2 can be obtained from the secular equations. To obtain absolute values of these coefficients another relationship between them is wanted and is provided by the normalization requirement that $\int \psi^2 \, d\tau = 1$, i.e.

$$1 = \int (c_1 \psi_1 + c_2 \psi_2)^2 \, d\tau$$

$$= c_1{}^2 \int \psi_1{}^2 \, d\tau + 2c_1 c_2 \int \psi_1 \psi_2 \, d\tau + c_2{}^2 \int \psi_2{}^2 \, d\tau$$

$$= c_1{}^2 + 2c_1 c_2 S_{12} + c_2{}^2$$

If the wave functions are orthogonal $S_{12} = 0$.

This procedure may be generalized for any number of terms in the expression for ψ. The secular equations are

$$c_1(H_{11} - \xi S_{11}) + c_2(H_{12} - \xi S_{12}) + c_3(H_{13} - \xi S_{13}) \ldots = 0$$
$$c_1(H_{21} - \xi S_{21}) + c_2(H_{22} - \xi S_{22}) + c_3(H_{23} - \xi S_{23}) \ldots = 0$$
$$c_1(H_{31} - \xi S_{31}) + \ldots, \text{etc.}$$

and their secular determinant is

$$\begin{vmatrix} H_{11} - \xi S_{11} & H_{12} - \xi S_{12} & H_{13} - \xi S_{13} & \ldots \\ H_{21} - \xi S_{21} & H_{22} - \xi S_{22} & H_{23} - \xi S_{23} & \ldots \\ H_{31} - \xi S_{31} & \text{etc.} & & \end{vmatrix} = 0$$

The normalization requirement then becomes

$$\sum c_i^2 + 2 \sum c_i c_j S_{ij} = 1 \tag{10.24}$$

or for orthogonal wave functions

$$\sum c_i^2 = 1$$

10.5. Diatomic Molecules

We have seen that the two chief theories of molecular structure require a combination of atomic wave functions, but since the molecular wave functions are only approximately correct there is no need to stick to atomic functions which are exact solutions of the Schrödinger equation for the atom. Let us consider which functions can be combined by the techniques discussed earlier in this chapter.

In the first place the value of ξ for a diatomic molecule involves the integral of $\psi H \psi \, d\tau$, where ψ is of the form $\psi_{a1}\psi_{b2} + \psi_{a2}\psi_{b1}$ or $\psi_a + \psi_b$. Now it is not difficult to show that the various potential terms in $\mathbf{H}$, which express the coulombic attractions between electrons and nuclei, will result in the biggest reduction in the value of the potential energy V when $\int \psi_a \psi_b \, d\tau$ is large. The *virial theorem* applied to systems in which the potential energy is electrostatic states that

$$E = -\bar{T} = \tfrac{1}{2}\bar{V}$$

where the bar indicates a time average. This theorem is not always completely satisfied in wave mechanical calculations, but at least $|\bar{V}| > |\bar{T}|$ and the total energy of the system is generally lowest when the overlap integral $S = \int \psi_a \psi_b \, d\tau$ is large[†]. There are two conditions

† A large value of S increases the denominator in the variation expression for the energy of a bonding orbital but this fact is of less significance.

necessary for S to be large: (a) the orbitals of the individual atoms must overlap to a large extent, (the *principle of maximum overlapping*), and (b) the wave functions of the atomic orbitals must be of the same phase, or sign.

Condition (a) requires p-type orbitals for example, to overlap 'end-on' rather than at an angle to one another and thereby gives a

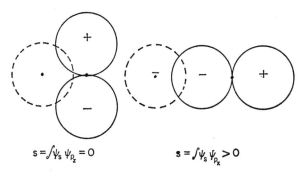

$$s = \int \psi_s \psi_{p_z} = 0 \qquad\qquad s = \int \psi_s \psi_{p_x} > 0$$

FIGURE 10.4   The overlap of atomic s and p orbitals, (not to scale).

directional character to the bonding.   Condition (b) restricts the symmetries of the orbitals which can combine.   This is illustrated in Figure 10.4 for the overlap of s and p orbitals.   Those orbitals which can and those which cannot be combined in forming molecular wave functions, for bonds lying along the x axis, are shown in Table 10.1.

TABLE 10.1.   COMBINATIONS OF ATOMIC ORBITALS
ψ_a AND ψ_b SITUATED ON THE z AXIS

ψ_a	ψ_b	
	Permitted	Forbidden
s	s, p_z, d_{z^2}	$p_x, p_y, d_{xy}, d_{yz}, d_{zx}, d_{x^2-y^2}$
p_z		
p_x	p_x, d_{zx}	$s, p_y, p_z, d_{xy}, d_{yz}, d_{z^2}, d_{x^2-y^2}$
d_{zx}		
d_{z^2}	s, p_z, d_{z^2}	$p_x, p_y, d_{xy}, d_{yz}, d_{zx}, d_{x^2-y^2}$
$d_{x^2-y^2}$	$d_{x^2-y^2}$	$s, p_x, p_y, p_z, d_{xy}, d_{yz}, d_{zx}, d_{z^2}$

There is also a third requirement.   The orbitals must have comparable energies if the binding between the atoms is to be effective. If this is not the case, the electrons will be largely concentrated round the one nucleus where their contribution to the chemical bonding would be small.

The above restrictions in forming likely molecular wave functions can also be considered in terms of the secular equations or determinant. Consider equation (10.23),

$$(H_1 - \xi)(H_2 - \xi) = (H_{12} - \xi S_{12})^2$$

The above restrictions require the overlap integral to be large and positive, and the exchange integral to be large and negative. Were this not the case $H_{12} - \xi S_{12}$ would be small and $\xi \simeq H_1$ or H_2. That is, the energy of the system would be close to the energy of one of the isolated atoms and the bond energy would be small.

With these preliminaries we are in a position to consider some typical diatomic molecules. In all cases only a simple treatment will be attempted—the actual wave functions can always be refined in the ways which have been discussed previously for molecular hydrogen.

Homonuclear Diatomic Molecules

Hydrogen Molecule Ion. This ion possesses just the one electron which could therefore be associated with either proton. The valence bond description is that resonance, indicated by a double ended arrow, occurs between two structures.

$$H_a H_b{}^+ \longleftrightarrow H_a{}^+ H_b$$

$$\psi_{a1} \qquad\qquad \psi_{b1}$$

The molecular wave function is consequently

$$\psi_\pm = N(\psi_{a1} \pm \psi_{b1})$$

In the alternative description the molecular orbital which the electron occupies is

$$\psi_\pm = N(\psi_a \pm \psi_b)$$

In the case of the hydrogen molecule ion, the wave functions from the two approximations are identical and describe a one-electron bond.

From the secular equations the energy of the bonding state is given by

$$\xi_+ = \frac{H_a + H_{ab}}{1 + S} = \frac{\alpha + \beta}{1 + S}$$

The appropriate Hamiltonian being

$$\mathbf{H} = -\frac{h^2}{8\pi^2 m} \nabla_1{}^2 - \frac{e^2}{r_a} - \frac{e^2}{r_b} + \frac{e^2}{r_{ab}}$$

and the numerical values of the integrals α, β, and S are evaluated for hydrogen $1s$ wave functions. (The nomenclature is the same as that employed previously.) This will give ξ as a function of the internuclear distance and has a minimum value of $-15\cdot355$ eV when $r_{ab} = 1\cdot32$ Å. Since $E_H = -13\cdot595$ eV, the calculated dissociation energy is $1\cdot76$ eV. (Experimental values are $D_e = 2\cdot791$ eV, $r_e = 1\cdot060$ Å.) As with the hydrogen molecule the calculation can be improved by suitably modifying the wave function. For example,

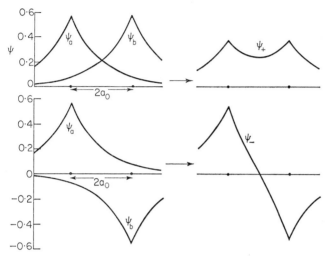

FIGURE 10.5 The formation of σ and $\sigma*$ ($1s$) radial functions for the hydrogen molecule ion.

with an effective nuclear charge $Z' = 1\cdot228$, $D_{e(calc.)} = 2\cdot25$ eV, and allowing for a polarization effect this becomes $2\cdot65$ eV with $r_e = 1\cdot06$ Å. Many other improvements and extensions have been made to the wave function, some of the most extensive data on the molecular orbitals of H_2^+ being given by Bates, Ledsham, and Stewart.[5]

In addition to the energy of the system the electron distribution in the molecule is also of interest. As with atoms, we consider the radial and angular factors separately. The combinations of two $1s$ wave functions in and out of phase with one another are shown diagrammatically in Figure 10.5. With the bonding orbital, the square of the molecular wave function, or charge distribution, is greater between the nuclei than half the sum of the charge distributions for unreacting atoms; in the antibonding case it is less and falls to zero at the mid-point, i.e. between the nuclei

$$(\psi_a + \psi_b)^2 > \tfrac{1}{2}(\psi_a{}^2 + \psi_b{}^2) > (\psi_a - \psi_b)^2$$

To obtain the complete electron distribution these functions have to be multiplied by the corresponding angular factors shown in Figure 10.6. In these and subsequent orbital diagrams accurate representation of the true orbital shapes and sizes has been sacrificed for clarity in seeing the positions of their lobes.

The diagram shows the nodal plane for the antibonding orbital very clearly. To signify that these orbitals are symmetrical about the internuclear axis they are called sigma (σ) orbitals—the antibonding one being distinguished by an asterisk.

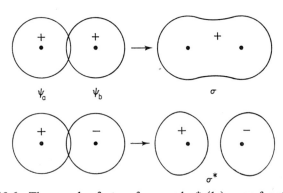

FIGURE 10.6   The angular factors for σ and σ^* ($1s$) wave functions for the hydrogen molecule ion.

So far only the ground state and the antibonding orbital formed from $1s$ atomic orbitals have been considered; others are possible in which ψ_a and ψ_b refer to excited states of the hydrogen atom. For a homonuclear diatomic molecule, particularly one containing just a single electron, the necessary conditions listed earlier for effective bonding require that the combining orbitals be identical. The wave functions could represent $2s$ atomic orbitals and give rise to $\sigma(2s)$ and $\sigma^*(2s)$ molecular orbitals. Their energy and size would be greater than for those formed from atomic $1s$ orbitals and the radial factor would possess a node close to each nucleus, but this has little physical significance. With the $2p$ orbitals there are two possibilities.

1. If the internuclear axis is taken to be the x axis then the $2p_x$ orbital of each atom could overlap to give a $\sigma(p)$-type orbital. The angular factors are shown schematically in Figure 10.7.
2. Once this bond has been formed the spacial distribution of the $2p_y$ and $2p_z$ atomic orbitals means that they cannot overlap in a similar manner. In fact they can only overlap sideways, and as the extent of overlap is generally less the bonds are weaker.

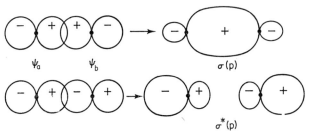

FIGURE 10.7   The angular factors for $\sigma(p)$ and $\sigma^*(p)$ wave functions for the hydrogen molecule ion.

The angular factors in Figure 10.8 are again purely diagrammatic. They differ from the previous orbitals in not being symmetrical around the internuclear axis, in fact, there is a nodal plane passing through the axis. Molecular orbitals with this symmetry are termed π orbitals. Another difference is that the orbitals are doubly degenerate—two π orbitals are formed from the atomic p_y and p_z orbitals. If both molecular orbitals contain either one or two electrons their resultant charge cloud would be symmetrical about the internuclear axis.

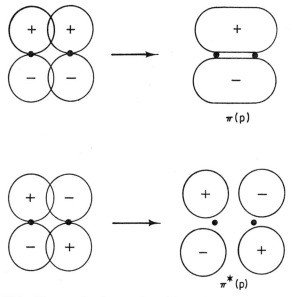

FIGURE 10.8   The angular factors for $\pi(p)$ and $\pi^*(p)$ wave functions for the hydrogen molecule ion.

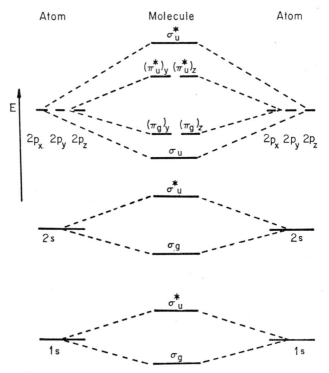

FIGURE 10.9   Molecular orbital energies for homonuclear diatomic
molecules.

Yet higher energy σ orbitals can be constructed from $3s$ atomic
orbitals, and σ- and π-type ones from $3p$ orbitals. In this third
quantum shell there are also the $3d$ orbitals; the d_{xy} and d_{zx} ones
can form molecular orbitals with π-type symmetry around the
internuclear axis—sometimes called d–π orbitals to distinguish them
from the p–π-type—and orbitals of δ symmetry by the sideways
overlap of d_{yz} atomic orbitals. δ symmetry implies two perpendicular
nodal planes passing through the internuclear axis.

The energies of some of these excited orbitals are shown schematically in Figure 10.9.†

† An alternative nomenclature for orbitals is due to Mulliken who used letters,
working backwards from z, in place of the symbol designating the atomic
orbital. Thus $z\sigma$ would mean that the lowest molecular orbital z had σ symmetry, and $y\sigma$ that the next orbital also had this symmetry. The classification is
of greater value for heteronuclear molecules. A third method is to call the lowest
orbital of σ symmetry the 1σ orbital, the next the 2σ, etc. Care must be taken
not to confuse these numbers with a principal quantum number.

Another symmetry classification of molecular orbitals in homonuclear diatomic molecules designates whether their wave functions are symmetrical g, or antisymmetrical u, to reflection in the midpoint along the internuclear axis. These symbols arise from the German words for even (*gerade*), and odd (*ungerade*). Thus the σ bonding orbitals are g and the corresponding antibonding orbitals u; designated σ_g and $\sigma_u{}^*$ respectively. The importance of this classification is that the quantized absorption and emission of dipole radiation when an electron jumps from one orbital to another must be accompanied by a change between g and u states. That is, by the formation or elimination of a nodal plane.

Hydrogen Molecule. This has already been considered. The valence bond description is a resonance hybrid of the canonical forms

$$\text{H—H} \leftrightarrow \text{H}^+\text{H}^- \leftrightarrow \text{H}^-\text{H}^+$$

in which the weights of the ionic forms are equal to preserve the non-polarity of the molecule. The molecular orbital description is one in which the two electrons with paired spins occupy the $\sigma 1s$ orbital, written as H_2, $(\sigma 1s)^2$. These descriptions can be improved along the lines previously indicated.

In principle, the energy of the system can be computed to any required accuracy. Historically, the work of James and Coolidge[6] is of interest. With a thirteen term expression for the wave function they calculated the bond energy to be 4·72 eV. These calculations took them three years to complete! Electronic computers considerably reduce the labour involved in such calculations so that recently Kolos and Roothaan[7] were able to employ a function with fifty terms (see also McLean, Weiss and Yoshimine[8]). They obtained $D_e = 4\cdot7467$ eV and $r_e = 0\cdot74127$ Å, which is to be compared with the experimental values of $D_e = 4\cdot7466 \pm 0\cdot0007$ eV and $r_e = 0\cdot74116$ Å.

An electronically excited state of the hydrogen molecule would arise by the combination of a normal atom H ($1s$) with an excited atom, say H ($2p$). In valence bond theory it could be represented by two one-electron bonds, bearing in mind that the resultant wave function would have to be either symmetrical or antisymmetrical to an exchange of electrons and of nuclei. The molecular orbital description of the same excited state is simply H_2, $(\sigma 1s)(\sigma 2p)$.

Homonuclear Molecules from He_2 *to* Cl_2. A simple description of the bonding in some homonuclear diatomic molecules is outlined below.

(*a*) $He_2{}^+$, $(He, (1s)^2)$

V.B. He: $\cdot He^+ \leftrightarrow He^+\cdot$:He

The 'dots' represent electrons. This has been called a three-electron bond and written He $\cdots$ He. It differs somewhat from a usual valence bond description in that electrons on the two atoms are not being paired together. Like H_2^+ (one-electron bond) the stability arises through the possibility of resonance involving two energetically equivalent structures.

M.O. $He_2^+, (\sigma 1s)^2(\sigma^* 1s)$

Two electrons occupy the bonding and one the antibonding σ orbital; the net result is a bonding power slightly less than that of a single $(\sigma 1s)$ electron.

(b) He_2, $(He, (1s)^2)$

V.B. In the ground state no electrons of the two atoms can be paired together, and no alternative canonical forms written. The coulombic repulsion between the charge clouds of the helium atoms is not countered by coulombic or resonance energies and the molecule does not exist as a stable entity.

M.O. $He_2, (\sigma 1s)^2(\sigma^* 1s)^2$

The antibonding tendency exceeds that of the bonding effect so that a stable He_2 molecule could not be formed. The molecule has a transient existence in an electronically excited state, but the excess energy would be lost very rapidly and the molecule revert to two independent atoms.

(c) Li_2, $(Li, (1s)^2(2s))$

V.B. $Li\!-\!Li \leftrightarrow Li^+Li^- \leftrightarrow Li^-Li^+$

The $1s$ electrons of each atom remain in their atomic orbitals but the $2s$ electrons form a two-electron bond. The ionic character of the resonance hybrid will differ from that in H_2 because of the different orbitals involved and the different ionization potentials and electron affinities of hydrogen and lithium atoms.

M.O. $Li_2, (\sigma 1s)^2(\sigma^* 1s)^2(\sigma 2s)^2$

or $KK(\sigma 2s)^2$

The bonding and antibonding tendencies of the $1s$ electrons virtually cancel out. The overlap of these $1s$, or K shell, electrons of the two atoms must be very small so they are normally considered to remain in these shells and are represented† as KK.

(*d*) Be$_2$, (Be, $(1s)^2(2s)^2$)

Beryllium resembles helium in possessing a pair of electrons in its outer orbital and does not form a stable Be$_2$ molecule.

(*e*) B$_2$, (B, $(1s)^2(2s)^2(2p)$)

V.B. Boron has three electrons in its second quantum shell. The valence bond description of B$_2$ therefore involves a $(2s)^2$ inert pair of electrons in each atom, and the pairing of their $2p$ electrons to form a two electron bond.

M.O. On the molecular orbital approach we would expect to obtain

$$B_2, KK(\sigma2s)^2(\sigma*2s)^2(\sigma2p)^2$$

Spectroscopic evidence however indicates that

$$B_2, KK(\sigma2s)^2(\sigma*2s)^2(\pi_y2p)(\pi_z2p)$$

with one electron in each of the two degenerate π orbitals (cf. Hund's rules) has a slightly lower energy. As a consequence the molecule has a triplet ground state.

(*f*) C$_2$, (C, $(1s)^2(2s)^2(2p)^2$)

V.B. Carbon, with one more electron than boron, would be expected to form two bonds by the mutual pairing of electron spins; one with σ and the other with π symmetry.

M.O. The molecular orbital description would be

$$C_2, KK(\sigma2s)^2(\sigma*2s)^2(\sigma2p_x)^2(\pi_y2p)(\pi_z2p)$$

with two electrons possessing parallel spins in the degenerate π orbitals, but the state

$$C_2, KK(\sigma2s)^2(\sigma*2s)^2(\sigma2p_x)(\pi_y2p)^2(\pi_z2p)$$

has almost the same energy, (less than 0·1 eV greater[9]). Each arrangement has six bonding and two antibonding electrons.

† The charge distribution of two electrons in a bonding and two in the corresponding antibonding orbital is

$$2\left[\frac{(\psi_a + \psi_b)^2}{2(1 + S)}\right] + 2\left[\frac{(\psi_a - \psi_b)^2}{2(1 - S)}\right] = \frac{2}{1 - S^2}[\psi_a{}^2 + \psi_b{}^2 - 2S\psi_a\psi_b]$$

For the $1s$ orbitals of lithium the overlap integral $s = 0.01$ so that the charge distribution is almost equal to $2(\psi_a{}^2 + \psi_b{}^2)$, which is the distribution for two non-interacting atoms. The value of S is much smaller still for the $1s$ orbitals of heavier atoms in the same period. This is the mathematical justification for ignoring any interaction or chemical bonding between inner shell electrons.

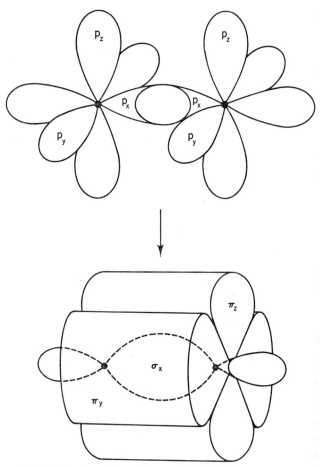

FIGURE 10.10   The formation of molecular orbitals for C_2, N_2, and O_2.

(g) N_2, (N, $(1s)^2(2s)^2(2p)^3$)

V.B.   The nitrogen atom has three unpaired electrons with parallel spins. The valence bond description is one in which three two-electron bonds are formed; one of σ and two of π symmetry.

M.O.   In molecular orbital language this would be written as

$$N_2, \ KK(\sigma 2s)^2(\sigma^*2s)^2(\sigma 2p_x)^2(\pi_y 2p)^2(\pi_z 2p)^2$$

Normally the overlap integral and bonding energies of p—π bonds are less than for p—σ bonds and are consequently more reactive chemically. The π bond becomes relatively stronger as the internuclear distance is reduced, and Mulliken[10] has demonstrated that in N_2 they are stronger than the σ bond. The molecular orbitals should therefore be written in the order,

$$N_2, KK(\sigma2s)^2(\sigma*2s)^2(\pi_y2p)^2(\pi_z2p)^2(\sigma2p_x)^2$$

The electron distribution is symmetrical about the internuclear axis. If the neutral molecule is ionized to give N_2^+ it is probably a $\sigma2p_x$ electron which is lost.

(h) O_2, $(O, (1s)^2(2s)^2(2p)^4)$

V.B. Oxygen has two unpaired electrons and from the valence bond theory we would expect a double bond to be formed. The molecule however is paramagnetic, with two unpaired electrons of the same spin. This could be explained by postulating an electron pair σ bond and two three-electron bonds.[11]

$$O \overset{\textstyle\cdot\cdot}{\underset{\textstyle\cdot\,\cdot}{\vphantom{.}}} O$$

M.O. On the molecular orbital approach it is natural from Hund's rules to assign one electron to each of the degenerate $\pi*2p$ orbitals (cf. Figure 10.9) and for their spins to be parallel.

$$O_2, KK(\sigma2s)^2(\sigma*2s)^2(\sigma2p_x)^2(\pi_y2p)^2(\pi_z2p)^2(\pi_y*2p)(\pi_z*2p)$$

Eight electrons are bonding and four antibonding, but since two of the latter have parallel spins the ground state should be paramagnetic and a triplet. The bonding power is roughly that of four electrons, equivalent to that of a double bond. In O_2^+ one of the $(\pi*2p)$ electrons is lost, the ion therefore has a smaller paramagnetism and, because of the decrease in antibonding character, a shorter bond length and greater dissociation energy. This is confirmed experimentally, the bond lengths and energies being O_2, $1\cdot207$ Å, $5\cdot08$ eV; O_2^+, $1\cdot123$ Å, $6\cdot48$ eV. This may be contrasted with the corresponding figures for nitrogen; N_2, $1\cdot098$ Å, $7\cdot38$ eV; N_2^+, $1\cdot116$ Å, $6\cdot35$ eV.

(i) F_2, $(F, (1s)^2(2s)^2(2p)^5)$

Since fluorine atoms have just one unpaired electron they can only form a single two-electron bond. We might, however, note that whereas the valence bond description involves only the one electron from each atom, the molecular orbital picture includes all the L shell electrons.

$$F_2, KK(\sigma2s)^2(\sigma*2s)^2(\sigma2p_x)^2(\pi_y2p)^2(\pi_z2p)^2(\pi_y*2p)^2(\pi_z*2p)^2$$

Excluding the bonding $(\sigma2p_x)^2$ electrons, the remaining orbitals have corresponding bonding and antibonding ones occupied, and though these tendencies almost cancel out there is a residual antibonding which may be interpreted as a coulombic repulsion between the electron pairs of the two atoms.

(j) Ne_2, (Ne, $(1s)^2(2s)^2(2p)^6$)

Finally, with neon, the second electron shell is complete and a diatomic molecule is not formed.

A point to note is that the relative order of the molecular orbitals for H_2^+ (Figure 10.9) can be altered somewhat for other homonuclear diatomic molecules. It will be recalled that a similar situation exists with atoms. The next period in the periodic table (Na → A) follows a similar pattern to the molecules just considered; the repulsion between the completely occupied K and L shells of each atom is greater, and the overlap of the bonding orbitals somewhat smaller because of their greater size.

Heteronuclear Diatomic Molecules

The general approach is the same as that for homonuclear di-atomics but a few modifications and extensions are necessary. There can be no g or u property because of the absence of a centre of symmetry in the molecule.

Valence Bond Method. A single bond between two atoms is represented by resonance between the structures

$$A—B \leftrightarrow A^-B^+ \leftrightarrow A^+B^-$$

In this case however less energy is required to produce the one ionic form than the other so that they have different weights.

$$\psi = c_1(\psi_{a1}\psi_{b2} + \psi_{a2}\psi_{b1}) + c_2\psi_{a1}\psi_{a2} + c_3\psi_{b1}\psi_{b2}$$
$$= c_1\psi_{A-B} + c_2\psi_{A^-B^+} + c_3\psi_{A^+B^-}$$

In principle the coefficients are evaluated from the appropriate secular equations, but except for some small molecules the calculations are difficult and in practice they are frequently estimated from the polarity of the molecule (see Chapter 14). To form A^- and B^+ an energy of $-E_A + I_B$ is required where E stands for electron affinity and I for ionization potential. Likewise, to transfer an electron from A to B requires an energy of $I_A - E_B$. If this energy $I_A - E_B$ is appreciably greater than for the first case $-E_A + I_B$, or in other words if $I_A + E_A \gg I_B + E_B$, the structure A^+B^- will contribute very little to the resonance hybrid and c_3 may then be neglected in comparison with c_2. We say that atom A is more *electronegative* than B; that is the bonding electrons spend, on the average, a greater time in the vicinity of A than of B. The values of I, E, and $I + E$, for the valence states of some atoms are presented in Table 10.2.

TABLE 10.2. THE ELECTRON AFFINITIES AND
IONIZATION POTENTIALS (IN eV) OF THE
VALENCE STATES OF SOME ATOMS

Atom	Valence State	E	I	$E + I$		
				s	p	sp Hybrid‡
H	s	0·747	13·59	14·34		
Li	s	0·54	5·39	5·92		
Na	s	0·74	5·14	5·88		
Cu	s	0·9	7·72	8·6		
Be	sp†	−0·24	5·96		5·72	9·20
	sp†	2·76	9·99	12·68		
Mg	sp	0·42	4·52		4·94	8·36
	sp	2·82	8·95	11·78		
Zn	sp	−0·31	4·90		4·60	9·42
	sp	3·29	10·95	14·24		
B	s^2p	−0·65	8·30		7·66	
	sp^2	0·12	8·53		8·66	12·68
	sp^2	5·58	15·15	20·72		
Al	s^2p	−0·05	5·98		5·94	
	sp^2	1·45	6·67		8·12	11·38
	sp^2	5·14	12·74	17·88		
C	s^2p^2	0·28	10·94		11·22	
	sp^3	0·58	11·42		12·00	16·60
	sp^3	9·26	21·43	30·40		
Si	s^2p^2	0·75	7·95		8·70	
	sp^3	3·02	8·98		12·00	15·36
	sp^3	7·53	17·93	25·46		
N	s^2p^3	0·85	13·83		14·68	
	sp^4	1·58	14·49		16·06	
	sp^4	13·79	27·5	41·3		
P	s^2p^3	1·29	10·15		11·44	
	sp^4	2·42	11·94		14·36	
	sp^4	8·60	24	32·6		
As	s^2p^3	1·37	9·62		11·00	
	sp^4	2·02	12·24		14·26	
	sp^4	8·32	24	32·4		
O	s^2p^4	2·70	17·28		19·98	
	sp^5	4·85	17·76		22·60	
	sp^5	19·85	35·30	55·14		
S	s^2p^4	2·70	12·50		15·20	
Se	s^2p^4	2·38	11·61		14·04	
Te	s^2p^4	2·62	10·6		13·22	
F	s^2p^5	3·65	20·98		24·64	
Cl	s^2p^5	3·82	15·09		18·88	
Br	s^2p^5	3·69	13·72		17·40	
I	s^2p^5	3·55	12·61		16·16	

† Where two values are quoted for the same valence state the first refers to the addition or removal of a p electron, the second to an s electron.

‡ The values of $E + I$ for sp hybrids are the means of the values for s and p electrons weighted according to the contribution each makes to the hybrid.

The values in the above table are after Pritchard and Skinner.[12,13]

If c_3 is negligble

$$\psi = c_1\psi_{A-B} + c_2\psi_{A-B+}$$

$$= N(\psi_{\text{covalent}} + \lambda\psi_{\text{ionic}})$$

where $\lambda = (c_2/c_1)$ is a constant determining the ionic, or polar character, of the bond. The weights of the covalent and ionic parts are in the ratio of $1^2:\lambda^2$, so that we could define the percentage ionic character of the bond as $100\lambda^2/(1 + \lambda^2)$. The most elementary way of estimating λ experimentally is from the dipole moment μ of the molecule, (but see Chapter 14). The covalent form is considered to be non-polar and it is assumed that

$$\mu = \mu_{\text{covalent}} + \frac{\lambda^2}{1 + \lambda^2}\mu_{\text{ionic}}$$

$$= 0 + \frac{\lambda^2}{1 + \lambda^2}er_{AB} \tag{10.25}$$

where er_{AB} is the dipole moment of the completely ionic form. In some cases λ is so large (e.g. KF) that the bonding is almost entirely due to the ionic form; such a situation is a special case of wave mechanics in which the laws of classical mechanics are valid.

Molecular Orbital Method. The formulation of the wave functions for heteronuclear diatomics differs from that for the homonuclear case by weighting the atomic functions to give a greater chance of finding the electron near the more electronegative atom. We write

$$\psi_\pm = N(\psi_a \pm \lambda\psi_b)$$

and in principle determine λ, the coefficient of mixing of the atomic orbitals, from the appropriate secular equations. As with the valence bond method this parameter is frequently estimated from the dipole moment of the molecule or from some other experimentally measured property. Let us consider the dipole moment method.

The electron in a bonding molecular orbital is visualized as a charge cloud with density

$$\rho = \psi_+^2 = N^2(\psi_a + \lambda\psi_b)^2$$

The normalizing factor is given by the relationship

$$\int \psi^2\,d\tau = N^2\int(\psi_a + \lambda\psi_b)^2\,d\tau = 1$$

or

$$N^{-2} = \int \psi_a^2\,d\tau + \lambda^2\int \psi_b^2\,d\tau + 2\lambda\int \psi_a\psi_b\,d\tau$$

$$= 1 + \lambda^2 + 2\lambda S \tag{10.26}$$

The internuclear axis will be a plane of symmetry for the molecule and the centroid of the charge cloud must lie on this axis at a distance $\bar{x}$ from its mid-point, Figure 10.11, where

$$\bar{x} = \int x\rho \, d\tau = \int x\psi^2 \, d\tau$$

The same relationship is obtained from equation (4.2),

$$\bar{x} = N^2 \int x(\psi_a{}^2 + \lambda^2\psi_b{}^2 + 2\lambda\psi_a\psi_b) \, d\tau$$

$$= N^2(\bar{x}_a + \lambda^2\bar{x}_b + 2\lambda\bar{x}_{ab}) \qquad (10.27)$$

In this equation $\bar{x}_a$ and $\bar{x}_b$ are average positions of an electron in the atomic orbitals ψ_a and ψ_b respectively. For the orbitals considered in Chapter 9 these would be at their atomic nuclei situated at

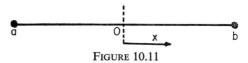

FIGURE 10.11

$x = -\frac{1}{2}r_{ab}$ and $x = \frac{1}{2}r_{ab}$ respectively. The term $\bar{x}_{ab}$ is the mean position of an electron averaged over the product of the two wave functions ψ_a and ψ_b; this product is only of real significance where the orbitals overlap, and since x is then small the value of $\bar{x}_{ab}$ is sometimes taken to be zero. We shall adopt this simplification for the moment and reserve a more detailed discussion for Chapter 14. Hence

$$\bar{x} = N^2[-\tfrac{1}{2}r_{ab} + \lambda^2\tfrac{1}{2}r_{ab} + 2\lambda(0)]$$

$$= N^2\tfrac{1}{2}(\lambda^2 - 1)r_{ab}$$

If two electrons occupied this molecular orbital their centroid of negative charge density would be at $\bar{x}$. There would also be one unit of positive charge at each nucleus which is equivalent to a charge of $+2e$ at the mid-point where $x = 0$. Consequently the dipole moment of the molecule is

$$\mu = 2e\bar{x} = N^2(\lambda^2 - 1)er_{ab}$$

$$= \frac{(\lambda^2 - 1)}{1 + \lambda^2 + 2\lambda S} er_{ab} \qquad (10.28)$$

The overlap integral may be evaluated fairly readily, particularly if the approximate Slater wave functions are employed, so that the value of λ may be computed from the measured dipole moment of the molecule. For many molecules S has a value of about $\frac{1}{3}$ and this figure has often been employed. It must be emphasized that this whole procedure for estimating the coefficient of mixing λ is very approximate, for reasons which will be considered later.

The space wave functions for two electrons in the same bonding orbital is obviously

$$\psi = N(\psi_a + \lambda\psi_b)_1(\psi_a + \lambda\psi_b)_2$$
$$= N[\psi_{a1}\psi_{a2} + \lambda^2\psi_{b1}\psi_{b2} + \lambda(\psi_{a1}\psi_{b2} + \psi_{a2}\psi_{b1})]$$

The three factors represent the two ionic forms, A^-B^+ and A^+B^-, together with the covalent form A—B.

Hybridized Orbitals. Little has so far been said about the actual atomic orbitals which are coupled together in both the valence bond and the molecular orbital theories. With a homonuclear diatomic, ψ_a and ψ_b naturally represent the same orbital for each atom, but in a heteronuclear molecule these might have very different energies. Electrons, or orbitals, of comparable energy have to be paired together in forming a chemical bond.

Consider hydrochloric acid. From Figure 9.2 it is seen that the $1s$ electron of hydrogen has an energy close to those of the $3s$ and $3p$ electrons in a chlorine atom. Hence on the valence bond theory the unpaired H($1s$) and Cl ($3p$) electrons would be coupled together giving

$$\psi = N[(\psi_{H(1s)_1}\,\psi_{Cl(3p)_2} + \psi_{H(1s)_2}\,\psi_{Cl(3p)_1}) + c\psi_{Cl(3p)_1}\,\psi_{Cl(3p)_2}]$$
$$= N[\psi_{H-Cl} + c\psi_{H^+Cl^-}].$$

The structure H^-Cl^+ is excluded by energetic considerations. The energy required to transfer an electron from H to Cl is 9·6 eV, but 12·3 eV are required to transfer one in the opposite direction to form H^- and Cl^+, and so this structure could only play a minor part in formulating the complete wave function.

On the alternative theory, the corresponding molecular orbital containing the pair of electrons has the wave function

$$\psi = N(\psi_{H(1s)} + \lambda\psi_{Cl(3p)})$$

The $3s$ orbital of chlorine has an energy only a little lower than that of the $3p$ orbital so couldn't one also have the molecular orbital

$$\psi = N(\psi_{H(1s)} + \lambda'\psi_{Cl(3s)})$$

It would be less likely because of the lower energy of the $3s$ orbital but it cannot be ruled out completely. A much better description of HCl would therefore be one in which the bonding molecular orbital had some of the characteristics of both, i.e.

$$\psi = N[(\psi_{H(1s)} + \lambda(\psi_{Cl(3s)} + \sigma\psi_{Cl(3p)})]$$
$$= N[\psi_{H(1s)} + \lambda\psi_{Cl(sp)}]$$

where the symbol *sp* stands for an 'atomic orbital' with some of the characteristics of a pure *s* and some of a pure *p* orbital. Such a mixed atomic orbital is called a *hybridized orbital.* Hybridized orbitals *do not exist* in the isolated atom, they simply provide a convenient method of describing the form of a molecular wave function. Molecular wave functions, as an approximation, are formulated in terms of atomic wave functions, but the expressions can be considerably improved by modifying them and hybridization is a very important and valuable way of doing this. Hybridized orbitals can be utilized in both valence bond and molecular orbital methods.

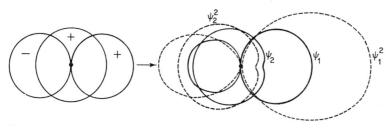

FIGURE 10.12   Hybridized orbitals from atomic *s* and *p* wave functions.

$$\psi_1 = \frac{1}{\sqrt{26}}(\psi_s + 5\psi_p), \quad \psi_2 = \frac{1}{\sqrt{1\cdot04}}(\psi_s - 0\cdot2\psi_p).$$

The angular part of a hybrid from atomic *s* and *p* orbitals with the hybridization parameter $\sigma = 5$ is shown in Figure 10.12. It is primarily of *p* character, but the one lobe where the individual *s* and *p* functions have the same phase has increased in size at the expense of the other lobe. If two orbitals are mixed together then it is obviously impossible to form just one hybridized orbital, the shape of both must be changed. If they are to remain orthogonal then for the two hybrids

$$\psi_1 = N_1(\psi_s + \sigma\psi_p)$$

and

$$\psi_2 = N_2(\psi_s + \delta\psi_p)$$

the integral of their product must be zero, i.e.

$$\int \psi_1\psi_2 \, d\tau = N_1N_2 \int (\psi_s + \sigma\psi_p)(\psi_s + \delta\psi_p) \, d\tau = 0$$

$$\int \psi_s{}^2 \, d\tau + \sigma\delta \int \psi_p{}^2 \, d\tau + (\sigma + \delta)\int \psi_s\psi_p \, d\tau = 0$$

or

$$1 + \sigma\delta + 0 = 0$$

Hence if $\sigma = 5$, as in Figure 10.12, $\delta = -0.2$. The other hybridized orbital, also shown in the figure, does not possess a nodal plane and bears a strong resemblance to an s-type orbital. From a purely geometrical standpoint these hybridized orbitals would overlap with a $1s$, or any other orbital, of the second atom to a greater extent than pure s and p orbitals, and should consequently form stronger bonds. This is confirmed by calculation of the overlap integral† and the bond energy. For any particular atom there are two opposing factors:

1. An s orbital has a lower energy than the p orbital of the same principal quantum number. Energy is therefore necessary to hybridize the orbitals.

† Consider for example a bond formed from an sp hybrid of atom a and the $1s$ orbital of a hydrogen atom. Let

$$\psi_a = N(\psi_s + \sigma\psi_p)$$

$$\equiv \psi_s \cos \alpha + \psi_p \sin \alpha$$

It is often convenient to express the orbital mixing in terms of $\cos \alpha$ and $\sin \alpha$ since this ensures that the wave function is always normalized (cf. (3.18) and (3.19)).

$$\psi_b = \psi_{H(1s)} = \psi_h$$

Then the overlap integral of the orbitals from these two atoms is

$$S_{ab} = \int \psi_a \psi_b \, d\tau$$

$$= \cos \alpha \int \psi_s \psi_h \, d\tau + \sin \alpha \int \psi_p \psi_h \, d\tau$$

$$= S_{sh} \cos \alpha + S_{ph} \sin \alpha$$

Where S_{sh} and S_{ph} are the overlap integrals of pure s and p orbitals on atom a with the $1s$ orbital of b. As the parameter α is varied from 0 to 90°, S_{ab} changes from S_{sh} to S_{ph} and in between these limits it will pass through a maximum when $dS_{ab}/d\alpha = 0$, or when $\tan \alpha = S_{ph}/S_{sh}$. Consequently,

$$(S_{ab})_{maximum} = (S_{sh}^2 + S_{ph}^2)^{1/2}$$

This is always greater than either S_{sh} or S_{ph}. From this result and the binomial expansion we also see that if $S_{sh} \ll S_{ph}$

$$(S_{ab})_{maximum} = S_{ph}\left[1 + \frac{S_{sh}^2}{2S_{ph}^2} + \dots\right]$$

$$\simeq S_{ph}.$$

Unless the s and p orbitals which are being hybridized are of about the same size, so that $S_{sh} \sim S_{ph}$, it is not worthwhile introducing the concept of hybridization.

2. The hybridized orbital is able to form a stronger chemical bond to another atom.

Hybridization may be considered to occur to some extent in all diatomic molecules, though the hybridization parameter is frequently small. It might be worth while emphasizing again that hybridized orbitals do not exist in the isolated atom, but it is convenient to think of them as being formed during the approach of two atoms to form a chemical bond.

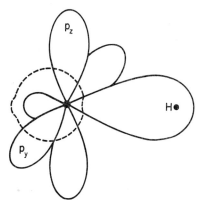

FIGURE 10.13   The occupied molecular and lone-pair orbitals for HCl.

Returning to HCl, a far better description of the electron distribution within the molecule is obtained by supposing that the hydrogen atom interacts with a hybridized chlorine atom. The amount of s character in the hybridized orbital is small, but its inclusion in the wave function greatly improves the calculated energy of the molecule and provides a reasonable explanation of the magnitude of its dipole moment (see Chapter 14). Another consequence is that one pair of electrons on the chlorine atom will now occupy the other hybridized orbital and have a directional character away from the hydrogen atom. The orbitals of HCl, each containing two electrons, are shown diagrammatically† in Figure 10.13. In addition, the inner $1s$, $2s$, and $2p$ orbitals of the chlorine atom each hold two electrons.

Carbon Monoxide. (CO, 1·128 Å, calculated from covalent radii, C=O, 1·22 Å, C≡O, 1·10 Å).

---

† This, and subsequent diagrams of molecular orbitals, are not drawn to scale. In particular p- and d-type orbitals are drawn much thinner than they should be, but if this is not done it is difficult to see at a glance which orbitals are present in the molecule.

M.O. Let us consider the molecule CO as another example. This molecule is isoelectronic with N_2 and the bonding is consequently similar. That is to say the same orbitals of the two atoms couple together as shown below.

$$\text{C} \qquad \text{O}$$

$(1s)^2 \quad (1s)^2$	In atomic orbitals
$(2s)^2 \quad (2s)^2$	Lone-pair atomic electrons
$(2p_x\text{—}2p_x)^2$	Form a σ bond
$(2p_y\text{—}2p_y)^2$	Form a π bond
$(2p_z\text{—}2p_z)^2$	Form a π bond

The nucleus of the oxygen atom has one more proton, and carbon one less, than nitrogen. The oxygen atom is therefore more electronegative than carbon and has a greater control over the bonding electrons. Also, the energies of the oxygen orbitals are somewhat less than the corresponding carbon ones; in fact Figure 9.2 implies that the $O(2p)$ orbitals have an energy between those of the $C(2s)$ and $C(2p)$ orbitals. Some sp hybridization of the carbon atom will therefore occur so that the σ bond is really formed from a carbon sp hybrid and the oxygen $2p_x$ orbital. (There will also be a little hybridization in the oxygen atom but less than in carbon.) This also means that the lone-pair electrons will not occupy the $2s$ orbital of carbon but the orthogonal sp hybrid directed away from the oxygen atom. These lone-pair electrons make a substantial contribution to the dipole moment in the sense $\leftarrow +$C O and oppose that arising through the charge asymmetry of the bonding orbitals. Carbon monoxide in fact has a very small net dipole moment of $0\cdot12D$. The directional character of the lone-pair also helps us to understand much of the chemistry of the molecule as these electrons would be readily donated to an acceptor atom.

All descriptions of the nature of the bonding between two atoms are approximations and in this case it is of interest to consider briefly a rather more elaborate treatment.[14-16] In it the $C(2s)$, $O(2s)$, and $O(2p_x)$ orbitals give rise to three *occupied* σ-type orbitals (1σ, 2σ, and 3σ), whilst the $2p_y$ and $2p_z$ orbitals of each atom form two occupied π molecular orbitals as before (π_y and π_z).

1σ. This is formed from the $O(2s)$ orbital with smaller but nearly equal contributions from the $C(2s)$ and $C(2p_x)$ orbitals. The charge cloud is concentrated between the nuclei but is rather nearer the oxygen atom—polarity $C + \leftrightarrow$ O. The calculated ionization potential is $43\cdot4$ eV.

2σ. This is essentially the lone-pair sp hybrid orbital of the oxygen atom with a centroid of charge near the oxygen atom but on the side remote from the carbon—polarity C O↔, ionization potential calculated 20·01 eV, experimental 19·07 eV.

3σ. This is the corresponding lone-pair of the carbon atom; the $2s$ and $2p_x$ electrons contribute nearly equally to the hybrid so that it is strongly directed away from the carbon nucleus. Polarity ↔+C O, and possessing the lowest ionization potential in the molecule, calculated 13·37 eV, experimental 14·01 eV. When one of these electrons is lost, giving C^+O, the number of bonding electrons is unaltered but the carbon atom becomes more electronegative, the bond energy increases, and the bond length decreases to 1·115 Å.

π_y, π_z. These are the degenerate π-type molecular orbitals. Calculation shows that electrons in these orbitals are about four times as likely to be near the oxygen as near the carbon nucleus— polarity C ↔ O. Calculated ionization potential 15·97 eV, experimental 16·58 eV.

The resultant dipole moment is calculated to be in the direction C ↔+ O. Finally, we quote some figures of Ransil which show the total extent to which the atomic orbitals are 'populated' by electrons in the molecule. These are obtained by summing the contribution of each to the atomic, lone-pair, and molecular orbitals.

	$1s$	$2s$	$2p_x$	$2p_y$	$2p_z$
Carbon	2·0	1·68	0·96	$0·62_5$	$0·62_5$
Oxygen	2·0	1·85	1·51	$1·37_5$	$1·37_5$

V.B. The simplest valence bond description of carbon monoxide is C=O, in which there is one σ and one π bond formed from the two unpaired p electrons of the oxygen atom. This is inadequate since the bond length (1·128 Å) is 0·10 Å shorter than in ketones and the bond strength consequently greater. Also the molecule has a very low dipole moment (0·12D) in spite of the oxygen atom being much more electronegative than carbon. The greater electronegativity would imply a substantial contribution from the structure C^+—O^- in which an electron has been transferred from carbon to oxygen. The shorter bond length implies a contribution from $C^-\equiv O^+$ in which an electron has been transferred in the other direction to give C^- and O^+, both atoms now having the electronic structure of nitrogen. This structure makes a significant contribution because the stability associated with a triply covalent bond counteracts the unfavourable charge distribution, and since it has the reverse polarity to the other forms it accounts for the low dipole moment. One final point may be mentioned about the valence bond description of carbon monoxide which also applies to all molecules. If the three canonical forms

$$C^+\!\!-\!\!O^- \leftrightarrow C\!\!=\!\!O \leftrightarrow C^-\!\!\equiv\!\!O^+$$

had any separate existence, their bond lengths would be very different. For resonance to occur they must be stretched or compressed to the common bond length of 1·128 Å. They do not represent carbon monoxide molecules with 'normal' single, double, and triple bonds. A considerable energy is necessary to adjust these bond lengths, (*compression energy*), which detracts to some extent from the additional stability which ensues from resonance between three canonical forms.

Nitric Oxide. (NO, 1·151 Å, calculated from covalent radii N=O, 1·18 Å, N≡O, 1·06 Å). The nitric oxide molecule has one electron more than N_2 and CO. The molecular orbital description will be similar to that for these molecules, bearing in mind that the extent of hybridization decreases in the order C > N > O, whilst the nuclear charge and electronegativity of the atoms are in the reverse order. The main problem is the additional electron. It must be in the molecular orbital of next greatest energy which is the antibonding π^* $2p$ orbital; consequently when it is removed to form NO^+, isoelectronic with N_2 and CO, the ion has a greater bond energy and shorter bond length (1·062 Å). It is also diamagnetic, no unpaired electrons, whereas nitric oxide itself is paramagnetic.

The unexpected stability of this molecule with one unpaired electron must be associated with the fact that this electron is distributed in a molecular orbital extending over both nuclei. The bonding in the dimer $(NO)_2$, which only exists at low temperatures, has been discussed by Orville-Thomas.[17]

The valence bond description involves a three-electron bond but is rather less satisfactory.

$$N\!\!=\!\!\ddot{O} \leftrightarrow \overset{-}{\ddot{N}}\!\!=\!\!\overset{+}{O} \quad \text{i.e. } N\!\!\vdots\!\!=\!\!O$$

BIBLIOGRAPHICAL REFERENCES

1. Bloch, F., *Z. Phys.*, 1928, **52**, 555.
2. Heitler, W., and London, F., *Z. Phys.*, 1927, **44**, 455.
3. Wang, S. C., *Phys. Rev.*, 1928, **31**, 579.
4. Rosen, N., *Phys. Rev.*, 1931, **38**, 2099.
5. Bates, D. R., Ledsham, K., and Stewart, A. L., *Phil. Trans. Roy. Soc.*, 1953, A**246**, 215.
6. James, H. M., and Coolidge, A. S., *J. Chem. Phys.*, 1933, **1**, 825.

7. Kolos, W., and Roothaan, C. C. J., *Rev. Mod. Phys.*, 1960, **32**, 219.
8. McLean, A. D., Weiss, A., and Yoshimine, M., *Rev. Mod. Phys.*, 1960, **32**, 211.
9. Ballik, E. A., and Ramsay, D. A., *J. Phys. Chem.*, 1959, **31**, 1128.
10. Mulliken, R. S., *J. Phys. Chem.*, 1952, **56**, 295.
11. Wheland, G. W., *Trans. Faraday Soc.*, 1937, **33**, 1499.
12. Pritchard, H. O., and Skinner, H. A., *Chem. Rev.*, 1955, **55**, 745.
13. Pritchard, H. O., and Skinner, H. A., *Trans. Faraday Soc.*, 1953, **49**, 1254.
14. Sahni, R. C., *Trans. Faraday Soc.*, 1953, **49**, 1246.
15. Ransil, B. J., *J. Chem. Phys.*, 1959, **30**, 1113.
16. Hurley, A. C., *Rev. Mod. Phys.*, 1960, **32**, 400.
17. Orville-Thomas, W. J., *J. Chem. Phys.*, 1954, **22**, 1267.

CHAPTER 11

POLYATOMIC MOLECULES I.
LOCALIZED ORBITALS

To develop the wave mechanical approach to polyatomic molecules it is simplest if we discuss a definite example. Let us consider the water molecule, in which the hydrogen atom has just one electron in its $1s$ orbital and the oxygen atom has three doubly occupied orbitals, $1s$, $2s$, and $2p_z$, together with two singly occupied degenerate $2p$ orbitals, $2p_x$ and $2p_y$.

11.1. Experimental Results

The distance of each hydrogen atom in the water molecule from the oxygen nucleus is the same (0·958 Å), and the $\widehat{HOH}$ angle is 104°27'. No chemical or physical distinction exists between the two hydrogen atoms so any theoretical treatment of water must recognize that the bonding between each hydrogen and the oxygen atom is identical. Experimental results also show that if one hydrogen atom is replaced by a different atom or radical X, then the properties associated with the OH bond in HOX are almost the same as in H_2O. The bond length, bond energy, force constant, and $\widehat{HOX}$ angle are all nearly independent of the nature of X. Even in the OH radical the bond length is only increased by 0·013 Å and the bond energy decreased by about 10 kcal/mole to 99·5 kcal. A successful description of the HOX molecule must therefore indicate that the bonding between H and O is not greatly influenced by the other atom. We might anticipate that the electrons which bind these atoms together are essentially *localized* around these atoms—as in a diatomic molecule.

160

The fact that it is possible to compile tables of bond energies, bond angles, and covalent atomic radii which are approximately independent of the molecule points to the conclusion that this state of affairs exists in many polyatomic molecules. There are exceptions however; the most obvious is the C—C bond whose length varies between about 1·20 and 1·54 Å in different molecules. In these cases we might suspect that the electron density between the two atoms, and their hybridization, can vary considerably from one molecule to another. The electrons may not be localized in two-centre orbitals.

11.2. Molecular Orbital Theory

The water molecule has ten electrons, two of which occupy the $1s$ orbital of oxygen and cannot be involved in the bonding because of their energy and orbital size. Let us first assume, as we did initially with diatomic molecules, that the paired electrons in the L shell of oxygen ($(2s)^2$ and $(2p_z)^2$) do not enter the into bonding but remain as lone-pairs. In the ground state the remaining four electrons occupy two similar molecular orbitals. We shall first formulate these as non-localized three-centre orbitals and then as localized two-centre orbitals.

Non-Localized Molecular Orbitals

The water molecule possesses two planes of symmetry and it would therefore seem natural to position the atomic orbitals so that they are either symmetrical or antisymmetrical to these planes. This has been done in Figure 11.1 which is self explanatory.

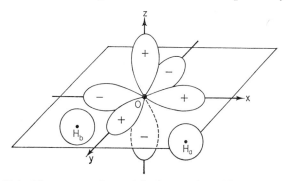

FIGURE 11.1   The oxygen $2p$ and hydrogen $1s$ orbitals utilized in the formation of H_2O.

The oxygen $2p_y$ orbital is symmetrical and the $2p_x$ orbital anti-symmetrical to reflection in the symmetry plane passing through the Oy and Oz axes. Since the hydrogen atoms are indistinguishable, their combined orbitals must also be symmetrical or antisymmetrical with respect to this plane. The individual hydrogen $1s$ wave functions do not have either of these symmetries and so we must employ either the combination $h_a + h_b$, or $h_a - h_b$, where h stands for $\psi_{H(1s)}$. Now the combination of orbitals with different symmetries is not possible so the only molecular orbitals which are allowed, and which extend over the three atoms, are

$$\Theta = N[(h_a + h_b) + \lambda p_y] \quad \text{(symmetrical)}$$

and

$$\Phi = N[(h_a - h_b) + \mu p_x] \quad \text{(antisymmetrical)}$$

where λ and μ are their coefficients of mixing. Each of these will contain two electrons so that the determinantal form of the molecular wave function, including spin, will be, (cf. (9.3)),

$$\psi = N \begin{vmatrix} (\Theta\alpha)_1 & (\Phi\alpha)_1 & (\Theta\beta)_1 & (\Phi\beta)_1 \\ (\Theta\alpha)_2 & (\Phi\alpha)_2 & (\Theta\beta)_2 & (\Phi\beta)_2 \\ (\Theta\alpha)_3 & (\Phi\alpha)_3 & (\Theta\beta)_3 & (\Phi\beta)_3 \\ (\Theta\alpha)_4 & (\Phi\alpha)_4 & (\Theta\beta)_4 & (\Phi\beta)_4 \end{vmatrix} \quad (11.1)$$

The value of a determinant is unaltered if multiples of the rows or columns are added or subtracted from one another. This property can be utilized to transform the orbitals Θ and Φ as follows[1]:

1. Add column two to column one thus giving the functions $\Theta + \Phi$ in column one.
2. Subtract one half of column one, i.e. $\frac{1}{2}(\Theta + \Phi)$, from column two thus obtaining the functions $\Phi - \frac{1}{2}(\Theta + \Phi) \equiv -\frac{1}{2}(\Theta - \Phi)$ in column two.
3. Repeat these operations on columns three and four.

The determinantal wave function then becomes

$$\psi = \frac{1}{2} \cdot \frac{1}{2}N \begin{vmatrix} [(\Theta + \Phi)\alpha]_1 & [(\Theta - \Phi)\alpha]_1 & [(\Theta + \Phi)\beta]_1 & [(\Theta - \Phi)\beta]_1 \\ [(\Theta + \Phi)\alpha]_2 & [(\Theta - \Phi)\alpha]_2 & [(\Theta + \Phi)\beta]_2 & [(\Theta - \Phi)\beta]_2 \\ [(\Theta + \Phi)\alpha]_3 & [(\Theta - \Phi)\alpha]_3 & [(\Theta + \Phi)\beta]_3 & [(\Theta - \Phi)\beta]_3 \\ [(\Theta + \Phi)\alpha]_4 & [(\Theta - \Phi)\alpha]_4 & [(\Theta + \Phi)\beta]_4 & [(\Theta - \Phi)\beta]_4 \end{vmatrix}$$

$$(11.2)$$

But this is the wave function which would have been obtained for two electrons in a molecular orbital

$$\Theta + \Phi = N(2h_a + \lambda p_y + \mu p_x)$$

and two electrons in

$$\Theta - \Phi = N(2h_b + \lambda p_y - \mu p_x)$$

Since p-type wave functions may be written in the form

$$p_x = xf(r)$$

and   (7.8)

$$p_y = yf(r)$$

it is possible to add these functions vectorially to give p-type functions which point in different directions, (cf. (7.12) and figure).

$$\lambda p_y + \mu p_x = (\lambda^2 + \mu^2)^{1/2} p_a$$
$$\lambda p_y - \mu p_x = (\lambda^2 + \mu^2)^{1/2} p_b \qquad (11.3)$$

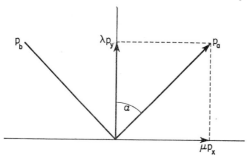

The molecular orbital $\Theta + \Phi$ can therefore be considered to result from the overlap of the hydrogen orbital h_a and an oxygen orbital p_a with p symmetry and directed towards the hydrogen atom at an angle $\alpha = \tan^{-1} \mu/\lambda$ to the y axis. The function $\Theta - \Phi$ represents a similar orbital involving the other hydrogen atom. These are shown diagrammatically in Figure 11.2. There are two possibilities.

1. If $\lambda = \mu$ than $\alpha = 45°$ and the oxygen orbitals p_a and p_b are mutually at right angles—or orthogonal—to one another. In this case the molecular orbitals $\Theta + \Phi$ and $\Theta - \Phi$ are also orthogonal. In other words they should be completely independent of one another and represent completely localized molecular orbitals for the O—H_a and O—H_b bonds. The description of the water molecule in terms of two delocalized three-centre orbitals Θ and Φ, is therefore entirely equivalent to a description in terms of two localized two-centre orbitals $\Theta + \Phi$ and $\Theta - \Phi$. The latter description is generally preferred since it corresponds closely to the older concept of a chemical bond. Further, as these orbitals are mutually independent the properties of each bond should be independent of the nature of the other atoms attached to the oxygen. This is only true to a first approximation.

2. If $\lambda \neq \mu$ then $\alpha \neq 45°$ and the two molecular orbitals are not completely orthogonal—each depends to some extent upon the other. Since one lobe of the atomic orbital p_y is well removed from the two hydrogen atoms, we might expect it to be slightly less involved in the bonding than p_x. In other words, μ/λ would be slightly greater than unity and $\alpha > 45°$. The experimental $\widehat{HOH}$ bond angle of $2\alpha = 104\frac{1}{2}°$ corresponds to $\mu/\lambda = 1\cdot29$. In this case the properties of the OH bond would not be entirely independent of the nature of the other atom attached to the oxygen.

Localized Molecular Orbitals

The problem of the water molecule can also be approached directly in terms of localized orbitals. The oxygen atom has two

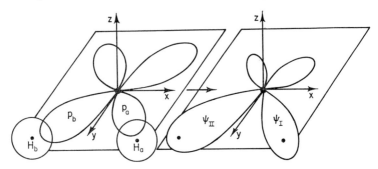

FIGURE 11.2   Localized molecular orbitals for H_2O.

singly occupied p orbitals—say p_a (or p_x) and p_b (or p_y). From our knowledge of the chemical and physical properties of the molecule and from the principle of maximum overlapping of orbitals, we might expect one hydrogen atom to interact with p_a and the other with p_b, as in Figure 11.2. The two molecular orbitals formed would each be localized on two atoms and have the wave functions

$$\psi_I = N(\psi_{H_a} + \nu\psi_{O(2p_a)})$$

and

$$\psi_{II} = N(\psi_{H_b} + \nu\psi_{O(2p_b)})$$

Further, the angle $\widehat{HOH}$ between them would be expected to be that between two atomic p orbitals—namely 90°. The molecular orbitals would be orthogonal and the properties associated with each bond independent of the other.

If we wish to employ these localized molecular orbitals then we must explain why the bond angle in water is $14\frac{1}{2}°$ greater than the angle between p orbitals. The first explanation was that the electronegative oxygen atom produced a low electron density near the hydrogen nuclei, which would consequently possess net positive charges. A charge of $+0\cdot32e$ at the nucleus of each hydrogen, and $-0\cdot64e$ on the oxygen atom would account for the dipole moment of the water molecule. The two positive charges would repel one another, but calculations[2] show that this could not increase the angle to more than 95°. In actual fact it would be much less, since it is now realized that the charges are less than quoted above (see Chapter 14). There will however be coulombic repulsions between the two pairs of bonding electrons which could open out the angle and might produce a bent bond.†

This idea can be extended further. Since the electron distribution round the oxygen atom in the molecule is not spherically symmetrical, the coulombic repulsion between the electrons in the bonding O—H molecular orbitals and the oxygen $(2s)^2$ and $(2p_z)^2$ lone-pair electrons would alter the shape and spacial distribution of each of these orbitals. Exchange interactions between the pairs of electrons are also possible. One convenient approximation to this problem is to employ hybridized atomic orbitals.

Both the molecular orbital and the valence bond descriptions given above predict that the $\widehat{HOH}$ bond angle should be something like 90°, and this provides the basis of the concept of directed valence. The theoretical description of the geometrical structure of molecules rests upon two principles:

1. The possibility of using localized, or nearly localized, orbitals.
2. The principle of maximum overlapping.

The Eight-electron Problem

As implied above a more elaborate and detailed treatment of the water molecule will involve the six electrons in the L shell of the oxygen atom in addition to the $1s$ electron of each hydrogen.

Employing non-localized molecular orbitals there would be two molecular orbitals in addition to Θ and Φ defined as before. The one would be formed from the oxygen $2s$ orbital and the symmetrical function for the two hydrogen atoms

$$\chi = N[(h_a + h_b) + \nu s]$$

† By a 'bent bond' is meant one in which the internuclear axis is not a symmetry line for the electron density in the bond.

The other would be the oxygen $2p_z$ orbital; this is not of a suitable symmetry to combine with the hydrogen $1s$ wave functions (cf. Table 10.1). The four functions, Θ, Φ, χ, and p_z could be employed in an eighth order determinantal function analogous to (11.1). Further this can readily be converted, by adding and subtracting columns in the determinant, into the orbitals

$$\tfrac{1}{2}(\Theta + \chi) + \Phi = N[2h_a + (\{\tfrac{1}{2}\lambda\}^2 + \mu^2)^{1/2}p_a + \nu s]$$

$$\tfrac{1}{2}(\Theta + \chi) - \Phi = N[2h_b + (\{\tfrac{1}{2}\lambda\}^2 + \mu^2)^{1/2}p_b + \nu s]$$

$$\Theta - \chi = N[\lambda p_y - \nu s]$$

and p_z

The first two of these are similar to the bonding orbitals $\Theta + \Phi$ and $\Theta - \Phi$ respectively except that they contain a little of the

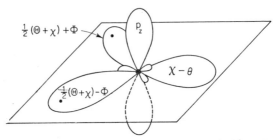

FIGURE 11.3   Localized molecular orbitals for H_2O.

oxygen atomic $2s$ orbital; they can be considered to be equivalent to bonds formed from two hybrid sp orbitals of the oxygen atom and the two hydrogen atoms. The third and fourth orbitals are centered entirely on the oxygen atom and hold the lone-pair electrons. The one has s and p character and represents a hybrid orbital pointing away from the hydrogen atoms, whilst the other is the atomic p_z orbital extending along the z axis above and below the plane of the molecule. These orbitals are illustrated in Figure 11.3. An alternative description is obtained by combining the columns which represent the lone-pair orbitals $\Theta - \chi$ and p_z in the determinant to give

$$(\Theta - \chi) + p_z = N(\lambda p_y - \nu s + p_z)$$
and
$$(\Theta - \chi) - p_z = N(\lambda p_y - \nu s - p_z)$$

The combination $p_y \pm p_z$ represents p-type orbitals in the y–z plane directed at angles of $\pm\alpha = \tan^{-1} 1/\lambda$ to the y axis. Hence

$\Theta - \chi \pm p_z$ are equivalent sp hybrid orbitals in these directions. This description of the water molecule is illustrated in Figure 11.4.

Figures 11.3 and 11.4 look different but in fact they give the same resultant electron distribution for the four lone-pair electrons and are entirely equivalent. This can be verified by comparing $(\Theta - \chi)^2 + p_z^2$ with $(\Theta - \chi + p_z)^2 + (\Theta - \chi - p_z)^2$, employing appropriate normalization factors. Since an s orbital is nondirectional the bond angle will still be controlled by the ratio μ/λ, and unless $\lambda = \mu$ the bonding O—H orbitals are not completely independent.

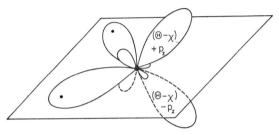

FIGURE 11.4   Localized molecular orbitals for H_2O.

Hybridized Orbitals

There is yet another approach which could be employed. From the discussion of hybridization in the previous chapter we would expect to be able to formulate orbitals for the water molecule in terms of the hydrogen $1s$ functions and a hypothetical hybridized oxygen atom. In this way, stronger O—H bonds could be formed than if pure p orbitals were utilized. Two hybridizations may be considered.

In the first the oxygen $2s$ orbital is mixed with the two singly occupied p orbitals. From these three pure atomic orbitals three hybridized orbitals result, they are known as sp^2 hybrids from their component orbitals. This is illustrated in Figure 11.5.

$$\psi_I = N(s + \lambda p_x)$$
$$\psi_{II} = N(s - \lambda' p_x + \mu' p_y) \equiv N[s + (\lambda'^2 + \mu'^2)^{1/2} p_a] \quad (11.4)$$
$$\psi_{III} = N(s - \lambda'' p_x - \mu'' p_y) \equiv N[s + (\lambda''^2 + \mu''^2)^{1/2} p_b]$$

Inspection of the signs of the lobes of the p_x and p_y orbitals shows that the main lobe of ψ_I must be directed along the x axis, whilst for ψ_{II}, x is negative but y positive, and for ψ_{III} both x and y are negative. In the water molecule two of these hybrids, say ψ_{II} and ψ_{III}, are entirely equivalent, apart from direction, and they overlap the

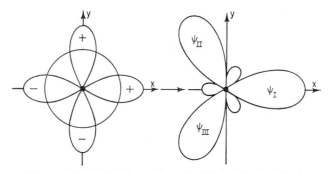

FIGURE 11.5   The formation of sp^2 hybridized orbitals.

hydrogen $1s$ orbitals to form two localized molecular orbitals. The third hybrid ψ_I, (cf. $\Theta - \chi$), holds a lone-pair of electrons. This description leads to the orbitals portrayed in Figure 11.3.

The other possibility is that the s orbital hybridizes with all three p orbitals, giving four sp^3 hybrids. The hybrid wave functions will be

$$\psi_I = N(s + \lambda p_x + \mu p_y + \sigma p_z) \equiv N(s + (\lambda^2 + \mu^2 + \sigma^2)^{1/2}p_1)$$

$$\psi_{II} = N(s + \lambda' p_x - \mu' p_y - \sigma' p_z) \equiv N(s + (\lambda'^2 + \mu'^2 + \sigma'^2)^{1/2}p_2)$$

$$\psi_{III} = N(s - \lambda'' p_x + \mu'' p_y - \sigma'' p_z) \equiv N(s + (\lambda''^2 + \mu''^2 + \sigma''^2)^{1/2}p_3)$$

$$\psi_{IV} = N(s - \lambda''' p_x - \mu''' p_y + \sigma''' p_z) \equiv N(s + (\lambda'''^2 + \mu'''^2 + \sigma'''^2)^{1/2}p_4)$$

$$(11.5)$$

The signs of the p terms in these wave functions show that the main positive lobes of the four hybrids will be tetrahedrally distributed about the central atom (Figure 11.6). The shape of one of these hybrids, to scale, is shown in Figure 11.7. In the water molecule they will be equivalent in pairs—two to form the localized O—H bonds with the hydrogen $1s$ wave functions, and two to hold the lone-pair electrons. The description is that of Figure 11.4.

In the previous chapter it was pointed out that energy is required to hybridize orbitals, but that the hybridized orbitals can then form stronger bonds. Also, the coulombic and exchange energies will differ from an unhybridized state. This can be very important. In the water molecule the repulsion between the lone-pairs could exceed that between the two O—H bonds. A compromise has to be reached, hence the different extents of hybridization between the bonding and lone-pair hybrids. This compromise, resulting in a minimum energy for the system, also controls the angles between the hybrids. Consider two atomic sp hybrids with their maxima in

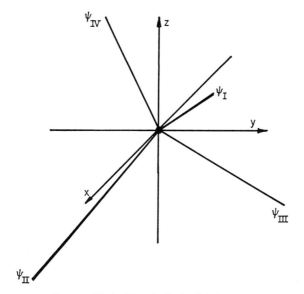

FIGURE 11.6   Tetrahedral sp^3 hybrids.

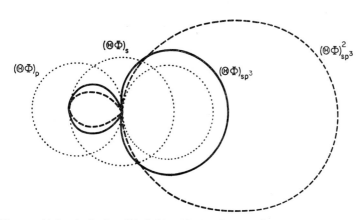

FIGURE 11.7   A single sp^3 hybrid orbital; sp^2 and sp^1 hybrids are virtually identical. The maximum value of the angular factors is s, 1; p, 1·732; sp^1, 1·932; sp^2, 1·992; sp^3, 2·000.

the directions a and b to be represented by

$$\psi_a = N_a(s + \lambda p_a)$$

and

$$\psi_b = N_b(s + \mu p_b)$$

They must be orthogonal, i.e.

$$\int \psi_a \psi_b \, \mathrm{d}\tau = 0$$

$$= N_a N_b \int (s + \lambda p_a)(s + \mu p_b) \, \mathrm{d}\tau$$

$$= N_a N_b \left[\int s^2 \, \mathrm{d}\tau + \lambda\mu \int p_a p_b \, \mathrm{d}\tau + \lambda \int s p_a \, \mathrm{d}\tau + \mu \int s p_b \, \mathrm{d}\tau \right]$$

$$= 1 + \lambda\mu \cos\theta_{ab} + 0 + 0 \qquad (11.6)$$

This follows because the s orbital is normalized, the s and p atomic orbitals are orthogonal, and p_b may be treated as a vector and resolved into components parallel and perpendicular to p_a. From Figure 11.8

$$\int p_a p_b \, \mathrm{d}\tau = \int p(p \cos\theta_{ab} + p \sin\theta_{ab}) \, \mathrm{d}\tau$$

$$= \cos\theta_{ab}$$

The perpendicular p orbitals must be orthogonal from their symmetry and for the parallel orbitals $\int p^2 \, \mathrm{d}\tau = 1$. From equation (11.6) therefore

$$1 + \lambda\mu \cos\theta_{ab} = 0 \qquad (11.7)$$

The angle between the hybrids is directly related to their hybridization parameters.

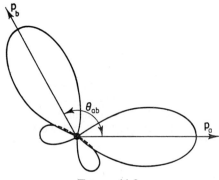

FIGURE 11.8

To give the experimental $\widehat{HOH}$ bond angle of $104\frac{1}{2}°$ the bonding hybrids would be

$$\psi = \sqrt{\tfrac{1}{5}}(s + 2p) \qquad (11.8)$$

the orthogonal lone-pair hybrid in Figure 11.3

$$\psi = \sqrt{\tfrac{1}{5}}(\sqrt{3}s + \sqrt{2}p)$$

and the two lone-pair orbitals in Figure 11.4

$$\psi = \sqrt{\tfrac{1}{10}}(\sqrt{3}s + \sqrt{7}p)$$

There is one final point. In HOX, the H—O and X—O bonds will be of different energies. If the HO bond is the stronger it will try to 'grab' a little more of the lower energy s orbital during the hybridization of the oxygen and the XO bond will have somewhat less. The bonding hybrids will no longer be equivalent and neither will be given accurately by equation (11.8). In this way the small variations found in the $\widehat{HOX}$ bond angles and in the physical properties of the O—H bond in different molecules can be understood.

The molecular orbital description of water has been considered at some length but the following general features emerge. Most complete wave functions of molecules can be interpreted in terms of either localized or delocalized molecular orbitals—those which cannot be considered as localized orbitals will be discussed in the next chapter. The choice arises from the determinantal form of the wave function, but we normally plump for localized orbitals as they approach most closely to the chemists' original conception of a 'bond' between two atoms. Localized orbitals are nearly, but not quite, orthogonal; the physical properties of the bond are consequently almost completely characteristic of the two atoms joined together. In the simplest treatment, only the unpaired electrons on the atoms are considered, but a much better description of molecules is obtained by including in the analysis all the electrons in the valence, or outermost, shell of each atom. These electrons may be considered together in a determinantal wave function but it is simpler, and chemically more revealing, if the individual localized molecular orbitals are considered separately. In this latter case, however, some account of the other valence electrons in the atom has to be introduced by employing hybridized orbitals. The degree of hybridization, i.e. the interaction between the bonding and the lone-pair electrons, is determined primarily by the lengths of the bonds and electronegativities of the atoms in the molecule and by the relative energies of the orbitals undergoing hybridization. The extent of hybridization is in turn the main factor controlling the precise values of the bond angles in the molecule.

11.3. Valence Bond Theory

In the valence bond description of diatomic molecules an unpaired electron in the one atom was considered to pair with an unpaired electron of comparable energy in the other atom, thus forming a localized two electron bond. This forms the basis of the valence bond description of polyatomic molecules.

Ignoring any ionic character of the bond its wave function is of the simple Heitler–London type.

$$\psi_\pm = N_\pm(\psi_{a1}\psi_{b2} \pm \psi_{a2}\psi_{b1}) \qquad (10.6, 10.7)$$

The energy of such a bond would be (cf. (10.11, 10.12))

$$\xi_\pm = E_a + E_b + \frac{Q \pm J}{1 \pm S^2} \qquad (11.9)$$

where E_a and E_b are the energies of the isolated atoms (this is not strictly correct if the bond is polar). The coulombic energy is given by

$$Q = \int \psi_{a1}\psi_{b2}(\mathbf{H} - E_a - E_b)\psi_{a1}\psi_{b2}\, d\tau$$

$$= \frac{e^2}{r_{ab}} + \int \psi_{a1}\psi_{b2} \frac{e^2}{r_{12}} \psi_{a1}\psi_{b2}\, d\tau - 2\int \psi_{a1} \frac{e^2}{r_{b1}} \psi_{a1}\, d\tau_1 \quad (10.14)$$

and the exchange energy by

$$J = \int \psi_{a1}\psi_{b2}(\mathbf{H} - E_a - E_b)\psi_{a2}\psi_{b1}\, d\tau$$

$$= \frac{e^2 S^2}{r_{ab}} + \int \psi_{a1}\psi_{b2} \frac{e^2}{r_{12}} \psi_{a2}\psi_{b1}\, d\tau - 2S\int \psi_{a1} \frac{e^2}{r_{b1}} \psi_{b1}\, d\tau_1 \quad (10.13)$$

At the equilibrium bond length these energies are negative, but numerically J is greater than Q.

Let us first consider the hydroxyl radical. The hydrogen atom could be paired either with the electron in the $2p_x$, or the one in the $2p_y$ orbital of the oxygen atom; suppose for the sake of argument that it pairs with the $2p_x$ orbital but is situated at an angle α to the symmetry axis of this atomic orbital (Figure 11.9). One electron in p_x together with one in the p_y orbital of oxygen, results in a uniform 'smoke-ring' electron distribution around the atom, (Section 7.2), so their coulombic interaction with the hydrogen's electron will be independent of the angle α. The coulombic repulsion from the lone-pair electrons in the oxygen $2p_z$ and $2s$ orbitals are also independent of α; the interaction with the former would incidentally tend to keep the hydrogen nucleus in the x–y plane. Hence the total coulombic energy Q is independent of α. Now consider the exchange energy J. We have seen that the energy ξ_+ is that of the bonding singlet level associated with paired spins; the other energy level ξ_- is that of the triplet state associated with parallel spins. Hence, if the hydrogen pairs up with the oxygen p_x electron their spins must

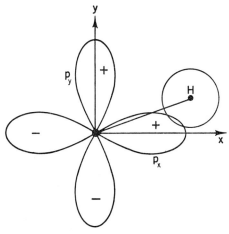

FIGURE 11.9   Hydrogen $1s$ and oxygen $2p_x$ and $2p_z$ atomic orbitals.

be paired and the exchange energy represented by $+J$ (N.B. J is negative). In this case there could be no relation between the spins of the hydrogen electron and that in p_y; or rather there would be three chances of their spins being parallel (exchange energy $-J$) to one chance of paired spins (exchange energy $+J$). The average energy would therefore be

$$\tfrac{3}{4}(-J) + \tfrac{1}{4}(+J) = -\tfrac{1}{2}(+J)$$

The exchange energy between the hydrogen atom and the oxygen electrons with which it is not paired increases the total energy of the system. For the hydroxide radical the net exchange energy with the oxygen p_x and p_y electrons is

$$+J_{p_x} - \tfrac{1}{2}J_{p_y}$$

Inspection of equation (10.13) for J shows that the product $\psi_{a1}\psi_{b1}$ occurs in the two integrals. This product increases with the extent of overlap of the two orbitals ψ_a and ψ_b, so we might anticipate that J is greatest when the orbitals overlap to the greatest extent. This is confirmed by a more detailed analysis and by numerical calculation and gives rise to the principle of maximum overlapping mentioned on page 137. Hence J_{p_x} will be a maximum when α is zero, and this condition also ensures that J_{p_y} is small.

No mention has been made so far of the overlap integral $S = \int \psi_{a1}\psi_{b1} \, d\tau$, in equation (11.9). Its magnitude is often about $\frac{1}{3}$ so that $(1 \pm S^2)$ can easily differ from unity by 10% or more; nevertheless it is frequently neglected. Following this course, equation (11.9) reduces to

$$\xi = E_a + E_b + Q \pm J$$

The conclusions reached in the above discussion may be summarized as follows:

(a) E_a and E_b could differ significantly from the energies of the isolated atoms if the bonds are very polar.

(b) The coulombic energy Q depends upon the distances between the atoms, but it is unlikely to depend to a great extent upon the relative positions of the orbitals in the two atoms. It would not therefore be markedly dependent upon the bond angles in a molecule.

(c) The exchange energy J is normally greater than Q and consequently of greater significance. For small atoms, Q is only about 15% of $(|Q| + |J|)$ if the bond is formed between s-type orbitals, but this percentage increases as the size of the atoms increases and when the orbitals are hybridized.[3-5] It is indeed fortunate that the coulombic energy is essentially non-directional, so that the relative magnitudes of Q and J do not effect the stereochemistry of the molecule; J increases with increasing overlap of the orbitals and is always the main factor. Three exchange energies exist in molecules:

1. $+J$ between electrons with paired spins.
2. $-J$ between electrons with parallel spins.
3. $-\frac{1}{2}J$ between electrons whose spins are completely random.

If S is neglected and the electrons in a molecule paired up to form two electron bonds, its energy may be expressed by the equation

$$\xi = \sum_{\substack{\text{all} \\ \text{atoms}}} E_{\text{atoms}} + \sum_{\substack{\text{all} \\ \text{atoms}}} Q_{ij} + \sum_{\substack{\text{paired} \\ \text{spins}}} J_{ij} - \sum_{\substack{\text{parallel} \\ \text{spins}}} J_{ij} - \tfrac{1}{2}\sum_{\substack{\text{random} \\ \text{spins}}} J_{ij} \quad (11.10)$$

This is known as the approximation of perfect pairing.[6] It is obviously rather crude, but has the merit of being simple and qualitatively is found to be surprisingly reliable. To illustrate its application, let us again consider the water molecule.

Consider the situation in which H_a forms a two electron bond with the p_x orbital of the oxygen atom, and H_b pairs with the p_y orbital, (Figure 11.2). Then according to the approximation of perfect pairing,

$$\xi = E_{(H_a)} + E_{(H_b)} + E_{(O)}$$
$$+ Q_{(p_x,h_a)} + Q_{(p_y,h_a)} + 2Q_{(p_z,h_a)} + 2Q_{(s,h_a)}$$
$$+ Q_{(p_x,h_b)} + Q_{(p_y,h_b)} + 2Q_{(p_z,h_b)} + 2Q_{(s,h_b)}$$
$$+ Q_{(h_a,h_b)} \tag{11.11}$$
$$+ J_{(p_x,h_a)} - \tfrac{1}{2}[J_{(p_y,h_a)} + 2J_{(p_z,h_a)} + 2J_{(s,h_a)}]$$
$$+ J_{(p_y,h_b)} - \tfrac{1}{2}[J_{(p_x,h_b)} + 2J_{(p_z,h_b)} + 2J_{(s,h_b)}]$$
$$- \tfrac{1}{2}J_{(h_a,h_b)}$$

If this rather lengthy expression is examined it will be seen to be quite simple. After the energies of the isolated atoms are three lines listing the various coulombic interactions—the first of these represents the interactions of H_a with the $(2s)^2 (2p_x)^1 (2p_y)^1 (2p_z)^2$ electrons of the oxygen atom, the second line the similar interactions for H_b, and the last coulombic term covers the repulsion between the two hydrogen atoms. The last three lines are the corresponding exchange energies. In addition, there will be coulombic and exchange energies between the various electrons in the oxygen atom.

Apart from the coulombic repulsion between the hydrogen atoms, the other coulombic terms confer no directional character upon the bonds, but the exchange terms would result in a minimum energy when the H$\widehat{O}$H angle was 90°. The interaction between the hydrogen atoms would increase this angle slightly (cf. the molecular orbital description). The exchange terms can actually be expressed as a function of the H$\widehat{O}$H angle so the way is open to calculate the energy, and hence the frequency, associated with the bending vibration of the molecule. In view of the approximations the agreement between the calculated and experimental frequencies, 1660 and 1595 cm^{-1} respectively, is surprisingly good.[7]

One final point about equation (11.11). If the interaction between the hydrogen atoms is neglected, then the second and fifth lines of this expression represent the energy of the O—H_a bond. These terms are independent of the other atom attached to the oxygen so that the valence bond approach also provides an explanation of the nearly constant physical properties of the O—H bond.

When dealing with diatomic molecules it was concluded that a better description of the molecule could be given by including resonance with ionic structures. For water the following structures would be included in the resonance hybrid.

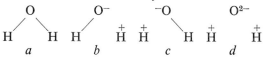

a b c d

Ideally the molecular wave function should be formulated as a linear combination of the wave functions for each of these four structures, weighted so as to minimize the energy. Equation (11.11) applies to the covalent form a and analogous expressions could be written for each of the other structures. However, the secular equations employed to carry out the energy minimization include coulombic and exchange terms for interactions between these complete structures and their calculation is very difficult. This approach is seldom followed.

The relative weights of the structures are often obtained in a semi-empirical manner from experimental data. *One* method is to employ the dipole moment of the molecule (1·84 D). If the relative weights of a covalent to an ionic bond are in the ratio of $x:y$, then

$$(a):(b):(c):(d) = xx:xy:yx:yy$$

subject to the condition that

$$x^2 + 2xy + y^2 = 1$$

The covalent bond is assumed to be non-polar so that the dipole moment of the molecule is given by

$$xy\mu_{(b)} + yx\mu_{(c)} + y^2\mu_{(d)} = 1·84$$

where the μ's are the dipole moments of the various structures, i.e.

$$(xy + yx)(r_{\mathrm{OH}} \cos \tfrac{1}{2}(\widehat{\mathrm{HOH}}))e + y^2(2r_{\mathrm{OH}} \cos \tfrac{1}{2}(\widehat{\mathrm{HOH}}))e = 1·84$$

From the experimental values of the bond length and angle the weights of the structures are (a) 45·4%, (b) 22·0%, (c) 22·0%, and (d) 10·7%. Another rather similar approach based upon the difference between the electronegativity of hydrogen and oxygen, (see Chapter 14), gives the result (a) 37%, (b) 24%, (c) 24%, and (d) 15%.

These figures are of interest, particularly when employed to compare different molecules, but we must not take them too seriously. Apart from approximations made in the general approach we must bear in mind that,

1. The canonical structures have no independent existence, so it is meaningless to assign relative weights to them.
2. The two bonds are not completely independent of each other.
3. The relative weight of structure (d) is undoubtedly too great, for if the O—H$_a$ bond is ionic the electronegativity of the oxygen would be considerably reduced and the covalent/ionic ratio for the second bond would be much less than x/y.
4. From the numerical point of view, the greatest error arises from a false assessment of the factors contributing to the

dipole moment of the molecule. This is discussed in Section 14.2.

Our valence bond treatment of water molecules has been based upon pairing schemes which involve the pure p atomic orbitals of oxygen. The exchange interactions and coulombic energies are more favourable to molecule formation if hybridized orbitals are employed in place of these p orbitals; they would be the same as those considered previously in the molecular orbital method.

11.4. Some Simple Polyatomic Molecules

A few simple polyatomic molecules will now be considered to extend the approaches developed above for handling the water molecule. The actual wave functions are formulated in similar ways and will not be discussed further.

The description of the hydrides of the Group VI elements, H_2S, H_2Se, and H_2Te, is very similar to that for H_2O. The principal quantum number of the valence electrons and hence the size of the atoms, increases in the order $O < S < Se < Te$. This in turn influences the detailed description of the molecular orbitals. The bond lengths are greater and this, together with the reduced electronegativity of the larger atoms, means that the bonding electrons are pulled further away from the central atom. Consequently the factors tending to increase the bond angle are reduced, and they approach more closely to that between pure p orbitals, (see Table 11.1). Alternatively, we may say that the benefits which accrue by hybridizing the s and p orbitals become less as the sizes of the orbitals increases, so that both the bonding and the lone-pair atomic orbitals approximate more closely to pure s and p orbitals.

The energy required to promote an electron from an s to a p orbital decreases with increasing principal quantum number and consequently should facilitate hybridization in the larger atoms. It has been argued[8,9] that the main factor determining the extent of hybridization is not the promotion energy but the relative repulsions between electrons in the lone-pair orbitals and those in the bonding orbitals. In H_2O the repulsion between the two lone-pairs shown in Figure 11.4 is slightly greater than that between the O—H bonds so the $\widehat{HOH}$ angle is a little less than the tetrahedral value. As the size of the central atom increases, repulsion between the bonds falls off much more rapidly than that between the lone-pairs; the $\widehat{HXH}$ angle decreases towards 90° whilst that between the lone-pairs increases towards the maximum of 180° (sp^1 hybrids).

TABLE 11.1

Molecule	Bond Angle (°)	Bond Length (Å)	Molecule	Bond Angle (°)	Bond Length (Å)
H_2O	104·45	0·958	NH_3	107·3	1·008
H_2S	93·3	1·346	PH_3	93·5	1·421
H_2Se	91	1·47	AsH_3	91·8	1·519
H_2Te	89·5	1·7	SbH_3	91·3	1·707
F_2O	103·2	1·418			

Similar changes occur if the hydrogen atoms are replaced by a more electronegative atom such as fluorine. The hydrides of the Group VII elements, NH_3, PH_3, AsH_3, and SbH_3, follow an analogous pattern with one lone-pair and three bonding orbitals. If ammonia were to lose one of its lone-pair electrons it could form an additional covalent bond. The existence of many ammonium compounds (NH_4^+) shows that this frequently takes place. In this ion the N—H bonds are all identical, so it could be considered to be constructed from N^+ in which sp^3 hybridization has produced four equivalent tetrahedral hybrids (Figure 11.6) each of which then forms a localized bond with one of the hydrogen atoms. Likewise oxonium compounds, such as $H_3O^+Cl^-$, have three covalent bonds and one which is predominantly ionic. With heavier atoms the energy of the additional bonds is lower, and the tendency for the above process to take place is reduced.

The valency of an atom can also be increased through promotion of one of its outermost electrons to an atomic orbital of greater energy. If a $3s$ electron in phosphorus is promoted to a vacant $3d$ orbital ($3s \rightarrow 3d$) its electronic structure becomes $P(1s^2 2s^2 2p^6 3s^1 3p^3 3d^1)$, and five localized two-electron bonds may be formed. The orbitals hybridize (sp^3d hybridization) to give a trigonal-bipyramidal arrangement of bonds around the phosphorus atom. Likewise in carbon $2s \rightarrow 2p$ promotion occurs which explains the normal quadrivalence of this atom. More than one electron may be promoted; to form SF_6, for example, a $3s$ and a $3p$ electron have to go into the $3d$ orbitals. Such promotions only occur if the additional bond energy of the resulting system exceeds the electronic promotion energy. It appears that excitation to an orbital of greater principal quantum number requires so much energy that it is extremely rare for it to take place. Pentacovalent nitrogen compounds, for example, do not exist. Likewise a particularly stable outer shell configuration, such as that possessed by an inert gas, requires so much energy to promote a p electron to a d orbital of the same quantum number that only a few of their compounds are known. Very recently XeF_2, XeF_4, XeF_6, oxides such as XeO_3, and oxyfluorides such as $XeOF_4$ have been isolated. The fluoride XeF_2 is linear, in XeF_4 the fluorine atoms have a square planar arrangement, and in XeF_6 they are octahedrally disposed around the xenon atom. The higher valency states can be described in terms of sp^3d^2 hybridization of the xenon atom, with the consequent formation of highly polar bonds,[10] or in terms of resonance between structures involving covalent and ionic bonds.

$$\overset{+}{F-Xe} \quad \overset{-}{F} \leftrightarrow \overset{-}{F} \quad \overset{+}{Xe-F}$$

This description indicates that the inert gas atoms must be large, so that their ionization potentials are low and the ligand must be highly electronegative and small.

So far we have assumed that all the electrons must be paired, but a number of exceptions are known. Nitric oxide and oxygen have already been mentioned, ClO_2 and NO_2 also contain unpaired electrons. Unpaired d electrons occur frequently in the transition elements; vanadium $(\ldots 3d^34s^2)$ for example, would be expected to have valencies of 3 and 5 (by promoting one of the $4s$ electrons) but it also displays valencies of 2 and 4, when unpaired d electrons must be present.

From the preceding discussion it is obvious that several possibilities arise in valence considerations of atoms. The molecular orbital and valence bond treatments of simple molecules are in substantial agreement, and can frequently be employed to predict the valencies of atoms and the geometrical structure of molecules. Theoretical considerations cannot however supersede experimental investigations and normally are only employed to explain and correlate the latter. The 'rules' of valence may be summarized as follows:

(a) A covalent bond is formed through two electrons binding the two atoms together; normally each atom provides one of the electrons. The maximum valence of an atom therefore equals its number of unpaired electrons.

(b) An electron may be transferred from one atom to another to form an ionic bond. This can result in a greater number of unpaired electrons in the cation which therefore possesses a greater covalency than the neutral atom.

(c) Electrons can be promoted to unoccupied, higher energy, orbitals. This seems to be restricted to orbitals with the same principal quantum number, and even then is not possible if the promotion energy is high (e.g. the inert gases). When it does occur the valence increases by two for each promoted electron.

(d) Unpaired electrons can exist in stable molecules so that the maximum valence is not always displayed. The unpaired electrons are normally either in a molecular orbital which extends over more than one nucleus, or in inner d or f atomic orbitals.

(e) In some cases both electrons forming the bond can come from the same atom. The resulting bond is covalent, but to denote its somewhat different origin it is often referred to as a coordinate or dative bond; it is highly polar. To form a coordinate bond the donor atom must have a lone-pair and must not be highly electronegative, whilst the acceptor atom must possess a low-lying vacant orbital and have a greater electronegativity.

(f) The geometry of the molecule is determined by the angles between the orbitals and the principle of maximum overlapping; the orbitals are normally hybridized to some extent.

11.5. Hybridization of Carbon

In the preceding chapter we saw that multiple bonds were formed in diatomic molecules when the atoms were small. This section is

TABLE 11.2

Molecule	$\widehat{HCH}$	$\widehat{HCCl}$	$\widehat{ClHCl}$
CH_4	109°28′	—	—
CH_3Cl	110°30′	108°26′	—
CH_2Cl_2	112°0′	108°17′	111°48′
$CHCl_3$	—	108°31′	110°24′
CCl_4	—	—	109°28′

devoted to a consideration of multiple bonds between carbon atoms. A quadrivalent carbon atom can only arise from the electronically excited state $C(1s^2 2s 2p_x 2p_y 2p_z)$. The excitation energy is about 96 kcal/mole,[11-13] but more than this is recovered through its being able to form four instead of two covalent bonds. If the carbon atom is attached to four other atoms the $2s$ and three $2p$ orbitals undergo sp^3 hybridization to give four tetrahedrally disposed hybrids (Figure 11.6). If the four atoms are identical (CH_4, CCl_4 etc.), the four hybrids are equivalent and each bond angle is 109°28′; if they are not, the hybrids are not entirely equivalent and the bond angle can depart slightly from this value, Table 11.2.

In ethylene only three atoms are attached to each carbon, so it is natural to consider that sp^2 hybridization occurs, leaving a pure p orbital on each carbon atom which can then link together to form a π bond (Figure 11.10). In benzene the geometry of the molecule forces the bond angles to be 120° and the hybrids are equivalent,

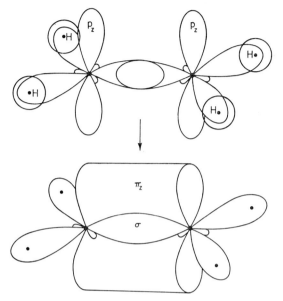

FIGURE 11.10   The σ and π molecular orbitals in ethylene.

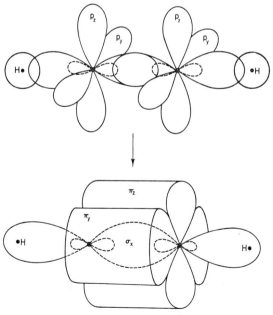

FIGURE 11.11   The σ and π molecular orbitals in acetylene.

but in ethylene this need not be the case. The experimental values of the angles are,[14–16] $\widehat{HCH} = 117°22'$, $\widehat{HCC} = 121°19'$.

In acetylene the carbon atoms are attached to only two other atoms, and sp^1 hybridization takes place leaving two pure p atomic orbitals, which give rise to two π bonds between the carbon atoms (Figure 11.11). The two hybrid orbitals are not necessarily equivalent.

The Strength of Hybrid Bonds

It has already been mentioned that hybridized orbitals form strong bonds. Let us consider this further for simple hydrocarbons.

TABLE 11.3. CARBON—HYDROGEN BONDS

Molecule	Hybridiza-tion	p Character (%)	Overlap Integral	Bond Length (Å)	Force Constant (dyne/cm)	Bond Energy (kcal)
—	s	0	0·55	—	—	—
C_2H_2	sp^1	50	0·749	1·060	$6·397 \times 10^5$	~113
C_2H_4	sp^2	$66\frac{2}{3}$	0·714	1·084	6·126	~103
C_2H_6	sp^3	75	0·687	1·094	5·387	~98
CH	p	100	0·46	1·120	4·490	80

Bonds between carbon atoms are complicated by multiple bond formation, but this is not the case for C—H bonds. There are four convenient measures of bond strength. A simple theoretical indication is given by the overlap integral S of the carbon and hydrogen orbitals. This is readily calculated for Slater-type functions. The other three are experimental quantities—the C—H bond length, the C—H stretching force constant, and the C—H bond energy.

The values of these various quantities are quoted in Table 11.3, from which it may be seen that as the overlap integral increases, the bond length decreases, and the force constant and bond energy increase. The overlap integral[17,18] increases with decreasing p character until it passes through a maximum of 0·758 at 39% p character, the extrapolated value for the bond length then being 1·051 Å. This trend is quite general—for a homonuclear bond the maximum of course would be for an sp hybrid with 50% p character.

Bond Angles Less than 90°

From the criterion of maximum overlapping we would anticipate that the smallest bond angle for an atom containing unpaired s and p electrons would be 90°, the angle between two pure p orbitals. In virtually all cases sp hybridization would increase this value. How can stable molecules such as cyclopropane C_3H_6 and tetraphosphorus P_4 exist as the bond angles are only 60°?

The bonding orbitals from each atom cannot overlap in the most efficient way but are at an angle to one another—the bonds are bent. The least strain would be present if the bonding atomic orbitals were pure p orbitals, but calculation indicates that even in these cases hybridization occurs; the larger angle between the hybrids is offset by the greater overlap possible with hybridized orbitals.

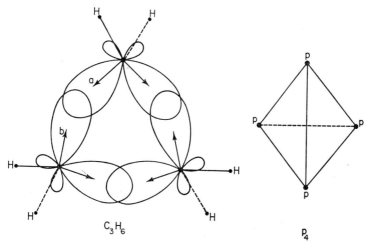

FIGURE 11.12   The cyclopropane and tetraphosphorus molecules.

Coulson and Moffitt[19] calculated that the best compromise in cyclopropane is obtained with hybridized carbon orbitals of 80% p character, the angle between the hybrids then being 104°. The non-linear overlap of hybrid orbitals from adjacent carbon atoms results in a loss of about 7·5 eV/mole, but some of this (ca. 1·2 eV) is recovered through the possibility of pairing the hybrids in alternative ways—a residual resonance energy.† A similar situation

† In polyatomic molecules the molecular orbitals are not completely localized so there is an error involved in treating them as such. In the valence bond approach this situation arises through the possibility of other pairing schemes existing and each should be incorporated in the complete wave function. In Figure 11.12, for example, orbital a would normally be paired with orbital b, but there would be a small contribution to the molecular wave function arising through pairing it with the other atomic orbitals in the molecule. The bonds would be delocalized to some extent. The energy of this residual resonance is normally very small, but can be of significance when the approximation of considering all the bonds to be localized is inadequate. This is likely to be so in molecules which contain bent bonds (i.e. bonds which are under strain) and when several of the bonds are very polar (this includes cases of abnormally high valence, such as in SF_6, TaF_8^{3-}, and $Mo(CN)_8^{4-}$, and many complexes formed by transition elements). The ionic character of highly polar bonds implies that the electrons are not completely localized between the two atoms.

7

exists in the tetraphosphorus molecule, only in this case it is possible to include a little $3d$ character in the hybridized orbitals. This cannot be done with carbon as there is no $2d$ orbital. Pauling and Simonetta[20] calculated that the hybrid which minimizes the energy of P_4 possesses 97·4% $3p$, 0·4% $3s$, and 2·2% $3d$ character (cf. Arnold[21]). The bonding is very largely between p orbitals, the small amount of d character serving primarily to reduce the strain in the molecule.

BIBLIOGRAPHICAL REFERENCES

1. Coulson, C. A., *J. Chim. Phys.*, 1949, **46**, 198.
2. Heath, D. F., and Linnett, J. W., *Trans. Faraday Soc.*, 1948, **44**, 556.
3. Eyring, H., and Polanyi, Z. *Phys. Chem.*, 1931, **B12**, 279.
4. Rosen, N., and Ikehara, S., *Phys. Rev.*, 1933, **43**, 5.
5. Fraga, S., and Mulliken, R. S., *Rev. Mod. Phys.*, 1960, **32**, 254.
6. Dirac, P. A. M., *Proc. Roy. Soc.*, 1929, A**123**, 714.
7. Van Vleck, J. H., and Cross, P. C., *J. Chem. Phys.*, 1933, **1**, 357.
8. Gillespie, R. J., and Nyholm, R. S., *Quart. Rev.*, 1957, **11**, 339.
9. Gillespie, R. J., *J. Chem. Educ.*, 1963, **40**, 259.
10. Allen, L. C., *Nature*, 1963, **197**, 896.
11. Bacher, R. F., and Goudsmit, S., *Phys. Rev.*, 1934, **46**, 948.
12. Ufford, C. W., *Phys. Rev.*, 1938, **53**, 568.
13. Shenstone, A. G., *Phys. Rev.*, 1947, **72**, 411.
14. Bartell, L. S., and Bonham, R. A., *J. Chem. Phys.*, 1957, **27**, 1414.
15. Allen, H. C., and Plyler, E. K., *J. Amer. Chem. Soc.*, 1958, **80**, 2673.
16. Dowling, J. M., and Stoicheff, B. P., *Canad. J. Phys.*, 1959, **37**, 703.
17. Cumper, C. W. N., *Trans. Faraday Soc.*, 1958, **54**, 1261.
18. Maccoll, A., *Trans. Faraday Soc.*, 1950, **46**, 369.
19. Coulson, C. A., and Moffitt, W. E., *Phil. Mag.*, 1949, **40**, 1.
20. Pauling, L., and Simonetta, M., *J. Chem. Phys.*, 1952, **20**, 29.
21. Arnold, J. R., *J. Chem. Phys.*, 1946, **14**, 351.

CHAPTER 12

POLYATOMIC MOLECULES II.
DELOCALIZED ORBITALS

In many molecules, particularly those classified as aromatic, some of the electrons can never be considered to be localized in a bond between two atoms, as there are comparable probabilities of finding them near three or more atoms. In this chapter these delocalized electrons are discussed in terms of the valence bond and molecular orbital approaches, and also by the free electron method.

The most convenient molecule to discuss first is butadiene, a planar non-linear hydrocarbon of four carbon atoms with the structure[1,2] shown in Figure 12.1. It can exist in *cis* and *trans* forms, but the latter is the more stable. Each carbon is attached to three other atoms and this, together with the planarity of these

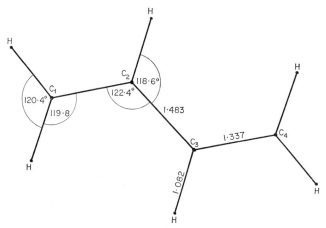

FIGURE 12.1   Butadiene.

atoms, shows that trigonal sp^2 hybrids are involved. As the bond angles are close to $120°$ the hybrids must be nearly equivalent. Each carbon, therefore, forms three *localized* two-electron bonds which are depicted by the lines in Figure 12.1. In addition the p_z orbital of each carbon atom, perpendicular to the plane of the paper in this diagram, holds one electron and it is these which become delocalized in the butadiene molecule. Nearly all theoretical calculations ignore any interaction between the σ and π electrons, but this is not really justifiable.

12.1. The Free Electron Theory

Consider a conjugated polyene such as butadiene stripped of its π electrons. Each carbon atom would possess a unit positive charge and in the free electron theory this is assumed to be spread out uniformly along the zigzag line joining the carbon atoms. The original periodic potential along this line is then replaced by a constant potential. If one π electron is added to this system the problem becomes that of a particle in a one-dimensional box. The best approximation would be a box with finite potential walls, but the one with infinite walls is normally employed since the Schrödinger equation has been solved explicitly in this case. The possible energy levels are

$$E_n = \frac{n^2 h^2}{8ma^2} \quad (n = 1, 2, 3 \ldots) \tag{3.5}$$

where the length of the box a is generally considered to extend half a bond length on either side of the ends of the conjugated chain. In a conjugated polyene $a \simeq 1 \cdot 4N$, Å where N is the number of conjugated carbon atoms. If the interaction between the electrons is neglected the total energy of the π electrons is obtained by placing them, two at a time, into the orbitals of lowest energy. The electron density distribution of each electron would be given by (see Chapter 3)

$$\rho_x = \psi^2 = \frac{2}{a} \sin^2 \frac{n\pi}{a} x$$

The electron density of the four π electrons in butadiene is illustrated in Figure 12.2.

This very crude theory provides a surprisingly good account of the electronic spectra of polyenes and of aromatic hydrocarbons.[3,4] It has also been employed to discuss bond lengths and chemical reactivity.[5]

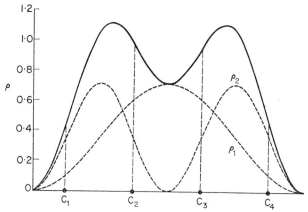

FIGURE 12.2 Electron density in butadiene calculated from the free electron theory. ρ_1 is the density for two electrons in the lowest orbital, ρ_2 for two electrons in the next orbital, and the full line is their sum.

12.2. Molecular Orbital Theory

The atomic p_z orbitals of the carbon atoms are illustrated in Figure 12.3. Let their atomic wave functions be ϕ_1, ϕ_2, ϕ_3, and ϕ_4 respectively. It is unrealistic to postulate that a localized π bond is formed between carbons 1 and 2 as the latter must also overlap the p^z orbital of carbon 3 to an appreciable extent. It is this which

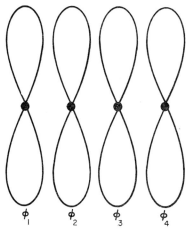

FIGURE 12.3 The atomic p_z orbitals of butadiene.

inhibits rotation about the C_2—C_3 bond and results in a planar molecule. These π electrons must therefore occupy molecular orbitals which are formulated as a linear combination of the four atomic p wave functions,

$$\psi = c_1\phi_1 + c_2\phi_2 + c_3\phi_3 + c_4\phi_4 \tag{12.1}$$

The electrons in these orbitals could be found near any of the carbon atoms—they are delocalized. The problem is to find the values of the weighting factors c_1, c_2, c_3, and c_4. This is done in the usual way by employing the variation principle and the secular determinant.

Minimizing the energy of the system with respect to the coefficient c_1 and employing the same nomenclature as used before, we obtain

$$\frac{\partial \xi}{\partial c_1} = c_1(H_{11} - \xi S_{11}) + c_2(H_{12} - \xi S_{12}) + c_3(H_{13} - \xi S_{13})$$
$$+ c_4(H_{14} - \xi S_{14}) = 0$$
$$= c_1(\alpha_1 - \xi) + c_2(\beta_{12} - \xi S_{12}) + c_3(\beta_{13} - \xi S_{13})$$
$$+ c_4(\beta_{14} - \xi S_{14}) = 0$$

($H_{ij} = \int \phi_i \mathbf{H} \phi_j \, d\tau$; $S_{ij} = \int \phi_i \phi_j \, d\tau$; $\alpha_i = H_{ii} =$ coulombic integral; $\beta_{ij} = H_{ij} =$ exchange integral.) The Hamiltonian involved in the H_{ij} terms is complicated but fortunately need not be considered explicitly. One of the main difficulties is that the electron distribution must be known before the coulombic terms in $\mathbf{H}$ can be formulated. There will be three more secular equations obtained by minimizing the energy in turn with respect to c_2, c_3, and c_4. They are

$$\frac{\partial \xi}{\partial c_2} = c_1(\beta_{21} - \xi S_{21}) + c_2(\alpha_2 - \xi) + c_3(\beta_{23} - \xi S_{23})$$
$$+ c_4(\beta_{24} - \xi S_{24}) = 0$$
$$\frac{\partial \xi}{\partial c_3} = c_1(\beta_{31} - \xi S_{31}) + c_2(\beta_{32} - \xi S_{32}) + c_3(\alpha_3 - \xi)$$
$$+ c_4(\beta_{34} - \xi S_{34}) = 0$$
$$\frac{\partial \xi}{\partial c_4} = c_1(\beta_{41} - \xi S_{41}) + c_2(\beta_{42} - \xi S_{42}) + c_3(\beta_{43} - \xi S_{43})$$
$$+ c_4(\alpha_4 - \xi) = 0$$

The secular determinant formed from the coefficients of the c's will be

$$\begin{vmatrix} \alpha_1 - \xi & \beta_{12} - \xi S_{12} & \beta_{13} - \xi S_{13} & \beta_{14} - \xi S_{14} \\ \beta_{21} - \xi S_{21} & \alpha_2 - \xi & \beta_{23} - \xi S_{23} & \beta_{24} - \xi S_{24} \\ \beta_{31} - \xi S_{31} & \beta_{32} - \xi S_{32} & \alpha_3 - \xi & \beta_{34} - \xi S_{34} \\ \beta_{41} - \xi S_{41} & \beta_{42} - \xi S_{42} & \beta_{43} - \xi_{43} & \alpha_4 - S\xi \end{vmatrix} = 0$$

This may be simplified without great loss of accuracy. Let us consider the approximations suggested by Hückel.[6] The first of these is to put all the overlap integrals equal to zero. This is legitimate for S_{13} and S_{14} as the orbitals are far apart, but can hardly be justified for S_{12} when the orbitals are on neighbouring atoms. Secondly, the exchange integrals between non-neighbouring atoms are ignored. With these approximations the secular determinant becomes

$$\begin{vmatrix} \alpha_1 - \xi & \beta_{12} & 0 & 0 \\ \beta_{21} & \alpha_2 - \xi & \beta_{23} & 0 \\ 0 & \beta_{32} & \alpha_3 - \xi & \beta_{34} \\ 0 & 0 & \beta_{43} & \alpha_4 - \xi \end{vmatrix} = 0 \qquad (12.2)$$

From the symmetry of the butadiene molecule

$$\alpha_1 = \alpha_4$$
$$\alpha_2 = \alpha_3$$
$$\beta_{12}(\equiv \beta_{21}) = \beta_{34}(\equiv \beta_{34})$$

The coulombic integrals α_1 and α_2 will depend upon the resultant electron density near these atoms and because the atoms have different environments these will not be the same; however let us take them as having the same value α. The C_1—C_2 bond is shorter than the C_2—C_3 bond so that $\beta_{12} > \beta_{23}$; again however, let us assume that all the resonance integrals have the same value β, then these final simplifications reduce the determinant to

$$\begin{vmatrix} \alpha - \xi & \beta & 0 & 0 \\ \beta & \alpha - \xi & \beta & 0 \\ 0 & \beta & \alpha - \xi & \beta \\ 0 & 0 & \beta & \alpha - \xi \end{vmatrix} = 0 \qquad (12.3)$$

Its solutions give four values for the energy

$$\xi = \alpha \pm 0 \cdot 618\beta$$
$$\xi = \alpha \pm 1 \cdot 618\beta$$

which correspond to four delocalized molecular orbitals. The integral β is negative so that the molecular orbitals of least energy are those with the positive signs, and since each orbital can accommodate two electrons the lowest energy state for butadiene results when two of the π electrons have the energy $\xi_1 = \alpha + 1 \cdot 618\beta$ and two have the energy $\xi_2 = \alpha + 0 \cdot 618\beta$.

For each eigenvalue the secular equations can be solved to obtain the ratio of the coefficients c; to obtain their absolute values another equation is required and is provided by normalizing the wave function. From equation (10.24) this gives

$$\sum c_i^2 + 2\sum_{i>j} c_i c_j S_{ij} = 1$$

or when the overlap integrals are neglected

$$\sum c_i^2 = c_1^2 + c_2^2 + c_3^2 + c_4^2 = 1$$

The values obtained are shown in Table 12.1. Valuable information may be obtained by analysing these results.

TABLE 12.1

Orbital	Energy	c_1	c_2	c_3	c_4
ψ_4	$\alpha - 1.618\beta$	+0.3718	−0.6015	+0.6015	−0.3718
ψ_3	$\alpha - 0.618\beta$	+0.6015	−0.3718	−0.3718	+0.6015
ψ_2	$\alpha + 0.618\beta$	+0.6015	+0.3718	−0.3718	−0.6015
ψ_1	$\alpha + 1.618\beta$	+0.3718	+0.6015	+0.6015	+0.3718

Electron Distribution. First of all a pictorial concept of the distribution of the electrons in the orbitals can be obtained. The clue is provided by the signs of the coefficients and the orbital shapes are shown pictorially in Figure 12.4. The orbital of least energy ψ_1

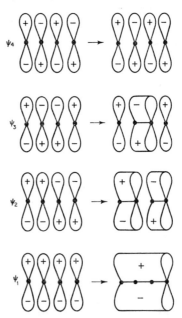

FIGURE 12.4   The delocalized molecular orbitals in butadiene.

has a bonding effect over the four carbon atoms whilst ψ_2, ψ_3, and ψ_4 have one, two, and three nodal planes respectively between the carbon atoms. In the ground electronic state the two electrons in ψ_1 will bond all the carbons together but the two in ψ_2 will only bind C_1 to C_2, and C_3 to C_4; there is a repulsion between C_2 and C_3. Hence there will be a considerable measure of π bonding between the outside pairs of carbon atoms but much less between the central pair. This is reflected in the different C—C bond lengths. In an excited state an electron might be promoted from ψ_2 to ψ_3. This would increase the bonding between C_2 and C_3 but reduce the strength of the other carbon bonds.

TABLE 12.2

Orbital	$c_i c_j$		
	C_1–C_2	C_2–C_3	C_3–C_4
ψ_1	0·2236	0·3618	0·2236
ψ_2	0·2236	−0·1381	0·2236
$\Sigma c_i c_j$ for two electrons in ψ_1 and in ψ_2	0·8944	0·4474	0·8944

This discussion can be put on a semi-quantitative basis by introducing the term *bond order*. A single bond is said to have a bond order of one, a double bond of two. In butadiene the C—C bonds have a σ bond order of unity and a π bond order of less than one. Bond order measures the electron density in the bond and for any orbital this will be greatest between atoms i and j when the product $c_i c_j$ is positive and large. Coulson[7] defined the π bond order as $\Sigma c_i c_j$, summed over all the electrons. These values are shown in Table 12.2. It will be noted that antibonding between two atoms makes a negative contribution.

The π bond order between the central atoms is only half that of the other bonds. If β_{23} had been taken to be less than β_{12}, as must be the case, then the π electron density between C_2 and C_3 would have been even smaller and that between the other carbons somewhat greater. In the excited state with two electrons in ψ_1 and one each in ψ_2 and ψ_3, the corresponding π bond orders are C_1—C_2 = C_3—C_4 = 0·447 and C_2—C_3 = 0·724. These π bond orders have been related to bond lengths (see p. 239).

$\Sigma c_i c_j$ gives a measure of the π electron density in the bonds, Σc_i^2 is a measure of the electron density associated with each atom. In butadiene Σc_i^2, summed over all the bonding electrons, is unity for each atom, so that the net charge on each atom is zero. This is always the case with alternant hydrocarbons.†

Bond Energy. The ground state configuration of two electrons in ψ_1 and two in ψ_2 has a π bond energy of

$$2\xi_1 + 2\xi_2 = 2(\alpha + 1\cdot618\beta) + 2(\alpha + 0\cdot618\beta)$$
$$= 4\alpha + 4\cdot472\beta$$

If the bonds were localized between C_1 and C_2, and between C_3 and C_4, i.e. C=C—C=C, the corresponding energy would be that of two doubly occupied ethylenic π bonds. The secular determinant for a localized π bond is

$$\begin{vmatrix} \alpha - \xi & \beta \\ \beta & \alpha - \xi \end{vmatrix} = 0$$

from which $\xi = \alpha \pm \beta$. Hence the four electrons in localized π bonds would have the energy

$$4(\alpha + \beta) = 4\alpha + 4\beta$$

Electron delocalization results in an additional stability of $0\cdot472\beta$, which may be termed the delocalization or resonance energy.

Finally, in the excited state mentioned earlier the corresponding energy would be

$$2\xi_1 + \xi_2 + \xi_3 = 2(\alpha + 1\cdot618\beta) + (\alpha + 0\cdot618\beta) + (\alpha - 0\cdot618\beta)$$
$$= 4\alpha + 3\cdot236\beta$$

The difference between this and the energy of the ground state, $(4\cdot472 - 3\cdot236)\beta = 1\cdot236\beta$, is an electron promotion energy which should correspond to an observable spectroscopic transition in the ultraviolet region.

The Magnitude of β. Because of the approximations made in the above analysis the numerical value of β cannot be calculated theoretically. Nevertheless it is not too much to expect that the values of α and β remain fairly constant for many unsaturated

---

† Alternant and non-alternant hydrocarbons may be distinguished as follows. Place a dot (.) over any carbon atom in the molecule, then put a cross (x) on the carbons which are directly attached to it and dots on the ones attached to those with crosses, etc. When all the carbons have been labelled then the hydrocarbon is *alternant* if two dots or two crosses are never on adjacent atoms, otherwise it is described as a *non-alternant* hydrocarbon. Benzene for example is alternant but fulvene is non-alternant (see figure).

hydrocarbons. Hence if the objective is just to compare conjugated hydrocarbons it is unnecessary to know their magnitudes.

β can be estimated experimentally from the energies discussed above. The resonance energy of a molecule can be estimated from tables of bond energies (Tables 14.1, 14.2, and 14.4) or from hydrogenation energies. If there were no delocalization the energy change in the hydrogenation of butadiene to give butane should be twice that of converting ethylene into ethane. The difference between this and the experimental value would be the resonance energy of $0 \cdot 472\beta$. Alternatively, the calculated promotion energies can be correlated with the energies of observed spectroscopic transitions. The two estimates differ somewhat, but there is a fair measure of agreement with different molecules; the value of β obtained from thermal data is about 16 kcal/mole in aromatic hydrocarbons.

The procedure just described is very simple to apply to conjugated molecules, but the approximations made in the treatment are too numerous for the results to be quantitatively reliable. Nevertheless they are of great value in comparing one molecule with another. Let us summarize some of the approximations.

(a) The molecular wave functions are assumed to be expressible as a linear combination of carbon p wave functions (equation (12.1)). The Hückel method is only concerned with the best choice for their coefficients.

(b) All the overlap integrals have been ignored. This is quite acceptable if the orbitals are far apart but cannot be justified when the atoms are adjacent. It is even illogical, since the resonance integrals between nearest neighbours are retained. The overlap integral between nearest neighbours can however be included without unduly complicating the calculation.[8,9] It has the effect of destroying the symmetry of the orbital energies about the value $\xi = \alpha$ (i.e. for the orbital $\xi = \alpha + k\beta$ there is no longer a corresponding orbital $\xi = \alpha - k\beta$), but for alternant hydrocarbons the inclusion of overlap does not alter the bond orders or the value of the charge on each atom.

(c) The coulombic integrals cannot be equal for each carbon atom in butadiene. The electron distribution is not uniform throughout the molecule and consequently the Hamiltonian cannot be the same near each atom. A molecule like benzene which possesses a high degree of symmetry, however, would have a regular electron distribution round the ring and consequently each carbon would then have the same coulombic integral.

(d) Much the same remarks can also be made about the integral β_{ij}. It depends upon the Hamiltonian, and since some of the factors include the product $\phi_i\phi_j$ it is also dependent upon the distance between the atoms. The C—C distances are constant in benzene but not in butadiene.

(e) Electron correlation is not taken into account; because of the repulsion between the electrons their positions are correlated to some extent. In butadiene this would tend to keep the π electrons towards opposite ends of the molecule, but in benzene this effect would give a uniform electron distribution round the ring.

(f) The interaction known to exist between the σ and π bonds has been neglected.

These criticisms are more serious in a molecule like butadiene than in one like benzene. In butadiene the terminal and central carbons differ, their chemical reactivity is different and so are the bond lengths. In ignoring this difference the Hückel approximation overemphasizes electron delocalization in the molecule—the terminal bonds are, in fact, more like ethylenic bonds and the central bond more like a single bond between two sp^2 hybridized carbon atoms than is implied in the analysis. In conjugated cyclic molecules like benzene, naphthalene, etc. the carbon atoms and C—C bonds are all fairly similar and the approximations of the Hückel method not nearly so serious. Further, in these cyclic molecules the average numerical values of α and β would be expected to vary less from one compound to another so that any comparison between them should be reliable.

Self-consistent Field Molecular Orbitals

In the Hückel method the Hamiltonian is not defined and the results of the calculations are only of value in comparing rather similar unsaturated molecules. In a self-consistent field method the Hamiltonian has to be defined explicitly. Coulombic and exchange interactions between all the electrons in the molecule are allowed for in the calculations. To do this, however, the wave functions of the electrons must first be known so that the Hamiltonian can be formulated. The position is very similar to that of the Hartree–Fock self-consistent field method for atoms (page 119) and a similar procedure of successive approximations has to be employed. The technique has been described by Roothaan[10] and gives results which are more accurate and more reliable than can be obtained by the elementary Hückel method.

The wave function of a conjugated or unconjugated molecule is approximated to by taking a linear combination of the atomic orbitals centred on each nucleus.

$$\psi_i = \sum_k c_{ik}\phi_k$$

A very large number of atomic wave functions should be included, but in practice many which contain inner electrons and those of great energy are not considered. With this form for ψ the coefficients c have to be determined. This is similar to the problem in the Hückel method and secular equations of the form

$$\sum_i c_{ik}(H_{lk} - \xi_i S_{lk}) = 0$$

and a secular determinant are formulated. The matrix elements H_{lk} however depend upon the wave functions ψ_i, that is upon the coefficients c_{ik}. An iterative procedure has to be used to solve the equations.

The Roothaan scheme involves a great number of integrals and unless the problem can be simplified by utilizing the symmetry of the molecule, only about six atoms may be included in the problem. Pariser and Parr[11], in their approximation, neglect all overlap integrals and so considerably simplify the secular determinant. Pople[12] goes even further by using a system of point charges, instead of a charge distribution, to compute the coulombic terms. These and other modifications to the Roothaan method have enabled the general self-consistent field approach to be applied more easily to complex molecules, but there is naturally some loss of accuracy.

12.3. Valence Bond Theory

A complete valence bond description of π electrons along the lines employed by Heitler and London for a σ bond in hydrogen is difficult and in practice is restricted to small molecules. The approximation of perfect pairing will be employed.

If the p electrons on carbons 1 and 2 and also on 3 and 4 in butadiene are paired together, the structure obtained is the one generally employed to describe this molecule.

$$\text{I} \qquad CH_2{=}CH{-}CH{=}CH_2$$

The binding energy of the four π electrons in this structure, given by equation (11.10), is

$$\xi_I = Q + J_{12} + J_{34} - \tfrac{1}{2}J_{23}$$

If the various exchange energies are assumed to be the same (that is equal bond lengths) this reduces to

$$\xi_I = Q + 1{\cdot}5J$$

The p electrons can be paired together in two other ways however.

$$\text{II} \quad CH_2 - CH = CH - CH_2$$

$$\xi_{II} = Q + J_{23} + J_{14} - \tfrac{1}{2}J_{12} - \tfrac{1}{2}J_{34}$$
$$= Q$$

The pairing of electrons 1 and 4 is just a formality—they are much too far apart to make any significant contribution to the stability of this structure and J_{14} is accordingly put equal to zero. This structure is less stable by $1{\cdot}5J$ than structure I. The third possible structure is

$$\text{III} \quad CH_2 - CH - CH - CH_2$$

$$\xi_{III} = Q + J_{13} + J_{24} - \tfrac{1}{2}J_{12} - \tfrac{1}{2}J_{23} - \tfrac{1}{2}J_{34}$$

It is not, however, independent of the first two. That is to say, its wave function may be compounded out of the wave functions of the other canonical forms. It has been shown that for $2N$ electrons in N different orbitals there are only

$$\frac{(2N)!}{N!(N+1)!} \tag{12.4}$$

independent structures possible with zero spin.[13] Chemical preference is for structures I and II.

The complete description of the interaction between these p electrons must incorporate all possible pairing schemes. Butadiene is therefore regarded as a resonance hybrid of I and II with

$$\psi = c_1\psi_I + c_2\psi_{II}$$

The secular determinant, from which the minimum energy associated with ψ is obtained, is

$$\begin{vmatrix} H_{I.I} - \xi S_{I.I} & H_{I.II} - \xi S_{I.II} \\ H_{II.I} - \xi S_{II.I} & H_{II.II} - \xi S_{II.II} \end{vmatrix} = 0$$

The matric elements for the above structures are

$$H_{I.I} - \xi S_{I.I} = \xi_I - \xi = Q + 1{\cdot}5J - \xi$$

and

$$H_{II.II} - \xi S_{II.II} = \xi_{II} - \xi = Q - \xi$$

The calculation of the 'cross terms' $(H_{I.II} - \xi S_{I.II})$ is more difficult. The procedure of Pauling will be described without proof. (For proof see Pauling[14]. Eyring and Kimball[15] give an alternative approach.) Only the overlap and exchange integrals between neighbouring p orbitals are considered.

First draw the skeleton bond structure of each form but including only the π bonds, viz.

$$\text{C—C} \quad \text{C—C} \qquad\qquad \text{C} \quad \text{C—C} \quad \text{C}$$

I   II

These are then superposed to give

$$\text{C—C—C—C}$$

The pattern consists of a number i of islands of closed contours. In butadiene $i = 1$. A quantity k is now defined as follows: 'k equals the number of pairs of orbitals on neighbouring atoms, whether bonded or not, in all the islands, less half the number of neighbour orbitals on separate islands.'

For the above case there is only the one island and this has three pairs of electrons on neighbouring carbon atoms (C_1—C_2, C_2—C_3, and C_3—C_4). Hence

$$k = 3 - \tfrac{1}{2}(0) = 3$$

The matrix element in the determinant is then given by the formula[14,16],

$$H_{\text{I,II}} - \xi S_{\text{I,II}} = \frac{1}{2^{(N-i)}} (Q - \xi + kJ)$$

$$= \frac{1}{2^{(2-1)}} (Q - \xi + 3J) \qquad \text{for butadiene}\dagger$$

$$(12.5)$$

Formula [12.5] actually holds for all the matrix elements, that is

† This might seem rather complicated, so let us consider as a second example the matrix element formed from one Kekulé (I) and one Dewar (II) form of benzene. The π bond skeletons and their superposition diagrams respectively are

I   II

In this case $i = 2$ ($\lhd$ and $\|$) containing three and one pairs of neighbour orbitals respectively, but in addition there are two pairs between the islands. Hence

$$k = (3 + 1) - \tfrac{1}{2}(2) = 3$$

The number of p electrons ($2N$) is six so that

$$H_{\text{I,II}} - \xi S_{\text{I,II}} = \frac{1}{2^{(3-2)}} (Q - \xi + 3J) = \tfrac{1}{2}(Q - \xi + 3J)$$

for $H_{I.I}$ as well as for $H_{I.II}$. Hence the secular determinant becomes

$$\begin{vmatrix} Q - \xi + 1\cdot 5J & \frac{1}{2}(Q - \xi + 3J) \\ \frac{1}{2}(Q - \xi + 3J) & Q - \xi \end{vmatrix} = 0$$

from which $\xi = Q + \sqrt{3}J$.

The resonance hybrid of structures I and II is therefore $(\sqrt{3} - 1\cdot 5)J = 0\cdot 232J$ more stable than the most stable individual structure (I). This is taken as the resonance energy of the molecule. For many conjugated hydrocarbons J has a value of about 30 kcal/mole.

The relative weights of structures I and II are in the ratio of $c_1{}^2 : c_2{}^2$. Substituting $\xi = Q + \sqrt{3}J$ into the secular equations $c_1 = (1 + \sqrt{3})c_2$, so that structure I contributes 88% and II contributes 12% to the resonance hybrid.

Bond Order

The C_1—C_2 and C_3—C_4 bonds have a double bond character in structure I alone—that is their π bond order is 88% of that for an ethylenic double bond or 0·88, that of the central C_2—C_3 bond being 0·12. These values differ from those obtained by the molecular orbital method but it must be remembered that they are based on very different definitions of bond order. Both have been related to bond lengths (see p. 189).

The approximations made in this method of perfect pairs are almost the same as those made in the molecular orbital method discussed previously. In addition to the assumptions of the perfect pairing procedure the overlap and exchange integrals between atomic orbitals which are not nearest neighbours are neglected, and the values of those included are taken to be the same. No ionic structures have been considered and any interaction between σ and π electrons ignored. Because the bonds are localized in each individual structure the positions of the electrons are correlated to a large extent.

One disadvantage of this method is that the total energy of all the electrons is obtained, there is no indication of how this is divided up amongst the individual electrons. Consequently to obtain the energy of an electronically excited state, and an estimate of the position of an absorption band in its ultraviolet spectrum, it is necessary to repeat the whole calculation.

Finally a word of warning about resonance energies. The resonance is an electronic resonance, the positions of the nuclei in the hybrid and in each canonical form must be the same. Experimental values of resonance energies therefore include the energy required to stretch or compress the C—C bonds from the normal values in ethane and ethylene (cf. Chapter 14). This *compression energy* would be small in butadiene but is very important in benzene, where the C—C bond lengths differ considerably from those of both single and double bonds.

12.4. Conjugation in Benzene, Pyridine, and Heteroatom Molecules

In butadiene the π orbitals are centred on carbon atoms. How are the molecular orbital and valence bond approaches to be

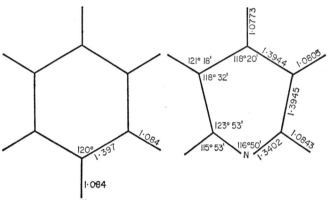

FIGURE 12.5   The geometrical structures of benzene and pyridine.

modified when the conjugated atoms differ? Let us compare benzene with pyridine. Both have planar hexagonal molecules with each ring atom sp^2 hybridized and having a single electron in a p_z orbital perpendicular to the plane of the ring. In pyridine one hybrid of the nitrogen atom holds a lone-pair of electrons. The bond angles and bond lengths[17-20] are shown in Figure 12.5.

Molecular Orbital Method. The secular determinant for a six-membered ring, corresponding to equation (12.2) for butadiene is

$$
\begin{vmatrix}
\alpha_1 - \xi & \beta_{12} & 0 & 0 & 0 & \beta_{16} \\
\beta_{21} & \alpha_2 - \xi & \beta_{23} & 0 & 0 & 0 \\
0 & \beta_{32} & \alpha_3 - \xi & \beta_{34} & 0 & 0 \\
0 & 0 & \beta_{43} & \alpha_4 - \xi & \beta_{45} & 0 \\
0 & 0 & 0 & \beta_{54} & \alpha_5 - \xi & \beta_{56} \\
\beta_{61} & 0 & 0 & 0 & \beta_{65} & \alpha_6 - \xi
\end{vmatrix} = 0
$$

[12.6]

Benzene. In benzene the bond lengths round the ring are all equal and the atoms identical so that the coulombic integrals and resonance energies must be equal. The six solutions of the determinant are

$$\xi_1 = \alpha + 2\beta \qquad \xi_4 = \alpha - \beta$$
$$\xi_2 = \alpha + \beta \qquad \xi_5 = \alpha - \beta$$
$$\xi_3 = \alpha + \beta \qquad \xi_6 = \alpha - 2\beta$$

The first three molecular orbitals are bonding and would each be occupied by two electrons giving a total energy of

$$\xi = 2\xi_1 + 2\xi_2 + 2\xi_3$$
$$= 6\alpha + 8\beta$$

The other three orbitals are antibonding and unoccupied in the ground state. Absorption of light in the ultraviolet region can however excite an electron into these levels.

The secular equations may be solved for each of these energies to obtain the coefficients c and analytical expressions for the wave functions. The second and third molecular orbitals are degenerate ($\xi_2 = \xi_3$) and so are the next two ($\xi_4 = \xi_5$). Their wave functions may therefore be represented in many ways, (cf. Sections 3.5 and 6.2). A real version of the orbitals is

Nodal Planes

$$\psi_1 = \frac{1}{\sqrt{6}}(\phi_1 + \phi_2 + \phi_3 + \phi_4 + \phi_5 + \phi_6)$$

$$\psi_2 = \frac{1}{\sqrt{12}}(2\phi_1 + \phi_2 - \phi_3 - 2\phi_4 - \phi_5 + \phi_6)$$

$$\psi_3 = \frac{1}{2}(\phi_2 + \phi_3 - \phi_5 - \phi_6)$$

$$\psi_4 = \frac{1}{\sqrt{12}}(2\phi_1 - \phi_2 - \phi_3 + 2\phi_4 - \phi_5 - \phi_6)$$

$$\psi_5 = \frac{1}{2}(\phi_2 - \phi_3 + \phi_5 - \phi_6)$$

$$\psi_6 = \frac{1}{\sqrt{6}}(\phi_1 - \phi_2 + \phi_3 - \phi_4 + \phi_5 - \phi_6)$$

The first orbital is bonding over all the carbon atoms whilst the next two orbitals each possess one nodal plane perpendicular to the ring. These are illustrated in Figure 12.6. The second pair of degenerate orbitals ψ_4 and ψ_5 have two nodal planes, whilst the orbital of greatest energy has three nodal planes. It might appear that a distinction is being made between the carbon atoms in some of these orbitals according to the position of the nodal planes. This is not really the case as the degenerate orbitals ψ_2 and ψ_3 are each doubly occupied in the ground state of benzene and their combined electron density, given by $(\psi_2{}^2 + \psi_3{}^2)e$, is seen to treat all the carbons alike. It is useful to think of their nodal planes as rotating around the ring in phase with one another so as to emphasize

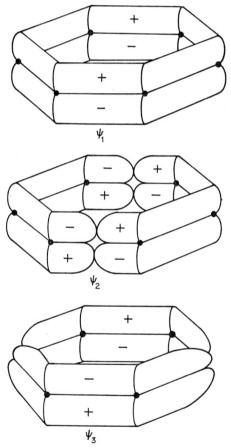

FIGURE 12.6 The bonding molecular orbitals in benzene. Each is occupied by two electrons in the ground state.

that the carbon atoms are identical. This equivalence of the carbon atoms is better expressed by replacing the above set of real functions by an equivalent set of complex functions.

$$\psi_1 = \frac{1}{\sqrt{6}} \left(\phi_1 + \phi_2 + \phi_3 + \phi_4 + \phi_5 + \phi_6 \right)$$

$$\psi_2 = \frac{1}{\sqrt{6}} \left(\phi_1 + e^{-\pi i/3}\phi_2 - e^{\pi i/3}\phi_3 - \phi_4 - e^{-\pi i/3}\phi_5 + e^{\pi i/3}\phi_6 \right)$$

$$\psi_3 = \frac{1}{\sqrt{6}} \left(\phi_1 + e^{\pi i/3}\phi_2 - e^{-\pi i/3}\phi_3 - \phi_4 - e^{\pi i/3}\phi_5 + e^{-\pi i/3}\phi_6 \right)$$

$$\psi_4 = \frac{1}{\sqrt{6}} \left(\phi_1 - e^{\pi i/3}\phi_2 - e^{-\pi i/3}\phi_3 + \phi_4 - e^{\pi i/3}\phi_5 - e^{-\pi i/3}\phi_6 \right)$$

$$\psi_5 = \frac{1}{\sqrt{6}} \left(\phi_1 - e^{-\pi i/3}\phi_2 - e^{\pi i/3}\phi_3 + \phi_4 - e^{-\pi i/3}\phi_5 - e^{\pi i/3}\phi_6 \right)$$

$$\psi_6 = \frac{1}{\sqrt{6}} \left(\phi_1 - \phi_2 + \phi_3 - \phi_4 + \phi_5 - \phi_6 \right)$$

Pyridine. Now consider pyridine. The secular equations and determinant are of precisely the same form as for benzene; the difference is in the values of the energies α and β. If the label 1 refers to the nitrogen atom, then because of its greater attraction for electrons, α_1 [or α_N] will be more negative than the other coulombic integrals. It is customary to express this difference in terms of β by writing,[21]

$$\alpha_1 \equiv \alpha_N = \alpha + k\beta$$

The parameter k has been taken to be proportional to the difference between the electronegativities of the two atoms.[22-23] In the case of a heterocyclic nitrogen atom, k was initially assumed to be 2, this was later revised to 0·5 but a value nearer 0·2 would be in better agreement with the charge distribution which results from more elaborate calculations.[24-26] The greater electronegativity of the nitrogen atom will pull electrons away from the carbons C_2 and C_6, thereby causing a small increase in their electronegativity, so that in some treatments the coulombic integrals of these atoms are also changed slightly by taking

$$\alpha_2 = \alpha_6 = \alpha + l\beta$$

When this modification is included in the calculation, l is usually taken to be about 10% of k. Finally, the introduction of the nitrogen atom will change the exchange integrals with carbons 2 and 6. Let

$$\beta_{12} = \beta_{16} = m\beta$$

The value of m may be estimated from bond energies by a method due to Lennard-Jones[27] and turns out to be close to unity for the

C—N bonds in pyridine—the precise value adopted for m has comparatively little effect upon the calculated energies.

The secular determinant for pyridine, corresponding to (12.6) is therefore

$$
\begin{vmatrix}
(\alpha + k\beta) - \xi & m\beta & 0 & 0 & 0 & m\beta \\
m\beta & (\alpha + l\beta) - \xi & \beta & 0 & 0 & 0 \\
0 & \beta & \alpha - \xi & \beta & 0 & 0 \\
0 & 0 & \beta & \alpha - \xi & \beta & 0 \\
0 & 0 & 0 & \beta & \alpha - \xi & \beta \\
m\beta & 0 & 0 & 0 & \beta & (\alpha + l\beta) - \xi
\end{vmatrix} = 0
$$

Taking $k = 0.2$, $l = \frac{1}{8}k = 0.025$, and $m = 1$ the energies, charge distribution and C—C π bond orders, calculated as for butadiene, are compared with the corresponding results for benzene in Figure 12.7. The orbital shapes are as in benzene, but the resultant charge cloud has 'flowed' slightly from the *ortho* and *para* positions to the nitrogen atom.

In more refined calculations the overlap integrals between neighbouring orbitals and resonance integrals between non-neighbouring atoms are introduced; also several methods have been described to determine the relative values of the coulombic and resonance integrals for differently situated atoms and bonds. These refinements do not affect the general conclusions of the simple treatment described above.

A set of values for the parameters k and m for various heteroatoms is given in Table 12.3. For each atom references could be given to cases where appreciably different values from those quoted have been adopted; strictly they are unique for each molecule so these are, at the best, averages. The values suggested are only for use in calculations where qualitative comparisons between molecules are made.

Valence Bond Method. The valence bond calculation, as with butadiene, reduces to the assignment of relative weights to the various structures. From equation (12.4) the π electrons in benzene and pyridine can be paired in five independent ways. These are normally taken to be the two Kekulé and three Dewar structures; the latter having the smaller binding energy because of the presence

ψ_I

ψ_II

ψ_III

ψ_IV

ψ_V

of a long bond. The resultant wave function will be

$$\psi = c_1\psi_I + c_2\psi_{II} + c_3\psi_{III} + c_4\psi_{IV} + c_5\psi_V \qquad (12.7)$$

Benzene. In benzene the individual Kekulé forms and the three Dewar forms are equivalent so their coefficients are the same.

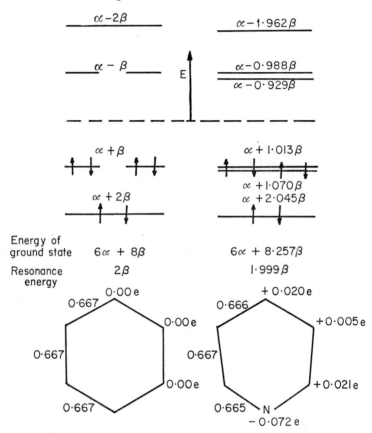

FIGURE 12.7   The energies of the delocalized molecular orbitals, atomic charges, and π bond orders in benzene and pyridine.

Equation (12.7) therefore reduces to

$$\psi = c_1(\psi_I + \psi_{II}) + c_3(\psi_{III} + \psi_{IV} + \psi_V)$$

The energy of each structure is expressed by the approximation of perfect pairing and a fifth order determinant solved as described for butadiene. The energies for some combinations of these structures are shown in Table 12.4. From the last function $c_3/c_1 = 0.434$

TABLE 12.3

Element		k	m	
B		−1	C—B	0·7
C		0	C—C	0·9
			$(C—C)_{aromatic}$	1·0
			C=C	1·1
N	$\dot{N}$	0·5	C—N	0·8
	$\ddot{N}$	1·5	$(C—N)_{aromatic}$	1·0
	N^+	2·0	N—O	0·7
O	$\dot{O}$	1	C—O	0·8
	$\ddot{O}$	2	C=O	1·0
	O^+	2·5		
F		3	C—F	0·9
Cl		2	C—Cl	0·8
Br		1·5	C—Br	0·7
CH_3†				
(1) Inductive effect	C_a	−0·5	$C_a—CH_3$	0
$\quad (C_a—CH_3)$				
(2) Hyperconjugation	C_b	−0·1	$C_a—C_b$	0·8
$\quad (C_a—C_b≡H_3)$	H_3	−0·5	$C_b≡H_3$	3
(3) Heteroatom	C_bH_3	2	$C_a—C_bH_3$	0·7
$\quad (C_a—C_bH_3)$				

† A methyl, or similar group, is generally considered to hypercon-jugate with an unsaturated system. Theoretically this has been treated as (1) an inductive effect by altering the k value of the atom to which the methyl is attached, as (2) a conjugation involving the C and H atoms in the methyl individually, and (3) by considering the methyl as a single 'heteroatom' attached to the unsaturated system.

TABLE 12.4

Canonical Forms		Energy	Resonance Energy
Single Kekulé	ψ_I	$Q + 1·5J$	—
Both Kekulé	$\psi_I + \psi_{II}$	$Q + 2·4J$	$0·9J$
Single Dewar	ψ_{III}	Q	—
Three Dewar	$\psi_{III} + \psi_{IV} + \psi_V$	$Q + 2·0J$	$0·5J$
All forms	$\psi_I + \psi_{II} + \psi_{III} + \psi_{IV} + \psi_V$	$Q + 2·6J$	$1·1J$

showing that the relative weights of each Kekulé and each Dewar structure is $1^2:0\cdot434^2$ or $1:0\cdot19$. We may therefore assign weights of 39% to each Kekulé and 7% to each Dewar structure. Each C—C bond is a double bond in one of the Kekulé and one of the Dewar structures so their π bond orders are $0\cdot39 + 0\cdot07 = 0\cdot46$.

In more elaborate calculations ionic structures are included. A very large number of these are possible, so the calculations become very much more difficult and are seldom attempted. Restricting the calculations to covalent structures, equation (12.4) shows that the secular determinant for naphthalene has an order of 42 and for anthracene 429. (In the molecular orbital method the determinants have orders, benzene 6, naphthalene 10, and anthracene 14.) As the number of conjugated atoms increases the problem soon becomes unmanageable and further drastic approximations have to be made. The calculations are also made more difficult by the introduction of a heteroatom. In pyridine the three Dewar structures no longer have equal weights—the one with the long bond to the nitrogen atom being different from the other two. To account for the greater electronegativity of the nitrogen atom it is now essential to include some ionic structures, the three most important ones being

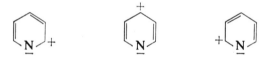

but many more could be included with advantage. It is obviously going to be difficult to decide the relative weights of all these covalent and ionic forms. In most cases the only feasible approach is to estimate them from experimental data such as resonance energies, electronegativities, dipole moments, or bond lengths.[28] In these circumstances the valence bond description is more qualitative and less valuable than the molecular orbital treatment.

BIBLIOGRAPHICAL REFERENCES

1. Alemenningen, A., Bastiansen, O., and Traetteberg, M., *Acta Chem. Scand.*, 1958, **12**, 1221.
2. Marais, D. J., Sheppard, N., and Stoicheff, B. P., *Tetrahedron*, 1962, **17**, 163.
3. Bayliss, N. S., *Quart. Rev.*, 1952, **6**, 319.
4. Kuhn, H., *Experimenta*, 1953, **9**, 41.
5. Scheer, C. W., *J. Chem. Phys.*, 1953, **21**, 1565, 1582.
6. Hückel, E., *Z. Phys.*, 1931, **70**, 204.

7. Coulson, C. A., *Proc. Roy. Soc.*, 1939, **A169**, 413.
8. Milliken, R. S., Rieke, C. A., and Brown, W. G., *J. Amer. Chem. Soc.*, 1941, **63**, 41.
9. Wheland, G. W., *J. Amer. Chem. Soc.*, 1941, **63**, 2025.
10. Roothaan, C. C. J., *Rev. Mod. Phys.*, 1951, **23**, 69.
11. Pariser, R., and Parr, R. G., *J. Chem. Phys.*, 1953, **21**, 466, 767.
12. Pople, J. A., *Trans. Faraday Soc.*, 1953, **49**, 1375.
13. Van Vleck, J. H., and Sherman, A., *Rev. Mod. Phys.*, 1935, **7**, 192.
14. Pauling, L., *J. Chem. Phys.*, 1933, **1**, 280.
15. Eyring, H., and Kimball, G. E., *J. Chem. Phys.*, 1933, **1**, 239.
16. McWeeny, R., *Proc. Roy. Soc.*, 1954, **A223**, 306.
17. Bak, B., Hansen-Nygaard, L., and Rastrup-Andersen, J., *J. Mol. Spectrosc.*, 1958, **2**, 361.
18. Stoicheff, B. P., *Canad. J. Phys.*, 1954, **32**, 339.
19. Langseth, A., and Stoicheff, B. P., *Canad. J. Phys.*, 1956, **34**, 350.
20. Almenningen, A., Bastiansen, O., and Fernholt, L., *Det. Kgl. Norske Vidensk. Selsk. Shrifter*, 1958, No. 3.
21. Pauling, L., and Wheland, G. W., *J. Amer. Chem. Soc.*, 1935, **57**, 2086.
22. Mulliken, R. S., *J. Chim. Phys.*, 1949, **46**, 497, 675.
23. Laforgue, A., *J. Chim. Phys.*, 1949, **46**, 568.
24. McWeeny, R., and Peacock, T. E., *Proc. Phys. Soc.*, 1957, **A70**, 41.
25. Odiot, S., and Roux, M., *J. Chim. Phys.*, 1953, **50**, 141.
26. Fernandez, J. I., *Compt. rend.*, 1951, **233**, 56.
27. Lennard-Jones, J. E., *Proc. Roy. Soc.*, 1931, **A158**, 280.
28. Pauling, L., *The Nature of the Chemical Bond*, 3rd edn., Cornell University Press, Ithaca, N.Y., 1960.

CHAPTER 13

EQUIVALENT ORBITALS

This chapter has been included to indicate the answer to a problem which might be worrying some readers; it is not required for an understanding of subsequent chapters (see also Pople[1]).

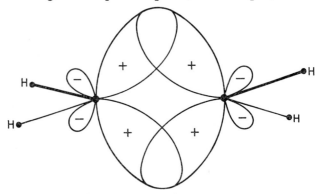

FIGURE 13.1   The overlap of sp^3 hybrids to form ethylene.

Consider the ethylene molecule. The C—C double bond was earlier described as being formed by the overlap of a trigonal sp^2 hybrid from each carbon to give a σ bond, and of the p_z orbitals to give a π bond. Why is the p_z orbital included in the hybridization (sp^3) when describing methane or ethane, but not when considering ethylene? Could the carbon atoms in ethylene be tetrahedrally hybridized and linked together as in Figure 13.1? In this case the carbon atoms would be joined by two equivalent bent bonds. True, the energy of each would be less than that of the single C—C bond in ethane, formed by the end-on overlap of two tetrahedral orbitals, but bent bonds do exist in cyclopropane, tetraphosphorus, and other molecules.

Let us formulate the molecular wave function according to molecular orbital theory for the σ plus π bond description. There

208

will be two electrons in each orbital so the complete determinantal wave function, including spin, is

$$\psi = N \begin{vmatrix} (\sigma\alpha)_1 & (\sigma\beta)_1 & (\pi\alpha)_1 & (\pi\beta)_1 \\ (\sigma\alpha)_2 & (\sigma\beta)_2 & (\pi\alpha)_2 & (\pi\beta)_2 \\ (\sigma\alpha)_3 & (\sigma\beta)_3 & (\pi\alpha)_3 & (\pi\beta)_3 \\ (\sigma\alpha)_4 & (\sigma\beta)_4 & (\pi\alpha)_4 & (\pi\beta)_4 \end{vmatrix}$$

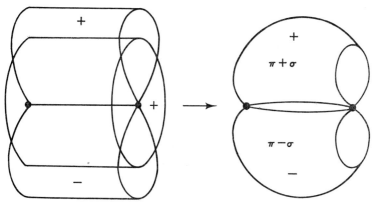

FIGURE 13.2 The formation of two equivalent orbitals for ethylene.

By adding and subtracting columns of this determinant it may be transformed into [cf. equation (11.2)]

$$\psi = N' \begin{vmatrix} [(\pi+\sigma)\alpha]_1 & [(\pi-\sigma)\alpha]_1 & [(\pi+\sigma)\beta]_1 & [(\pi-\sigma)\beta]_1 \\ [(\pi+\sigma)\alpha]_2 & [(\pi-\sigma)\alpha]_2 & [(\pi+\sigma)\beta]_2 & [(\pi-\sigma)\beta]_2 \\ [(\pi+\sigma)\alpha]_3 & [(\pi-\sigma)\alpha]_3 & [(\pi+\sigma)\beta]_3 & [(\pi-\sigma)\beta]_3 \\ [(\pi+\sigma)\alpha]_4 & [(\pi-\sigma)\alpha]_4 & [(\pi+\sigma)\beta]_4 & [(\pi-\sigma)\beta]_4 \end{vmatrix}$$

In other words, it is entirely equivalent to having two electrons in the molecular orbital $\pi + \sigma$ and two in $\pi - \sigma$. These two orbitals are *equivalent orbitals*; their shapes are illustrated diagrammatically in Figure 13.2 and are such as would be formed by the overlap of the tetrahedral hybrids in Figure 13.1.

The description of the C—C bonds as a σ plus a π bond with sp^2 hybridized carbons is equivalent to describing them as two equivalent bent bonds formed from sp^3 hybrids. The four tetrahedral hybrids in ethylene however are not equivalent since the $\widehat{HCH}$ angle[2-4] is $117°22'$, which is considerably greater than the tetrahedral angle in methane ($109°28'$). The hybrids which form the C—C bonds would have to possess rather more p character and those forming the C—H bonds rather less than in methane. This has already been implied in the above determinants where the σ part of the wave functions is that of trigonal sp^2 hybrids. The angle between equivalent sp^2 hybrids is 120°, and since aromatic organic compounds have bond angles very close to this figure the σ and π orbital approach gives a simpler representation of these molecules than the equivalent orbital method. With many non-cyclic organic compounds containing single and double bonds however, the angle between the two single bonds is close to the tetrahedral value of 109°28′ (or 125° between the single and double bond). In these cases the bent bond approach might seem to be the more logical description. The tricovalent nitrogen atom has a significantly smaller angle of about 113° between single and double bonds in many molecules.

Calculations by the valence bond method[5] show that the energy obtained with the σ and π bond model is lower, and therefore better, than that for bent tetrahedral bonds. Wave mechanical calculations can of course always be improved by employing more elaborate functions. Pauling[6] for example, showed that a more favourable distribution of charge in the tetrahedral bent bond model of ethylene occurred if the hybrids had about $2\frac{1}{2}\%$ of $3d$ and of $4f$ character, and the calculated energies were then superior to those obtained with the simpler σ plus π bond functions.

Nitrogen. Equivalent orbitals can always be formed when unsaturation is present. The N_2 molecule, for example, was described as having one σ and two π bonds on page 146.

$$N_2, \ \sigma_x{}^2 \ \pi_y{}^2 \ \pi_z{}^2$$

By manipulating the determinantal wave function for the complete nitrogen molecule these may be transformed into three equivalent-orbital wave functions (Figure 13.3).

$$\psi_1 = \sigma + \pi_y$$

$$\psi_2 = \sqrt{\tfrac{1}{2}}(\sigma - \pi_y) + \pi_z$$

and

$$\psi_3 = \sqrt{\tfrac{1}{2}}(\sigma - \pi_y) - \pi_z$$

In either description the electron density is symmetrical about the N—N axis. In $N_2{}^+$ this would no longer be the case in the equivalent orbital description, and a combination of ψ_1, ψ_2, and ψ_3 would have to be employed so as not to differentiate between the bonds.

In the older and more conventional description, the removal of a σ electron would not destroy the axial symmetry, but if a π electron is lost a combination of the π_y and π_z wave functions would be required to describe the molecule. (The same situation arises with p electrons in an isolated atom.) It is rather easier to appreciate that two energy states exist for N_2^+ according to whether a σ or a π electron is removed, than with the equivalent orbital method.

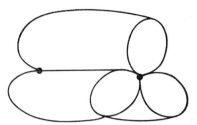

FIGURE 13.3 Equivalent orbitals for nitrogen.

Methane. Finally, let us consider the concept of equivalent orbitals by reference to saturated hydrocarbons. Figure 13.4 shows a set of reference axes and the positions of the four hydrogen atoms in methane.

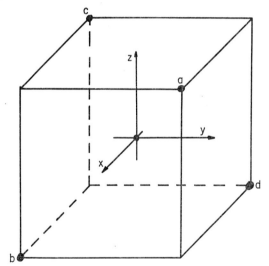

FIGURE 13.4 Reference axes for methane.

The carbon $2s$ wave function has the same phase in all quadrants, so may be combined with a group orbital formed from the four hydrogen $1s$ wave functions (represented by a, b, c, and d respectively).

$$\psi_1 = \lambda s + \mu(a + b + c + d)$$

The $2p_x$ carbon orbital has its lobe of plus phase directed towards hydrogens a and b, but the lobe of minus sign is nearest hydrogens

c and d. Hence it can only form a bonding orbital with a group orbital of the form $a + b - c - d$ giving

$$\psi_2 = \lambda' p_x + \mu'(a + b - c - d)$$

The other two molecular orbitals are similar with wave functions

$$\psi_3 = \lambda' p_y + \mu'(a - b - c + d)$$

and

$$\psi_4 = \lambda' p_z + \mu'(a - b + c - d)$$

Of these four delocalized orbitals only three, ψ_2, ψ_3, and ψ_4, are equivalent, but they may be transformed into four equivalent orbitals. One of these is

$$\psi_a = N[\lambda s + \lambda'(p_x + p_y + p_z) + (\mu + 3\mu')a + (\mu - \mu')(b + c + d)]$$
$$= N[\lambda s + \sqrt{3}\lambda' p_a + (\mu + 3\mu')a + (\mu - \mu')(b + c + d)]$$

where p_a is an orbital of p symmetry directed towards hydrogen a. The first three terms in this equation represent a localized bond between a tetrahedral sp^3 hybrid of carbon and the hydrogen atom a. The last factor implies that there is a possibility of an electron in this orbital appearing near the other hydrogen atoms. This delocalization, a form of hyperconjugation, is frequently neglected, but numerical calculations[7] show that

$$\psi_a = 2 \cdot 56s + 2 \cdot 94 p_a + 3 \cdot 31a - 0 \cdot 69(b + c + d) \qquad (13.1)$$

and there is a chance of $0 \cdot 69^2$ to $2 \cdot 56^2 + 2 \cdot 94^2 + 3 \cdot 31^2$, or 1 in 55 of the electron being either on b, or on c, or on d. The other three equivalent orbitals represent the bonds to the other hydrogen atoms and may be obtained from (13.1) above by the cyclic interchange of a, b, c, and d.

With saturated hydrocarbons the approach in terms of sp^3 hybridization is an equivalent orbital method and is the one normally employed. The above process can be reversed if required by taking a linear combination of equivalent bond orbitals, the L.C.B.O. approximation.

$$\psi = c_a \psi_a + c_b \psi_b + c_c \psi_c + c_d \psi_d$$

where the wave functions ψ_a, ψ_b, ψ_c, and ψ_d are equivalent bond orbitals for the four C—H bonds. The secular determinant, obtained from the corresponding secular equations, is

$$\begin{vmatrix} H_{aa} - \xi S_{aa} & H_{ab} - \xi S_{ab} & H_{ac} - \xi S_{ac} & H_{ad} - \xi S_{ad} \\ H_{ba} - \xi S_{ba} & H_{bb} - \xi S_{bb} & H_{bc} - \xi S_{bc} & H_{bd} - \xi S_{bd} \\ H_{ca} - \xi S_{ca} & H_{cb} - \xi S_{cb} & H_{cc} - \xi S_{cc} & H_{cd} - \xi S_{cd} \\ H_{da} - \xi S_{da} & H_{db} - \xi S_{db} & H_{dc} - \xi S_{dc} & H_{dd} - \xi S_{dd} \end{vmatrix} = 0$$

The orbitals are normalized, almost orthogonal, and of the same energy, so that

$$S_{aa} = 1; \ S_{ab} = 0, \text{etc.}$$

$$H_{aa} = H_{bb} = \alpha, \text{etc.}$$

$$H_{ab} = H_{ba} = \beta, \text{etc.}$$

The determinant therefore reduces to

$$\begin{vmatrix} \alpha - \xi & \beta & \beta & \beta \\ \beta & \alpha - \xi & \beta & \beta \\ \beta & \beta & \alpha - \xi & \beta \\ \beta & \beta & \beta & \alpha - \xi \end{vmatrix} = 0$$

It has the solutions

$$\xi_1 = \alpha + 3\beta \quad \text{(once)}$$

$$\xi_2 = \alpha - \beta \quad \text{(three times)}$$

Hence, whereas in the equivalent orbital approach all the bonding electrons have the same energy, in this L.C.B.O. approximation two electrons have one energy ξ_1, and six have a different energy ξ_2. The equivalent orbital approach is not convenient for discussing the ionized molecule CH_4^+, since when one electron is removed the charge distribution is no longer equivalent in the four orbitals. This defect is not present in the L.C.B.O. description and Koopmans[8] has shown that ξ_1 and ξ_2 are good approximations to the first and second ionization potentials of methane, (13·04 and 20 eV respectively). Hall[9], by extending this analysis to other paraffinic hydrocarbons was able to calculate their ionization potentials, and he obtained excellent agreement with the experimental values.

In this short chapter we have attempted to show by means of examples, as in fact we already knew from the discussion of the water molecule in Chapter 11, that the wave functions of molecules may be formulated and interpreted in many alternative ways. The results obtained with each approach, (energies, electron distribution, etc.), may be entirely equivalent, but whether this is so depends upon what refinements are included in each analysis—particularly the allowance made for configuration interactions. All approaches are of some value but some descriptions seem more logical for certain molecules than for others, particularly if we wish to visualize the electron distribution within the molecule. The discussion of ionization potentials in the preceding paragraphs was included to demonstrate that the more usual approach in terms of localized bonds is not always the most convenient for mathematical calculation.

BIBLIOGRAPHICAL REFERENCES

1. Pople, J. A., *Quart. Rev.*, 1957, **11**, 273.
2. Bartell, L. S., and Bonham, R. A., *J. Chem. Phys.*, 1957, **27**, 1414.
3. Allen, H. C., and Plyler, E. K., *J. Amer. Chem. Soc.*, 1958, **80**, 2673.
4. Dowling, J. M., and Stoicheff, B. P., *Canad. J. Phys.*, 1959, **37**, 703.
5. Coulson, C. A., and Moffitt, W. E., *Phil. Mag.*, 1949, **40**, 1.
6. Pauling, L., *Nat. Acad. Sci.*, 1958, **44**, 211.
7. Coulson, C. A., *Trans. Faraday Soc.*, 1942, **38**, 433.
8. Koopmans, T., *Physica*, 1933, **1**, 104.
9. Hall, G. G., *Proc. Roy. Soc.*, 1951, A**205**, 541.

PART III

Some Chemical Applications of Wave Mechanics

CHAPTER 14

PROPERTIES OF ATOMS
AND BONDS

In this chapter it is proposed to consider properties which can be associated with individual atoms and bonds. Most bonding electrons in atoms and molecules are essentially localized between two atoms. This is confirmed by experiment since, to a good approximation, many properties associated with chemical bonds are independent of the remainder of the molecule. Some molecular properties should therefore be approximately equal to the sum of the extents to which the property is possessed by each bond in the molecule; molar refraction and energy are examples. It might also be possible to break down some bond properties into contributions from the two atoms. Any additivity of atom or bond properties would almost certainly give incorrect results for molecules which possess delocalized electrons. The difference between the observed and predicted value of a property could then serve as a measure of the extent of delocalization and be employed to decide the relative weightings of canonical structures in the valence bond method, or the values of parameters such as β and k in the molecular orbital method.

Three properties which characterize a bond and which are strongly interdependent will be considered. They are bond energies, the asymmetric distribution of the bonding electrons, and bond lengths.

14.1. Bond Energy

Localized Bonds

Several books and review articles[1-4] deal thoroughly with the problem of bond energies; these are considered here for the light they throw upon the character of covalent bonds. It may be desirable to remind ourselves that bond energy can mean at least

217

two things, and that the experimental measurements in some cases may be in error.

For a diatomic molecule the *bond dissociation energy* is defined as the energy needed to break the bond, both the molecule and its two fragments being in their ground states. For a polyatomic molecule in which all the bonds are identical (e.g. P_4, S_8, CH_4, H_2O), the experimental energy of atomization required to break the molecule into its component atoms, in their ground states, may be divided by the number of bonds in the molecule to give their *average bond energy*. Now the energy, bond dissociation energy, required to break just one bond in the molecule can also be measured. In polyatomic molecules, bond dissociation energy and average bond energy can differ by several kcal/mole. Consider breaking one C—H bond in methane to give $CH_3\cdot$ and $H\cdot$. In addition to the actual breaking of the bond the configuration of the radical changes—in methane the carbon atom is sp^3 hybridized and the hydrogens are tetrahedrally disposed around it, whereas the methyl radical is planar, or very nearly planar,[5-6] and the carbon in an sp^2 hybridized state. The bond dissociation energy differs from the average bond energy by the reorganization energy of the methyl radical. A similar situation arises in going from $CH_3\cdot$ to $\cdot CH_2\cdot + H\cdot$, but there is now an additional complication. The hydrogen atom which is being removed from CH_4 to give $CH_3\cdot$ interacts with the carbon and three hydrogen atoms, whilst, when a second hydrogen is removed, it only interacts with the carbon and two hydrogen atoms.

In considering chemical binding it is the energy invested in each bond in the molecule which would be of the greatest interest. This is best given by the average bond energy—often abbreviated to *bond energy*. When the bonds in a molecule are identical the bond energy can readily be determined from the heat of atomization. Most molecules, however, possess more than one type of bond so it is necessary to assume that bond energies are additive. Consider methyl chloride. If the energy of the C—H bond is the same as in methane (91·1 kcal/mole), then the C—Cl bond energy is 70·0 kcal/mole. The same value is obtained from the heat of atomization of carbon tetrachloride. This additivity of bond energies is found in a number of molecules. Bond energies for some single bonds appear in Table 14.1 and those for multiple bonds in Table 14.2. These are average values, some being determined directly, whereas for others the addivitity property has been employed.

Homopolar Bonds. It will be seen from Table 14.1 that in each group of the periodic table the energy of single bonds between identical atoms decreases as the size of the atoms increases, the exceptions are the N—N, O—O, and F—F bonds. The reason is that only the bonding valence electrons have a negative exchange

TABLE 14.1. THE ENERGIES OF SINGLE BONDS

(a) *Bonds of the type X—X*

						He
H 104·2						0
Li 26·5	B 83	C 83·1†	N 38·4	O 33·2	F 36·6	Ne 0
Na 18·0		Si 42·2	P 51·3	S 50·9	Cl 58·0	A 0
K 13·2		Ge 37·6	As 32·1	Se 44·0	Br 46·1	Kr 0
Rb 12·4		Sn 34·2	Sb 30·2	Te 33	I 36·1	Xe 0
Cs 10·7			Bi 25			

† Based upon 171·7 kcal/mole for the latent heat of sublimation of graphite.

(b) *Bonds of the type X—Y*

	H	C	N	O	F	Si	P	S	Cl	As	Se	Br	I
H	104	98·8	93·4	110·6	134·6	70·4	76·4	81·1	103·2	58·6	66·1	87·5	71·4
C		83·1	69·7	84·0	105·4	69·3		62·0				65·9	57·4
N			38·4		64·8			47·7					
O				33·2	44·2	88·2		48·5					
F					36·6	129·3		71	60·6	111·3			
Si						42·2		54·2	85·7			69·1	50·9
P							51·3	79·1				65·4	51·4
Cl								59·7	58·0	68·9		52·3	50·3
Br								50·7		56·5		46·1	42·5

energy, resulting in an attraction between the atoms, whilst there is a considerable coulombic and exchange repulsion between all the remaining electrons. The heavier the atom the greater will be the number of non-bonding electrons contributing to this repulsion. Also, the larger the atom the less effectively will the charge clouds of the bonding electrons be able to overlap to form a strong bond. Both theory and experiment demonstrate that the repulsive forces increase very rapidly as the distance between the atoms is reduced below the value at which the charge clouds of the non-bonding electrons begin to overlap.

These are also the reasons why multiple bonds are restricted to the smaller atoms. The increased binding of a multiple bond reduces the bond length below that of the corresponding single bond. This shortening greatly increases the repulsions between the non-bonding

TABLE 14.2. THE ENERGIES OF MULTIPLE BONDS

C=C 147	C=N 147	C≡C 194
C=O 171 (aldehydes)	O=O 96	N≡N 226
174 (ketones)	N=N 100	C≡N 213
C=S 114		

electrons and if the atoms have many electrons, multiple bonds would be so weak compared to an equivalent number of single bonds that the molecule would be too reactive for it to be isolated.

Why are the N—N, O—O, and F—F bonds exceptions? Being light they might be expected to have much larger bond energies. The answer seems to be that these atoms are also very small. The electrons in the atoms are tightly held by the nucleus, therefore when the two atoms approach one another they have to be very close for the overlap of the bonding electrons to be effective. This means, however, that the repulsion between the compact charge clouds of the non-bonding electrons is then particularly large, and it results in the formation of a rather weak bond. In the case of the halogens, F_2, Cl_2, Br_2, and I_2, Caldow and Coulson[7] have demonstrated the dominating effect of the coulombic repulsion. Another interesting series where the electron repulsions are important is provided by hydrazine and its singly and doubly protonated molecules. The N—N bond lengths and vibration frequencies in Table 14.3 show that the strongest N—N bond exists in the doubly protonated molecule. Evidently the repulsion between the two positive charges is more than offset by the smaller number of non-bonding electrons.

TABLE 14.3

Molecule	Bond Length (Å)	Frequency (cm^{-1})
$H_2N—NH_2$	1·47	880
$H_2N—\overset{+}{N}H_3$	1·45	965
$\overset{+}{H_3}N—\overset{+}{N}H_3$	1·42	1030

The repulsion between non-bonding electrons plays a great part in determining the conformation of molecules. Hydrazine for example, is not symmetrical in the gaseous phase, likewise H_2O_2, H_2S_2, biphenyl, and very many other molecules are not planar.

Returning to the data in Table 14.1, it will be observed that bonds between alkali metals are particularly weak. This is undoubtedly due to the small overlap possible between two s-type orbitals. Orbitals of p symmetry form stronger bonds and sp hybrids should be able to form even stronger bonds. For atoms in which hybridization is frequently postulated (e.g. carbon and nitrogen), the bond energies quoted in Tables 14.1 and 14.2 are rather inadequate since they will depend upon the extent of hybridization. The most extensive data is available for hydrocarbons, and in Table 14.4 C—C and C—H bond energies and bond lengths are presented for different hybridizations.

TABLE 14.4[8-11]

Hybridization	Bond Type	Bond Energy (kcal/mole)	Bond Length (Å)
Carbon—Hydrogen Bonds			
sp^3	CH_4	99·49	1·094
	$—CH_3$	98·46	1·102
	CH_2	97·57	1·110
	$—CH$	97·26	1·112
sp^2	$=CH_2$	103·0	1·085
sp^1	$\equiv CH$	113·0	1·059
Carbon–Carbon Bonds			
sp^3–sp^3	$—C—C—$	85·45	1·538
sp^3–sp^2	$—C—C$	91·60	1·503
sp^3–sp^1	$—C—C\equiv$	103·2	1·459
sp^2–sp^2	$C—C$	101·8	1·476
	C (phenyl)	99·6	1·486
	(biphenyl)	98·2	1·493
sp^2–sp^1	$C—C\equiv$	109	1·426
	$—C\equiv$ (phenyl)	110·2	1·419
sp^1–sp^1	$\equiv C—C\equiv$	124·8	1·376
sp^2–sp^2	$C=C$	127·3	1·338
sp^2–sp^1	$C=C\equiv$	132·8	1·309
sp^1–sp^1	$=C=C=$	~150	1·285
	$—C\equiv C—$	167·4	1·205
Benzene	$C\text{:::}C$	117·5	1·397
Graphite		113·0	1·421

Ionic Resonance Energy

If we select any bond A—B between unlike atoms, then we might expect its bond energy $D(A—B)$ to be the mean of the A—A and B—B bond energies. This implies that the distribution of the bonding electrons in the three bonds is similar, in particular that the bonding electrons are equally shared by the two atoms. Suppose that B attracts electrons more strongly than A—that is to say, it has a greater electronegativity. The valence bond description would be one involving resonance between covalent and ionic forms.

$$A—B \leftrightarrow \overset{+}{A} \;\; \overset{-}{B}$$

$$\psi = c_1\psi_{\text{covalent}} + c_2\psi_{\text{ionic}}$$

The variation principle shows that this resonance hybrid would possess a greater bond energy than a purely covalent form A—B, the additional energy acquired by including the ionic structure being termed the *ionic resonance energy*. Pauling postulated that the mean of $D(A—A)$ and $D(B—B)$ gave the energy of the *covalent* structure, and he did in fact find that this was less than the experimental value of $D(A—B)$. Initially the arithmetic mean was employed, but the later results of Pauling and Sherman suggested that the geometric mean was more acceptable if the two bond energies differed greatly.[12]† Hence the ionic resonance energy was defined by

$$\Delta = D(A—B) - \sqrt{[D(A—A)D(B—B)]} \qquad (14.1)$$

This definition and the concept of ionic resonance energy Δ has no firm theoretical basis,‡ but it is a very valuable and practicable idea which has been employed extensively in discussions on the ionic character of bonds, and the relative electron attracting powers of different atoms (see Section 14.2). Some typical values of Δ are given in Table 14.5.

Delocalization Energy

Delocalization energies for conjugated molecules were discussed in the previous chapter, where it was seen that their theoretical values are normally expressed in terms of β (molecular orbital theory) or J (valence bond theory). It is also possible to obtain

---

† The arithmetic and geometric means of two numbers do not differ greatly when the numbers are not vastly different, e.g. The arithmetic mean of 30 and 50 is 40, whilst the geometric mean is only 1.3 units less.

‡ If the arithmetic mean is employed, the ionic resonance energy would equal the heat liberated in the reaction,

$$\tfrac{1}{2}A_2 + \tfrac{1}{2}B_2 \rightarrow A—B$$

each substance being in the gaseous state.

estimates of these energies from experimental observations. Let us take benzene as an example.

The heat of combustion of benzene is 789·1 kcal/mole and when allowance is made for the heats of formation of the products of combustion, CO_2 and H_2O, and the heat of atomization of graphite and hydrogen, the heat of atomization of benzene is 1,323 kcal/mole. From the bond energy data in Table 14.4 we would expect a single Kekulé structure to have the energy,

$$3D(C—C) + 3D(C\!=\!C) + 6D(C—H)$$
$$= 3(101·8) + 3(127·3) + 6(103·0) = 1,305·3$$

The difference between these values, 18 kcal/mole, may be taken as the resonance energy of benzene. (The somewhat greater numerical

TABLE 14.5. IONIC RESONANCE ENERGIES

	C	N	O	F	Si	P	S	Cl	As	Br	I
H	5·8	30·1	41·8	72·9	4·0	3·3	8·3	25·4	0·8	18·2	10·1
C		13·2	31·5	50·2	10·0		−2·4	9·1		4·0	2·6
N			27·0					0·5			
O				9·3	50·7			4·6			
F					90·0		27·8	14·5	77·0		
Si							7·8	36·2		25·0	11·8
P										16.7	8.3
Br								18·0			1·7

values often quoted do not make full allowance for the dependence of C—C and C—H bond energies on bond type.) An alternative approach is based upon heats of hydrogenation. The hydrogenation of benzene to give cyclohexane liberates 49·8 kcal/mole. This is 18 kcal/mole less than three times the heat of hydrogenation of cyclohexene and again has been identified as the resonance energy.

The resonance energies of a large number of hydrocarbons have been estimated in similar ways, and on the whole are reasonably consistent and correlate with theoretical estimates of delocalization energies. The results of such comparisons are in fact used to estimate the values of β and J (see p. 284). The complete picture is not as simple as that presented above however. The numerical estimates of the resonance energy of benzene have been based on a cyclohexatriene molecule with *alternate single and double bonds*, not upon a Kekulé structure with all the C—C bond lengths the same. The distortion energy required to equalize the lengths of the C—C bonds of cyclohexatriene has been estimated as 27, 37, or 35 kcal/mole.[13–16] This would increase the numerical value of the delocalization energy by a corresponding amount. The position should be clear from the energy cycle shown in Figure 14.1 in which a distortion

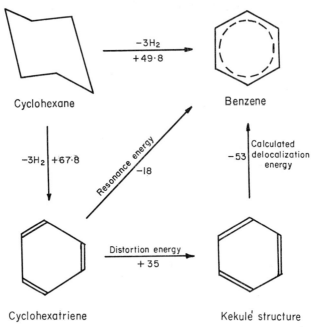

Cyclohexane

Benzene

Resonance energy

$-3H_2$ | $+67.8$

-18

$-3H_2$
$+49.8$

Calculated
-53 | delocalization
energy

Distortion energy
$+35$

Cyclohexatriene

Kekulé structure

FIGURE 14.1   Energy relationships between six membered rings.

energy of 35 kcal/mole has been employed. There is an error in this diagram which arises through assuming that the hydrogenation energy of cyclohexatriene is three times the hydrogenation energy of cyclohexene; steric effects caused by conformational changes (e.g. between cyclohexene and cyclohexane) have been neglected.

It is obvious that the greatest possible care must be exercised in using and comparing numerical estimates of resonance and delocalization energies for different molecules. Further, the values of β and J calculated from these energies should only be employed in energy calculations and not for estimating other properties, such as ultraviolet transition frequencies.

14.2. Bond Polarity

There are two topics to discuss under this heading. We shall first of all outline the wave mechanical concept of the factors contributing to the electric dipole moment of a molecule, and then consider the ionic character of a bond.

Dipole Moments

Let us develop an analysis given in Chapter 10. An electron in a localized bonding molecular orbital with wave function

$$\psi = N(\psi_a + \lambda\psi_b) \tag{14.2}$$

would have its centroid of negative charge density at a point $\bar{x}$ from the mid-point along the internuclear axis, where

$$\bar{x} = \int x\psi^2 \, d\tau$$

$$= N^2\left[\int x\psi_a^2 \, d\tau + \lambda^2 \int x\psi_b^2 \, d\tau + 2\lambda \int x\psi_a\psi_b \, d\tau\right] \tag{14.3}$$

$$= N^2[\bar{x}_a + \lambda^2\bar{x}_b + 2\lambda\bar{x}_{ab}] \tag{10.27}$$

and

$$N^{-2} = 1 + \lambda^2 + 2\lambda S. \tag{10.26}$$

In equation (10.27) above, the first term gives the centroid of charge density of an electron in an atomic orbital ψ_a, the second for an electron in the atomic orbital ψ_b, and the third term for one averaged over the product $\psi_a\psi_b$. To proceed further and obtain the equation given previously for the dipole moment of the bond (10.28) drastic assumptions had to be made. These must now be reconsidered.

Homopolar Dipole. Mulliken[17] pointed out that a bond with no ionic character whatever could still have a dipole moment. This arises from the last term in equation (14.3) which was neglected in our previous treatment. Consider a bond formed from atomic $1s$ and $3p$ orbitals (Figure 14.2). The directional character and size of the $3p$ orbital means that the product $\psi_a\psi_b$ has its maximum value nearer the smaller atom. The centroids of positive and negative charge do not coincide and a *homopolar dipole* in the sense $\overset{\longleftarrow +}{A\text{—}B}$ results. For hydrogen $1s$ and chlorine $3p$ orbitals its magnitude is about $1{\cdot}0D$.

Atomic Dipole. The other major assumption of our previous analysis was that the atomic orbitals were pure $s, p, d \ldots$ orbitals, so that the electrons they contained had their centroid of negative charge at the atomic nucleus. The first two integrals in equation

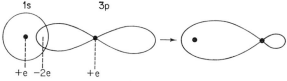

FIGURE 14.2   A molecular orbital formed from atomic $1s$ and $3p$ orbitals.

(14.3) consequently referred to the positions of the atomic nuclei. What if they are hybridized orbitals? The lobes of a bonding hybridized orbital are not symmetrical about the nucleus but are more strongly directed towards the other atom. An electron in such an orbital would have its centre of charge displaced from the nucleus towards the other atom, thus giving rise to an *atomic dipole*. The consequent reduction in the calculated bond moment may be estimated as follows.

Consider mixing pure s and p orbitals of the same atom to give the hybrid

$$\psi = N(\psi_s + \sigma\psi_p)$$

where

$$N^{-2} = 1 + \sigma^2$$

For the hybrid pointing along the x axis, its centroid of charge density is at a distance $\bar{x}$ from the nucleus, where

$$\bar{x} = \int x\psi^2 \, d\tau = N^2 \int x(\psi_s + \sigma\psi_p)^2 \, d\tau$$

$$= N^2 \left[\int x\psi_s^2 \, d\tau + \sigma^2 \int x\psi_p^2 \, d\tau + 2\sigma \int x\psi_s\psi_p \, d\tau \right]$$

$$= N^2 \left[0 + 0 + 2\sigma \int x\psi_s\psi_p \, d\tau \right]$$

$$= \frac{2\sigma}{1 + \sigma^2} \int x\psi_s\psi_p \, d\tau \tag{14.4}$$

The integral is independent of the hybridization parameter σ so that $\bar{x}$ attains its maximum value of $\int x\psi_s\psi_p \, d\tau$ when σ is unity (sp^1 hybridization). When $\sigma = 0$ (s orbital) or when $\sigma = \infty$ (p orbital), $\bar{x}$ is zero. The magnitude of this dipole can be considerable. With a carbon atom for example, the integral in equation (14.4) is about 0·47 Å, and when $\sigma = 1$ the atomic dipole has a value of about $0\cdot47e = 2\cdot2D$ per electron. Even when σ is only 0·1 the atomic dipole would be about 0·4D.

Atomic dipoles can make large contributions to the theoretical values of bond moments; in many molecules, however, the atomic dipoles of all the hybridized orbitals formed from a particular atom cancel out, in which case there is no need to consider them in estimating the dipole moment of the whole molecule. Tables of bond moments have been obtained empirically by partitioning the measured dipole moments of molecules among their various bonds, and when doing this it is often considered undesirable to make any allowance for atomic dipoles.

Lone-Pair Moment. There is one situation where the moment resulting from hybridization is of the utmost importance and must be considered in the calculations. This is when lone-pair electrons occupy a hybridized orbital. For sp hybrids the moment would be given by equation (14.4), but since atoms normally have two electrons in these non-bonding atomic orbitals their contribution towards the moment of the molecule outweighs that of the atomic dipole.

Two examples will serve to illustrate the importance of hybridization. Hydrogen chloride was discussed in Chapter 10; it has a dipole moment of $1 \cdot 1 D$, $\overset{+\longrightarrow}{\text{H—Cl}}$. For a bond formed from H($1s$) and Cl($3p$) orbitals the homopolar dipole is about $1 \cdot 0 D$ in the opposite direction ($\overset{\longleftarrow+}{\text{H—Cl}}$), and so the ionic character or charge asymmetry of the molecule would have to contribute about $2 \cdot 1 D$ to give the experimental result. Energy calculations and infrared spectroscopy studies show that this is impossible. The calculated moment of covalent H—Cl (including the lone-pair moment), however changes from $1 \cdot 0 D$ ($\overset{\longleftarrow+}{\text{H—Cl}}$) to $2 \cdot 5 D$ ($\overset{+\longrightarrow}{\text{H—Cl}}$) as the chlorine orbital is changed from being a pure p to an sp^1 hybrid. Evidently quite a small hybridization with the $3s$ orbital could explain the observed dipole moment.[18-20] The second example is provided by the water molecule (see Chapter 11). Its dipole moment is $1 \cdot 84 D$ so that the elementary concept of bond moments requires each O—H bond to have a moment of $1 \cdot 84/2 \cos \frac{1}{2}(\widehat{\text{HOH}}) = 1 \cdot 51 D$ ($\overset{\longleftarrow+}{\text{O—H}}$). Duncan and Pople[21] however, calculated that the lone-pair electrons in hybridized orbitals contribute $3 \cdot 03 D$ towards the dipole moment. This is opposed by a bond moment of $0 \cdot 97 D$ ($\overset{+\longrightarrow}{\text{O—H}}$)— in the reverse direction to the simple treatment for this molecule. Other calculations give similar results but the most recent one[22] indicates smaller lone-pair ($0 \cdot 69 D$) and O—H ($0 \cdot 14 D$) moments. The moment associated with lone-pair electrons is also the reason why the dipole moment of F_2O ($0 \cdot 18 D$) is much less than that of water. From the asymmetry of the bonding electrons the O—H and O—F bond moments should be very similar, though in opposite directions.

The resultant dipole moment of a molecule with covalent σ bonds therefore involves:

1. An effect due to the charge asymmetry of the bonding molecular orbital—related to the electronegativity difference between the atoms as portrayed by the coefficient λ in equation (14.2).
2. A homopolar dipole resulting from the different sizes of the bonded atoms and directed from the larger to the smaller.

3. Atomic and lone-pair moments arising through the use of hybrid orbitals.

In an actual molecule these factors are augmented (a) by each bond moment polarizing the remainder of the molecule (inductive effect) and (b) by interactions between the moments of adjacent bonds (for details see Smith[23] and Smyth[24]). If electrons tend to be drawn away from an atom in one bond then its electronegativity is increased and this in turn affects the ionic character of other bonds to this atom. When there is unsaturation in the molecule its π-type electrons are particularly polarizable. If it possesses delocalized electrons then there may also be a substantial primary π electron moment from the asymmetric distribution of the electrons over the delocalized molecular orbitals. The π electron charge distribution in pyridine, which is illustrated in Figure 12.7, would give rise to a π electron moment of $0.50D$. (This charge distribution is rather idealized as the π electron cloud is spread round the whole pyridine ring and not localized on the individual atoms.) Brown and Heffernan[25] calculated a σ bond moment of $1.97D$ for pyridine so that the total calculated moment would be $2.47D$, only $0.26D$ greater than the experimental value.

The preceding discussion of dipole moments has been based upon the molecular orbital theory, but a similar treatment can be advanced in terms of the valence bond method. In place of equation (14.2) the wave function for a polar bond is

$$\psi = N[\psi_{\text{covalent}} + \lambda\psi_{\text{ionic}}]$$

The expression for $\bar{x}$, entirely analogous to equation (10.27), is therefore

$$\bar{x} = \frac{\bar{x}_{\text{cov.}} + \lambda^2 \bar{x}_{\text{ionic}} + 2\lambda \bar{x}_{\text{cov. ionic}}}{1 + \lambda^2 + 2\lambda \int \psi_{\text{cov.}}\psi_{\text{ionic}}}$$

from which

$$\mu = \frac{\mu_{\text{cov.}} + \lambda^2 \mu_{\text{ionic}} + 2\lambda \mu_{\text{cov. ionic}}}{1 + \lambda^2 + 2\lambda \int \psi_{\text{cov.}}\psi_{\text{ionic}}} \qquad (14.5)$$

The first term in this equation represents the dipole moment of the covalent structure; this is usually taken to be zero, though from what has just been said about homopolar, atomic, and lone-pair moments this cannot be correct. The second factor involves a purely ionic bond, $\mu_{\text{ionic}} = er$, where r is the bond length. The last term, $\mu_{\text{cov. ionic}}$ is a cross-term analogous to the one giving rise to the homopolar dipole in equation (14.3). Again this is frequently, but quite unjustifiably, neglected. In the denominator $\int \psi_{\text{cov.}}\psi_{\text{ionic}}$

TABLE 14.6

Molecule	HF	HCl	HBr	HI
$\mu_{observed}(D)$	1·98	1·03	0·79	0·38
r (Å)	0·92	1·28	1·43	1·62
λ	0·90	0·45	0·36	0·23
Ionic character $100\lambda^2/(1+\lambda^2)$ (%)	45	17	12	5

replaces the overlap integral of the previous equation and if this is also assumed to be zero

$$\mu = \frac{\lambda^2}{1+\lambda^2}\mu_{ionic}$$

$$= \frac{\lambda^2}{1+\lambda^2}er \qquad (14.6)$$

It is obvious that many serious approximations have been made in deriving this equation, but it is nevertheless frequently used to estimate the value of λ and hence the ionic character of the bond. Some examples are given in Table 14.6. In spite of the inadequacy of equation (14.6) these figures seem reasonable and consistent. The reliability of this procedure however is very suspect when the atomic orbitals are hybridized to an appreciable extent.

Bond Following. Before concluding this discussion of dipole moments one other aspect should be mentioned. During the course of a molecular vibration the dipole moment of the molecule fluctuates—indeed this is a necessary requirement for the vibration to interact with infrared radiation. Let us consider one example, the bending vibration of water.

The molecular orbital description of the equilibrium state of this molecule is represented in Figure 14.3(a), (cf. Figure 10.3). During

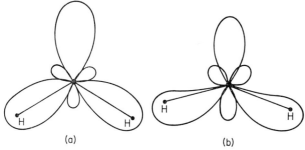

FIGURE 14.3   The bending vibration in H_2O.

the bending vibration the $\widehat{HOH}$ bond angle oscillates about the mean value of $104\frac{1}{2}°$. This is accompanied by three contributions to the fluctuation of the dipole moment,[22] and hence to the intensity of the corresponding infrared absorption band, for the molecule.

(a) The bonding and lone-pair hybrid orbitals of the oxygen atom are orthogonal. Consequently as the bond angle varies the percentage p character of the lone-pair hybrids changes and with it the lone-pair moment.

(b) The component of the dipole moment along the O—H bond alters owing to the associated change in the atomic dipole and the electron distribution in the bond. The small changes in the bond angle will have a very small effect upon the vector sum of the bond moments.

(c) The third factor arises from a component of the dipole moment perpendicular to the O—H bonds. This is due to the electron distribution in the bond not remaining symmetrically distributed about the O—H bond direction during the course of the vibration (Figure 10.3(b)).

The failure of the molecular orbital to 'follow' a bond during molecular vibrations is a feature common to all molecules, although the magnitude of the effect can vary considerably. Its existence, however, should put us on our guard when comparing bond moments derived from the intensities of infrared absorption bands with empirically determined static bond moments.

The calculated magnitudes of the three factors for the water molecule are rather surprising. The second factor only contributes about 5% to the overall change in the moment, the remainder being accounted for to nearly equal extents by (a) and (c). These relative contributions would be expected to be very dependent upon the actual molecule and vibrational mode.

The preceding discussion raises the question as to what is meant by a bond. This topic will not be taken up here but interested readers are referred to some comments by Coulson.[26]

Ionic Character of a Bond and Electronegativity

Great care must be exercised in assessing the asymmetry of electron distribution in a bond from the experimental dipole moment of the molecule. Is there another way in which the ionic character of a bond, as implied by its wave function, may be estimated? Pauling tackled this problem by devising a numerical scale of atom electronegativity.

The starting point is the ionic resonance energy Δ, the extra bond energy which results from including an ionic structure in the valence bond approach to molecular wave functions. It is a measure of the asymmetric distribution of charge in the bond and is related to the different abilities of atoms to attract the electrons binding them together, which is what chemists understand by the term electronegativity. A scale of electronegativity values should be additive in the sense that the difference between their values for any two atoms should indicate the electron distribution in a bond formed

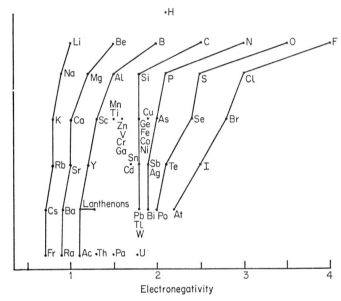

FIGURE 14.4   The Pauling electronegativity scale.

between these atoms. The Δ values themselves do not satisfy this requirement but their square roots are approximately additive.

$$\sqrt{\Delta_{AB}} + \sqrt{\Delta_{BC}} \simeq \sqrt{\Delta_{AC}}$$

Pauling[27] therefore suggested that

$$|x_A - x_B| = \sqrt{\Delta_{AB}} \qquad (14.7)$$

where x_A and x_B are electronegativity values of atoms A and B and Δ_{AB} is measured in electron volts. An arbitrary zero has to be chosen for this scale but this is of no consequence. The Pauling scale[28] is depicted in Figure 14.4. In agreement with the general chemical behaviour of the elements their electronegativity increases with increase in group number in the periodic table but decreases down each column. In general the smaller an atom the greater is its electronegativity.

Very many physical and chemical properties of molecules depend upon the different abilities of atoms to attract electrons. Bond moments, the distribution of π electrons in conjugated molecules, the inductive and mesomeric effects, electronic energy levels and electronic spectra, screening constants in nuclear magnetic resonance, and the rates of chemical attack by one molecule upon another, are some of the experimental observations which have been discussed in terms of electronegativity. Here we are only concerned with a theoretical discussion of the electron distribution in molecules so that these general aspects of electronegativity will not be pursued.

Malone[29,30] pointed out that there is a roughly linear relation between bond moments and the electronegativity difference between two atoms, but from our previous discussion of dipole moments we would not expect an exact correlation as the charge asymmetry in the bond is only one of several factors which contribute to its moment and there are indeed several serious exceptions to the above correlation.

In Table 14.6 estimates of the percentage ionic character in some polar diatomic molecules were given. The figures are almost a linear function of the electronegativity difference between the atoms concerned, one of the most satisfactory empirical relationships[31] between the quantities being

$$\text{Percentage ionic character} = 16\,|x_A - x_B| + 3 \cdot 5\,|x_A - x_B|^2 \quad (14.8)$$

This, or a similar relationship, has been employed extensively to determine the ionic character of bonds, and hence the weighting of the covalent and ionic structures in valence bond theory. To illustrate this let us consider the water molecule once again. One method of weighting the four structures

has already been mentioned [p. 176]. From Figure 14.4, $|x_O - x_H| = 1 \cdot 4$ and so by equation (14.8) the O—H bond has 39% ionic character and 61% covalent character. The relative weights of the canonical structures for water are therefore in the ratio,

$$a:b:c:d = 61 \times 61 : 61 \times 39 : 39 \times 61 : 39 \times 39$$

$$= 1 : 0 \cdot 64 : 0 \cdot 64 : 0 \cdot 41.$$

The completely covalent structure contributes to the extent of 37% to the resonance hybrid, each of the half-and-half structures b and c 24% and the completely ionic structure 15%.

This approach to ionic character and the weighting of canonical structures in the complete wave function for a molecule is simple and has been employed extensively. In comparing one molecule with another the results obtained are generally consistent with their chemical behaviour but we must not lose sight of the fact that it is an empirical method based upon arguments which involve a succession of assumptions and approximations. All the same, it works in practice.

There are alternative methods of estimating the ionicity of chemical bonds. One interesting method is based upon the measurement of nuclear quadrupole coupling constants.[32,33]

The Electroneutrality Principle.[34,35] In discussing the stability of complex ions Pauling developed the *electroneutrality principle*. It states that in a stable complex there can be no high concentration of either positive or negative charge.

Consider the hydrated aluminium ion $Al[H_2O]_6^{3+}$. The Al^{3+} ion has a formal charge of $+3$ and if the Al—O bonds were completely ionic this would be its charge in the complex ion. In fact it is reduced by the covalency of the six Al—O bonds. The electronegativity difference between Al and O is 2·0 corresponding, by equation (14.8), to 46% ionic and 54% covalent character. The covalent character of the bonds therefore results in the donation of $6 \times 0·54 = 3·24$ valence electrons to the aluminium ion, making its net charge only $-0·24$. Each oxygen would have a corresponding charge of $+0·54$, but this is relieved by a flow of charge from the two hydrogen atoms owing to the ionic character of the O—H bond. The O—H bond has 39% ionic character, so that the net charge on each oxygen atom is actually $0·54 - 2(0·39) = -0·24$, and each hydrogen atom has a charge of $+0·39$. Summarizing these results for $Al(H_2O)_6^{3+}$ the net charges on each atom are

$$Al = -0·24, \qquad O = -0·24, \qquad \text{and} \quad H = +0·39$$

Similarly for $Al(NH_3)_6^{3+}$ the corresponding charges are

$$Al = -1·08, \qquad N = +0·17, \qquad \text{and} \quad H = +0·17$$

These values are admittedly only approximate, but whereas all the charges are relatively low in $Al(H_2O)_6^{3+}$ the high charge on the aluminium ion in $Al(NH_3)_6^{3+}$ would, from the electroneutrality principle, imply a lower stability for this ion.

Other Electronegativity Scales. The Pauling electronegativity scale which we have been considering was the first of several such scales. An outline of two others will now be given and naturally they can be utilized in place of the Pauling scale.

The Mulliken Scale.[36,37] During the discussion of heteronuclear diatomic molecules the sum of the ionization potential I and electron affinity E of an atom was mentioned as a measure of its electronegativity. Mulliken actually defined his electronegativity numbers as $\frac{1}{2}[I + E]$, in electron volts. Numerically the Mulliken and

Pauling scales are very similar—the electronegativity difference between two atoms on the Mulliken scale being about 2·78 times the difference on the Pauling scale.

Mulliken does not use the actual values of I and E for free atoms but corrects them to the value expected for the valency state of the atom as it occurs in the molecule. In this way he is also able to recognize the effect of hybridization. It is worth noting that an sp^1 hybridized carbon atom is more electronegative than an sp^2 hybridized atom, which in turn is more electronegative than an sp^3 atom.

The Sanderson Scale.[38-42] Sanderson proposed an interesting scale based upon the average electron density (E.D.) in atoms.

$$E.D. = \frac{Z}{\frac{4}{3}\pi r^3}$$

where Z is the number of electrons and r the covalent radius of the atom or ionic radius of an ion (see next section). Electronegative atoms are very compact and have a high E.D. value whilst the metals, whose outermost electrons are readily lost, have low E.D. values. In addition to depending upon the electronegativity of the atom, the E.D. value also depends upon the number of electrons it contains. Sanderson sought to eliminate this last factor by defining a stability ratio (S.R.) as follows:

$$S.R. = \frac{E.D.}{(E.D.)_i}$$

where $(E.D.)_i$ is the average electron density of an isoelectronic inert atom, i.e. either an inert gas or a value obtained by linear interpolation between the E.D. values of the inert gases which precede and follow the atom in the periodic table. The inert gases therefore have a S.R. of unity, the electronegative elements a value greater than unity, and the metals less than unity.

The S.R. values (Appendix 8) follow the general trends of the Pauling and Mulliken electronegativity numbers but there are some interesting differences. For example, phosphorus (S.R., 2·0) is more electropositive than both nitrogen (S.R., 3·1) and arsenic (S.R., 2·5). A similar discontinuity occurs in the triad sulphur (S.R., 2·5), selenium (S.R., 2·9), and tellurium (S.R., 2·6). It will be recalled that pentacovalent compounds of phosphorus tend to be more stable than those of arsenic and that quadri- and hexa-valent selenium compounds are better oxidizing agents than either sulphur or tellurium in their higher oxidation states. We might also note that, within a particular group in the periodic table, the transition from an 8 electron inner shell to one of 18 electrons results in an increased electronegativity.

When a chemical bond is formed charge flows towards the atom of higher electronegativity, thereby reducing its S.R. value, and at the same time increasing the S.R. value of the less electronegative atom. It has been postulated that this flow proceeds until each atom has the same S.R. value, which has been taken as the geometric mean of the S.R. values of all the atoms in the molecule.

The above postulates permit one to estimate the bond lengths in a molecule (see next section), and also the net charges on the atoms. These in turn are connected with the stability and dipole moments of the molecule. This interesting approach to electronegativity and ionic character will not be developed further.

14.3. Bond Length and Atomic Radius

The distances between atomic nuclei in molecules[†] is a quantity which may be measured directly by spectroscopic and diffraction techniques; in this respect it differs radically from bond energies and bond moments in polyatomic molecules, which can only be inferred from measured properties of the whole molecule. Except where there is good reason to believe that delocalized electrons are present, the distance between any two covalently bonded atoms is remarkably constant. This naturally suggests that it is possible to express bond lengths as the sum of the radii of the atoms forming the covalent bond.

$$r_{A-B} = r_A + r_B \qquad (14.9)$$

This simple relationship holds to within 0·01–0·02 Å in a large number of cases. One set of atomic radii[28,44,45][‡] is presented in Table 14.7 and a more extensive list in Appendix 8. It will be observed that the general trends in these radii are as expected from the atoms' positions in the periodic table, and that double bond radii are about 0·01 Å less than the single bond radius.

From our knowledge of the nature of bonds it is logical to expect that their lengths depend upon the hybridization of the atoms. This has been studied most extensively for carbon, the atomic radii

† Many bond lengths quoted in this book have been taken from *Tables of Interatomic Distances and Configuration in Molecules and Ions*, published by The Chemical Society[43].

‡ Somewhat smaller radii have been suggested for the more electronegative elements when the bonds which they form are appreciably polar. Slightly different radii have also been suggested for coordination numbers greater than four.

TABLE 14.7. COVALENT RADII

	H 0·36(0·82–0·88)†		
	C	N	O	F
Single	0·77(1·22)	0·74(1·12)	0·74(1·12)	0·72(1·11)
Double	0·67	0·62	0·62	0·60
Triple	0·60	0·55	0·55	
	Si	P	S	Cl
Single	1·17(1·57)	1·10(1·53)	1·04(1·46)	0·99(1·44)
Double	1·07	1·00	0·94	0·89
	Ge	As	Se	Br
Single	1·22(1·61)	1·21(1·63)	1·17(1·58)	1·14(1·56)
Double	1·12	1·11	1·07	1·04
	Sn	Sb	Te	I
Single	1·40(1·80)	1·41(1·83)	1·37(1·79)	1·33(1·73)
Double	1·30	1·31	1·27	1·23

† The values in brackets are 'constant energy radii' (see the main text).

are summarized[46,47] in Table 14.8 and more detailed values of
C—C and C—H bond lengths have been included in Table 14.4.

The greater the percentage s character in the hybrid carbon
orbital the smaller is its radius. This is demonstrated by the study
of C—C bonds (Table 14.8) and C—H bonds[52,53] (cf. Table 11.3).

It is generally found that two atoms of greatly differing electronegativity are somewhat closer together than predicted using the
radii in Table 14.7. Schomaker and Stevenson[44] formulated

TABLE 14.8. THE COVALENT RADIUS OF CARBON

Bond Multiplicity	C—	C=	C≡
sp^3	0·767		
sp^2	0·737†	0·669	
sp^1	0·687	0·642	0·604

† There is considerable doubt about the length
of an sp^2–sp^2 carbon bond. Coulson[48,49] proposed a length of 1·50 Å, Mulliken[50], 1·51, and
Bak, and Hansen-Nygaard[51], 1·517 Å. These
are greater than the value quoted in the above
table and the one by Dewar and Schmeising[16],
1·48 Å.

empirical relationships which make the bond length dependent upon the Pauling electronegativity difference between the atoms.

$$r_{A-B} = r_A + r_B - 0.09 |x_A - x_B| \quad \text{for single bonds}$$

$$r_{A-B} = r_A + r_B - 0.06 |x_A - x_B| \quad \text{for double bonds}$$

These modified relationships give better agreement with experimental values for some polar bonds but are not always an improvement upon the simpler expression.[54] Other rather analogous expressions have also been suggested.

TABLE 14.9

Molecule	r_C	r_F	$r_C + r_F$	Molecule	r_C	r_{Cl}	$r_C + r_{Cl}$
CF_4	0.691	0.741	1.432	CCl_4	0.721	1.007	1.728
CHF_3	0.725	0.777	1.502	$CHCl_3$	0.736	1.029	1.765
CH_2F_2	0.737	0.790	1.527	CH_2Cl_2	0.752	1.052	1.804
CH_3F	0.761	0.815	1.576	CH_3Cl	0.769	1.075	1.844

Sanderson's treatment of electronegativity helps us to see why polar bonds are characteristically shorter than the sum of the non-polar covalent radii. If electronic charge is considered to be transferred from one atom to the other in forming these bonds, then both the E.D. values of Sanderson and also a comparison of the covalent and ionic radii of atoms (Appendix 8) implies that the linear contraction of the initially less electronegative atom exceeds the expansion of the more electronegative atom; the bond length is consequently reduced. Combining the expressions given in the previous section for the average electron density E.D., and stability ratio S.R. of an atom, its radius is given by

$$r^3 = \frac{Z}{\frac{4}{3}\pi(S.R.)(E.D.)_i}$$

If the S.R. value in this formula is taken to be the geometric mean of those for all the atoms in the molecule, then r will depend upon the polarities of all the bonds it forms with other atoms and is therefore an effective radius of the atom in the molecule. These effective radii, and the predicted values of the corresponding bond lengths, for fluorinated and chlorinated methanes are listed in Table 14.9. They may be compared with the experimental values given in Table 14.10 and with the constant bond lengths obtained by addition of the atomic radii in Table 14.7, C—F = 1.49 Å, C—Cl = 1.76 Å, or if the Schomaker and Stevenson equation is used, 1.36 and 1.72 Å respectively.

TABLE 14.10

Molecule	Bond Length		Molecule	Bond Length	
	C—H	C—F		C—H	C—Cl
CH_4	1·094				
CH_3F	1·109	1·385	CH_3Cl	1·11	1·781
CH_2F_2	1·092	1·358	CH_2Cl_2	1·068	1·772
CHF_3	1·098	1·332	$CHCl_3$	1·073	1·767
CF_4		1·323	CCl_4		1·766

Other methods of improving equation (14.9) have been suggested. One of the more interesting and valuable approaches being by Huggins,[55] who suggested that strong bonds were shorter than otherwise expected and proposed a simple relationship between bond length and bond energy,

$$r_{A-B} = r_A' + r_B' - \tfrac{1}{2} \log D(A - B)_i$$

The numerical factor of $\tfrac{1}{2}$ is an empirical constant and r_A' and r_B' are *constant energy radii* which are appreciably greater than the values we have been considering so far. They are shown in brackets in Table 14.8.

Conjugated Molecules

If delocalized electrons are present, the bond lengths are intermediate between those in the various canonical structures. In benzene, for example, the C—C bond length is 1·397 Å, compared with 1·54 and 1·34 Å for single and double bonds respectively. Since it requires more energy to stretch a double bond than to compress a single bond the experimental bond length is somewhat closer to that of the double bond than would be expected for a linear dependence of bond length upon the π bond order in the molecule. Several empirical relationships between bond order (or double bond character) P and bond length have been suggested. Naturally most of the results refer to C—C bonds, though C—N, N—N, C—O, and C—S bonds have also been discussed.[56,57]

The simplest and best procedure if adequate data are available is to plot the π bond order for a series of bonds against their experimental bond lengths. A smooth curve may then be drawn through the points and used for interpolation purposes. This may be done using either the valence bond or the molecular orbital definitions and values of bond order†. Some rather less reliable empirical

† There are other approaches to bond order which will not be considered, e.g. Penney.[58] It has been suggested[52] that a separate bond order, bond length curve, should be constructed for sp^1, sp^2, and sp^3 hybridized carbon atoms.

equations have also been proposed. Pauling and his co-workers,[59,60] employing the valence bond method, suggested that

$$r = r_s - \frac{(r_s - r_d)P}{\frac{2}{3}P - \frac{1}{3}}$$ (14.10)

where r is the experimental bond length and r_s and r_d the lengths of pure single and double bonds respectively. In this equation the double bond character, or bond order, P is defined as the ratio between the number of Kekulé structures† in which the bond in question is double to the total number of Kekulé structures. In benzene for example $P = \frac{1}{2}$ for each C—C bond and in naphthalene P is $\frac{1}{3}$ or $\frac{2}{3}$ as shown in Figure 14.5. A rather similar equation was

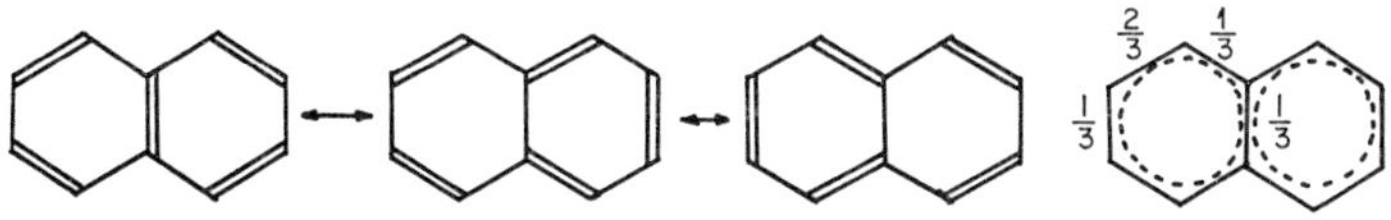

FIGURE 14.5   The double bond character in naphthalene.

suggested by Coulson[61] using the molecular orbital method

$$r = r_s - \frac{r_s - r_d}{1 + K[(r - P)/(P - 1)]}$$ (14.11)

Where P is now the molecular orbital value of the π bond order and K a constant dependent upon the nature of the bonded atoms. Several other similar formulae have been described.

These empirical graphs and formulae have been used in two ways.

(a) From a measured bond length its double bond character may be inferred, and this in turn has been utilized in weighting the canonical structures of a resonance hybrid and in obtaining a measure of the extent of conjugation within the molecule. In butadiene, for example, the central C_2—C_3 bond has a length of 1·483 Å, implying a double bond character of about 25% according to the molecular orbital theory. If we employ the data in Table 14.9, however, then this length is just about the value expected for a single bond between two sp^2 hybridized carbon atoms and there can be little π electron conjugation across this central bond. Dewar and Schmeising[16,62] conclude, in fact, that there is little conjugation in the ground states of all molecules which can only be represented classically by a single unexcited structure.

† Kekulé structures are those covalent structures which do not contain a long (or formal) bond. Structures with one long bond are sometimes called Dewar or first excited structures, with two long bonds they are second excited structures, etc.

TABLE 14.11. COMPARISON OF EXPERIMENTAL AND
THEORETICAL BOND LENGTHS IN CRYSTALLINE
NAPHTHALENE AND ANTHRACENE

Bond	Experimental	Pauling Valence Bond Method	Molecular Orbital Method
Naphthalene			
2,3	1·415 Å	1·421	1·406
1,2	1·364	1·375	1·384
1,9	1·421	1·421	1·416
9,10	1·418	1·421	1·424
Anthracene			
2,3	1·419	1·434	1·410
1,2	1·368	1·365	1·382
1,11	1·436	1·434	1·420
9,11	1·399	1·397	1·406
11,12	1·428	1·434	1·430

(*b*) From the calculated bond orders, the bond lengths in the molecule may be estimated. Substantial agreement with experimental values has been obtained in many cases. Table 14.11 illustrates this for naphthalene and anthracene.[63,64]

BIBLIOGRAPHICAL REFERENCES

1. Gaydon, A. G., *Dissociation Energies and Spectra of Diatomic Molecules*, Chapman and Hall, London, 1953.
2. Cottrell, T. L., *The Strengths of Chemical Bonds*, Butterworths, London, 1954.
3. Szwarc, M., *Quart. Rev.*, 1951, **5**, 22.
4. 'Discussion on Bond Energies and Bond Length,' *Proc. Roy. Soc.*, 1951, A**207**, 1.
5. Herzberg, G., and Shoosmith, J., *Canad. J. Phys.*, 1956, **34**, 523.
6. Cole, T., Pritchard, H. O., Davidson, N. R., and McConnell, H. M., *Mol. Phys.*, 1958, **1**, 406.
7. Caldow, G. L., and Coulson, C. A., *Trans. Faraday Soc.*, 1962, **58**, 633.
8. Bernstein, H. J., *Trans. Faraday Soc.*, 1962, **58**, 2285.
9. Mackle, H., and Mayrick, R. G., *Trans. Faraday Soc.*, 1962, **58**, 53.
10. Lide, D. R., *Tetrahedron*, 1962, **17**, 125.
11. Stoicheff, B. P., *Tetrahedron*, 1962, **17**, 135.
12. Pauling, L., and Sherman, J., *J. Amer. Chem. Soc.*, 1937, **59**, 1450.
13. Coulson, C. A., and Altmann, S. L., *Trans. Faraday Soc.*, 1952, **48**, 293.

14. Parr, R. G., *J. Chem. Phys.*, 1951, **19**, 799.
15. Mulliken, R. S., and Parr, R. G., *J. Chem. Phys.*, 1951, **19**, 1271.
16. Dewar, M. J. S., and Schmeising, H. N., *Tetrahedron*, 1959, **5**, 166.
17. Mulliken, R. S., *J. Chem. Phys.*, 1935, **3**, 573.
18. Robinson, D. Z., *J. Chem. Phys.*, 1949, **17**, 1022.
19. Kastler, D., *J. Chim. Phys.*, 1953, **50**, 556.
20. Duncan, A. B. F., *J. Amer. Chem. Soc.*, 1955, **77**, 2107.
21. Duncan, A. B. F., and Pople, J. A., *Trans. Faraday Soc.*, 1953, **49**, 217.
22. Burnelle, L., and Coulson, C. A., *Trans. Faraday Soc.*, 1957, **53**, 403.
23. Smith, J. W., *Electric Dipole Moments*, Butterworths, London, 1955.
24. Smyth, C. P., *Dielectric Behavior and Structure*, McGraw-Hill, New York, 1955.
25. Brown, R. D., and Heffernan, M. L., *Aust. J. Chem.*, 1957, **10**, 493.
26. Coulson, C. A., *Molecular Spectroscopy* (Eds Thornton, E., and Thompson, H. W.), Pergamon Press, Oxford, 1959, p. 195.
27. Pauling, L., *J. Amer. Chem. Soc.*, 1932, **54**, 3570.
28. Pauling, L., *The Nature of the Chemical Bond*, 3rd edn, Cornell University Press, Ithaca, N.Y., 1960.
29. Malone, J. G., *J. Chem. Phys.*, 1933, **1**, 197.
30. Smyth, C. P., *J. Amer. Chem. Soc.*, 1938, **60**, 183.
31. Hannay, N. B., and Smyth, C. P., *J. Amer. Chem. Soc.*, 1946, **68**, 171.
32. Gordy, W., *Disc. Faraday Soc.*, 1955, **19**, 14.
33. Dailey, D. P., and Townes, C. H., *J. Chem. Phys.*, 1955, **23**, 118.
34. Pauling, L., *J. Chem. Soc.*, 1948, 1461.
35. Ferreira, R., *Trans. Faraday Soc.*, 1963, **59**, 1064, 1075.
36. Mulliken, R. S., *J. Chem. Phys.*, 1934, **2**, 782.
37. Mulliken, R. S., *J. Chem. Phys.*, 1935, **3**, 573.
38. Sanderson, R. T., *J. Amer. Chem. Soc.*, 1952, **74**, 4792.
39. Sanderson, R. T., *J. Chem. Educ.*, 1952, **29**, 539.
40. Sanderson, R. T., *J. Chem. Educ.*, 1954, **31**, 2, 238.
41. Sanderson, R. T., *J. Chem. Educ.*, 1955, **32**, 140.
42. Sanderson, R. T., *J. Phys. Chem.*, 1959, **63**, 745.
43. Sutton, L. E. (Ed.), *Tables of Interatomic Distances and Configuration in Molecules and Ions*, Chem. Soc. Special Publication, No. 11, 1958; No. 18, 1965.
44. Schomaker, V., and Stevenson, D. P., *J. Amer. Chem. Soc.*, 1941, **63**, 37.
45. Gordy, W., *J. Chem. Phys.*, 1947, **15**, 81.
46. Bastiansen, O., and Skancke, P. N., *Advanc. Chem. Phys.*, 1961, **3**, 323.
47. Bastiansen, O., and Tratteberg, M., *Tetrahedron*, 1962, **17**, 147.
48. Coulson, C. A., *Proc. Roy. Soc.*, 1951, A**207**, 91.
49. Coulson, C. A., *J. Phys. Chem.*, 1952, **56**, 311.
50. Mulliken, R. S., *Tetrahedron*, 1959, **6**, 68.
51. Bak, B., and Hansen-Nygaard, L., *J. Chem. Phys.*, 1960, **33**, 418.
52. Coulson, C. A., *Victor Henri Memorial Volume, Étude de la Structure Moléculaire*, Desoer, Liège, 1948.
53. Cumper, C. W. N., *Trans. Faraday Soc.*, 1958, **54**, 1261.
54. Wells, A. F., *J. Chem. Soc.*, 1949, 55.

55. Huggins, M., *J. Amer. Chem. Soc.*, 1953, **75**, 4123, 4126.
56. Lofthus, A., *Mol. Phys.*, 1959, **2**, 367.
57. Cox, E. G., and Jeffrey, G. A., *Proc. Roy. Soc.*, 1951, A**207**, 110.
58. Penney, W. G., *Proc. Roy. Soc.*, 1937, A**158**, 306.
59. Pauling, L., Brockway, L. O., and Beach, J. Y., *J. Amer. Chem. Soc.*, 1935, **57**, 2705.
60. Pauling, L., and Brockway, L. O., *J. Amer. Chem. Soc.*, 1937, **59**, 1223.
61. Coulson, C. A., *Proc. Roy. Soc.*, 1939, A**169**, 413.
62. Dewar, M. J. S., and Schmeising, H. N., *Tetrahedron*, 1960, **11**, 96.
63. Cruickshank, D. W. J., and Sparks, R. A., *Proc. Roy. Soc.*, 1960, A**258**, 270.
64. Cruickshank, D. W. J., *Tetrahedron*, 1962, **17**, 155.

CHAPTER 15

THREE-CENTRE BONDING AND ELECTRON-DEFICIENT MOLECULES

In this chapter molecules, or parts of molecules, will be considered in which orbitals extend over three atomic centres. Some unsaturated systems will first be described by the conventional method of localized σ bonds together with two- or three-centre π bonds and then by a brief analysis in terms of delocalized σ and π bonds. The majority of molecules possess sufficient electrons to bind the component atoms together with a series of two electron σ bonds. In a few cases, however, this is not possible and these 'electron deficient' compounds will also be considered.

15.1. The Carboxylate and Nitro Groups

The R—COO^- and R—NO_2 systems are isoelectronic and, being planar, their central atom (C or N) must be in an sp^2 hybridized state. One of these hybrids bonds to the R group and the other two may be considered to form localized bonds with the oxygen atoms. In the simplest description the oxygen atom is considered to employ a pure p orbital, but a more realistic approach requires a little sp hybridization to occur (cf. Section 10.5). This is illustrated in Figure 15.1.

One lone-pair on each oxygen atom occupies the other sp hybrid orbital and because of its p character it is directed away from the central atom. The p_y orbitals of each oxygen atom are in the plane of the molecule and hold another pair of electrons. The remaining four electrons have to be accommodated in π orbitals formed from

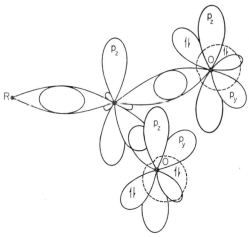

FIGURE 15.1   The atomic orbitals utilized in forming $R—COO^-$ and $R—NO_2$.

the atomic p_z orbital on each of the three atoms. Since both bonds are of the same length the valence bond description includes a resonance between the alternative pairing schemes

$$R—C \overset{\displaystyle O}{\underset{\displaystyle O^-}{}} \quad \text{and} \quad R—C \overset{\displaystyle O^-}{\underset{\displaystyle O}{}}$$

$$R—N \overset{\displaystyle O}{\underset{\displaystyle O}{}} \quad \text{and} \quad R—N \overset{\displaystyle O}{\underset{\displaystyle O}{}}$$

Carbon atoms are considerably less electronegative than those of nitrogen so that the C—O bonds have the greater polarity. The negative charge of the carboxylate anion is consequently located on the oxygen atoms but the description of both systems could be further improved by including some ionic structures.

In the molecular orbital method three-centre delocalized orbitals are formed from the p_z orbital of each atom. They may be formulated as

$$\psi_1 = c_1 \psi_{O_1} + c_2 \psi_C + c_1 \psi_{O_2}$$

$$\psi_2 = c_1' \psi_{O_1} \qquad - \qquad c_1' \psi_{O_2}$$

$$\psi_3 = c_1'' \psi_{O_1} - c_2'' \psi_C + c_1'' \psi_{O_2}$$

The first of these molecular wave functions is bonding over all three atoms and contains two electrons; ψ_2 contains the other two electrons but has a nodal plane perpendicular to the plane of the molecule and passing through the central atom. The electrons in it are much more likely to be found near the oxygen atoms than near the carbon atom. Finally, ψ_3 is antibonding with a node between the central atom and each oxygen but is unoccupied in the

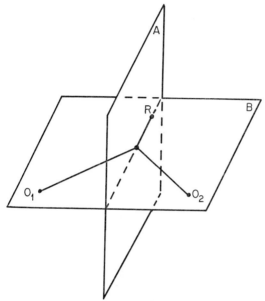

FIGURE 15.2   Symmetry planes for R—COO$^-$ and R—NO$_2$.

ground state. The form of these orbitals can be obtained by solving the appropriate secular equations or from symmetry considerations.

The groups have two symmetry planes (Figure 15.2), and the orbitals must be symmetrical or antisymmetrical to reflection in them. That is to say, the mathematical sign (phase) of the wave function must be unchanged or must change upon reflection. Each p_z orbital is antisymmetrical to reflection in plane B, but that of the central atom is symmetrical to reflection in plane A. The p_z orbitals of the oxygen atoms interchange places upon reflection in plane A so their linear combinations must be employed; $(p_z)_1 + (p_z)_2$ is symmetrical and $(p_z)_1 - (p_z)_2$ antisymmetrical to reflection in A. Only orbitals of the same symmetry can be combined together so that ψ_1, ψ_2, and ψ_3 above are obtained. Figure 15.3 is an energy diagram of these orbitals.

In forming carboxylic acids the proton makes a two electron bond with the p_y orbital of one of the oxygen atoms, thereby so increasing its electronegativity that it maintains a strong hold on the electrons in its p_z orbital. The bonding O—H orbital is actually hybridized as in water (Section 11.2). The carbon atom then forms what is essentially a localized two-electron π bond with the other oxygen.

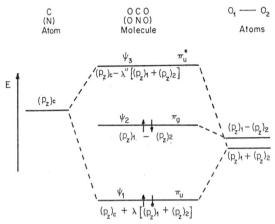

FIGURE 15.3 π molecular orbitals in R—COO$^-$ and R—NO$_2$.

Carboxylic acids and esters have a strong tendency to assume a planar conformation in which the hydrogen is situated between the oxygen atoms[1-3] so there must still be a little π electron delocalization in the molecule.

15.2. Carbon Dioxide

Carbon dioxide, with the same number of electrons as the —COO$^-$ system, differs from it in two major respects. In the first place it is linear, and secondly, the carbon atom is sp^1 not sp^2 hybridized. The two sp^1 hybrids form σ bonds with the oxygen atoms, as considered above for —COO$^-$.

The valence bond description of the remaining electrons involves two localized π bonds between the carbon and each oxygen atom and lone-pairs in pure p orbitals on the oxygen atoms (Figure 15.4). The π bonds would be orthogonal as in allenes ($>C{=\!=}C{=\!=}C<$). This description is inadequate, however, as the CO bond length of 1·160 Å is 0·07 Å shorter than in aldehydes and only 0·03 Å longer than in carbon monoxide. There is an equivalent alternative formulation in which the roles of the p_y and p_z orbitals are reversed. Resonance must occur between these structures giving complete symmetry about the O—C—O axis. This description can be further extended by including the ionic structures $\overset{+}{O}{\equiv}C{-}\overset{-}{O}$ and $\overset{-}{O}{-}C{\equiv}\overset{+}{O}$.

In the molecular orbital approach[4,5] delocalized three-centre orbitals are considered to be formed from the p_y orbitals and also from the p_z orbitals of each atom. They will be of the same form

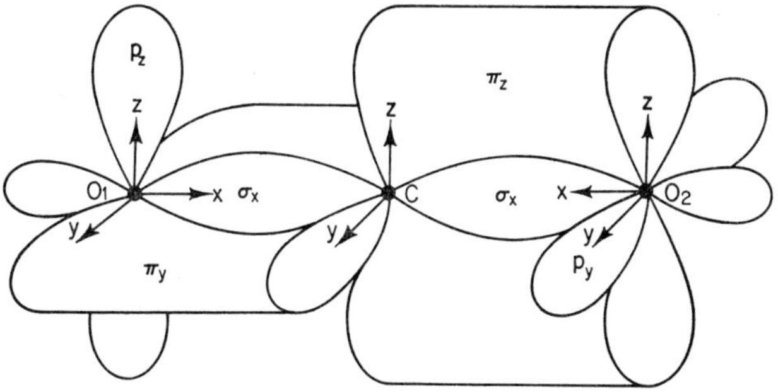

FIGURE 15.4   Valence bond description of σ, π, and lone-pair orbitals in carbon dioxide.

as the ones just described for $RCOO^-$. In each set the two molecular orbitals of lowest energy will be doubly occupied.

Carbon disulphide and carbonyl sulphide have similar structures to carbon dioxide.

15.3. Delocalized σ- and π-Bond Description

An alternative description of the bonding in triatomic molecules may be obtained through generalizing the symmetry arguments presented above for the π orbitals to cover all the valence orbitals. In a linear molecule which has a centre of symmetry, such as CO_2, the atomic and molecular orbitals may be classified according to whether they are σ, π, or δ orbitals and also as to whether they are g or u, [p. 143]. In CO_2 the orbitals are g if they are symmetrical in shape and phase to reflection in the nucleus of the carbon atom, but if there is a change of phase they are u. To confer this symmetry upon the two oxygen atoms combinations of their orbitals must be taken. Defining cartesian axes for the individual atoms as in Figure 15.4 the orbital classification is presented in Table 15.1. Only orbitals of the same symmetry may be combined in forming molecular orbitals.

9

π *Orbitals.* The delocalized π_z molecular orbitals have already been considered and their energies illustrated in Figure 15.3. A degenerate and orthogonal set are formed from the atomic p_y orbitals. Each of the two bonding π_u and two π_g molecular orbitals hold two electrons.

TABLE 15.1. SYMMETRY CLASSIFICATION
OF ATOMIC ORBITALS IN CO_2

Symmetry		Atomic Orbitals	
g	u	C	$O_1 — O_2$
σ_g		s_C	$s_1 + s_2$
			$(p_x)_1 + (p_x)_2$
	σ_u	$(p_x)_C$	$s_1 - s_2$
			$(p_x)_1 - (p_x)_2$
π_g		none	$(p_y)_1 - (p_y)_2$
			$(p_z)_1 - (p_z)_2$
	π_u	$(p_y)_C$	$(p_y)_1 + (p_y)_2$
		$(p_z)_C$	$(p_z)_1 + (p_z)_2$

σ *Orbitals.* An energy correlation diagram for the orbitals of σ symmetry is given in Figure 15.5. (The relative energies of orbitals lying close together may be incorrect.) In the ground state the four delocalized orbitals of lowest energy hold eight electrons.

The σ_u and σ_g molecular orbitals of least energy are centred round the two oxygen atoms alone—repulsion from the carbon atom will polarize them so that there will be a greater chance of finding their electrons on the side of the oxygen atom remote from the carbon†. The electrons in these delocalized σ_u and σ_g orbitals are therefore equivalent to an unshared pair on each oxygen atom. The electrons of the other delocalized three-centre σ_u and σ_g orbitals bind the three atoms together—they are entirely equivalent to the previous description of localized two-centre bonds between the carbon and each oxygen atom, formed from sp hybridized atomic orbitals.

In an unsymmetrical linear molecule X—Y—Z the energies would be modified and the g or u symmetry destroyed. More orbitals could be combined together, and this is conveniently incorporated in the description by hybridizing the s and p orbitals of the oxygen atoms. The modification would not alter the number of electrons,

† This is usually incorporated in the description by saying that the s and p_x orbitals of the oxygen atoms hybridize.

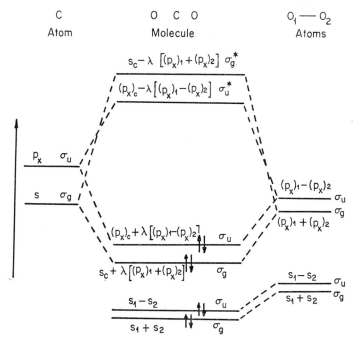

FIGURE 15.5 Energy correlation diagram for the σ orbitals in carbon dioxide.

sixteen, required to fill all the bonding orbitals and this is known to be a particularly stable arrangement in chemistry. For example, the following all possess sixteen valency electrons:

O—C—O   Does not form CO_2^+ or CO_2^- readily

(S—C—S)

(O—N—O)⁻ NO_2 (bent) readily forms the linear NO_2^- ion

(N—C—O)⁻   A stable linear ion

(N—N—N)⁻   A stable linear ion unlike N_3

In forming CO_2^+ a π_g electron is lost, but as this is essentially from a non-bonding orbital the ion would still be linear and the bond lengths changed only slightly. In CO_2^- or NO_2 the seventeenth electron would have to enter the high energy antibonding π_u^* molecular orbital. Rather than do this the energy of the system is lower if the molecule bends so as to reduce the antibonding tendency.

Consider NO_2 (Figure 15.6a). The orbitals of σ symmetry are similar to those of CO_2 but the π_y and π_z systems are no longer degenerate (Figures 15.6b and 15.6c). The three p_z orbitals are parallel and form three delocalized molecular orbitals of the forms discussed already (Figure 15.3). The p_y orbitals have a different symmetry however—the bonding π_y molecular orbital formed from them is

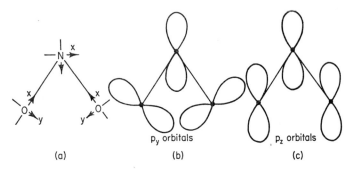

(a)   (b)   (c)

FIGURE 15.6   The p_y and p_z orbitals in NO_2.

weaker but so also is the antibonding tendency of the $\pi_y{}^*$ orbital. It is this last orbital which holds the seventeenth valence electron in NO_2. When two extra electrons have to be accommodated, the bond angle and the overall π bonding is further reduced (Table 15.2).

TABLE 15.2

Number of Valence Electrons		$\stackrel{\frown}{ONO}$ Bond Angle (°)	N—O Bond Length (Å)
$NO_2{}^+$	16	180	1·154
NO_2	17	134	1·188
$NO_2{}^-$	18	115	1·236

Electron-Deficient Molecules

In contrast to the above molecules a few do not have sufficient electrons for there to be a pair in each of the localized σ orbitals. They have been called electron-deficient molecules and occur whenever n atoms are bonded by less than $2(n - 1)$ valence electrons.

15.4. Boron Hydrides

The boron hydride B_2H_6 was initially considered to have the ethane-like structure H_3B—BH_3. This has seven localized σ bonds

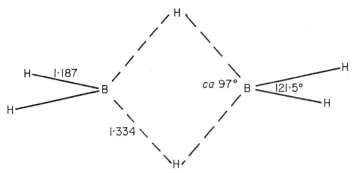

FIGURE 15.7 Diborane.

but the molecule has only twelve valence electrons instead of the required fourteen. It is now known that the structure[6,7] is as in Figure 15.7, which poses a further problem in the form of divalent hydrogen.

The valence bond description is one of resonance between various structures each having six covalent bonds. Four of these structures are shown in Figure 15.8. This is not a very convincing explanation of why the hydride is not BH_3, or informative about the nature of the bridge hydrogens.

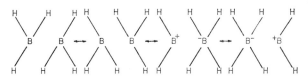

FIGURE 15.8 Valence bond description of diborane.

The results of an analysis of the infrared spectrum of diborane,[8] the similarity between the ultraviolet spectra of diborane and ethylene,[9] and the short $B \cdots B$ distance of 1.77 Å, only about 0.17 Å longer than expected for a direct covalent bond, led Pitzer[10] to suggest structure I containing a protonated double bond. Experimental evidence[11] however, shows the electron charge round

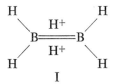

the bridge protons to be greater than near the terminal ones, and in any case the π bond character would be small at a bond length about 0.4 Å longer than predicted for B=B. The accepted molecular orbital approach is nevertheless a development of this structure.[12-16]

The terminal hydrogens are thought to form two-electron σ bonds to the boron atoms, leaving four electrons to bind the boron and bridge hydrogens together. Consider the interaction of the bridge hydrogens with the σ and π electrons of a B $\cdots$ B double bond. The wave function for a B—B bond formed from sp^2 hybrids (σ_1 and σ_2) of the boron atoms can be written as

$$\psi = N(\sigma_1 + \sigma_2)$$

This has the same symmetry as the combined function $s_3 + s_4$ of the bridge hydrogen $1s$ orbitals (Figure 15.9a). They may be combined to give two four-centre orbitals

$$\psi_\pm = N[(\sigma_1 + \sigma_2) \pm \lambda(s_3 + s_4)]$$

Similarly $s_3 - s_4$ has the symmetry of the π component of the B $\cdots$ B double bond and together these give another two four-centre orbitals (Figure 15.9b)

$$\psi_\pm' = N'[(p_1 + p_2) \pm \lambda'(s_3 - s_4)]$$

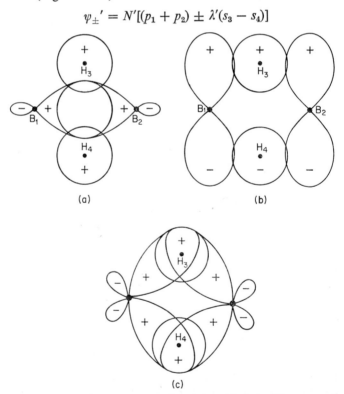

(a)

(b)

(c)

FIGURE 15.9   Combinations of atomic orbitals in diborane.

The orbitals ψ_+ and ψ_+' are bonding and are considered to hold two electrons each, the other two molecular orbitals being vacant. An alternative description is obtained by combining these bonding four-centre orbitals as follows:

$$\phi_1 = N(\psi_+ + \psi_+') = N[(\sigma + \mu p)_1 + (\sigma + \mu p)_2 + \delta s_3]$$
and
$$\phi_2 = N(\psi_+ - \psi_+') = N[(\sigma - \mu p)_1 + (\sigma - \mu p)_2 + \delta s_4]$$

Examination of these functions shows them to represent three-centre orbitals, formed by sp^3 hybrids of each boron and the s

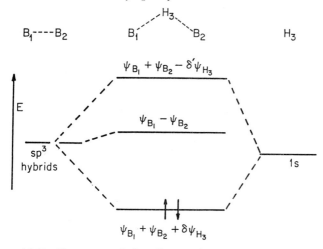

FIGURE 15.10   Energy correlation diagram for $B_1 \cdots H_3 \cdots B_2$ molecular orbitals. Similar orbitals are formed with H_4.

orbital of one of the bridge hydrogen atoms (Figure 15.9c). (cf. The description of ethylene in terms of equivalent orbitals on p. 209). In the ground electronic state ϕ_1 and ϕ_2 would each accommodate two electrons. The electron density will be greatest where the component atomic orbitals overlap—namely near the hydrogen atoms.† Figure 15.10 is an energy diagram showing the formation of three-centre $B \cdots H \cdots B$ orbitals.

Bonding in the other boron hydrides has also been described[17-19] in terms of two electron, two- and three-centre molecular orbitals. (For a summary of their structures, see Lipscomb.[20]) In each case the available electrons are just sufficient to fill every bonding

† More detailed calculations (Hamilton[15,16]) show that the three-centre orbital includes a small contribution from the other sp^3 hybrid of each boron atom and that the gross atomic populations from the orbitals are B, 0·78 and H, 1·22 electrons.

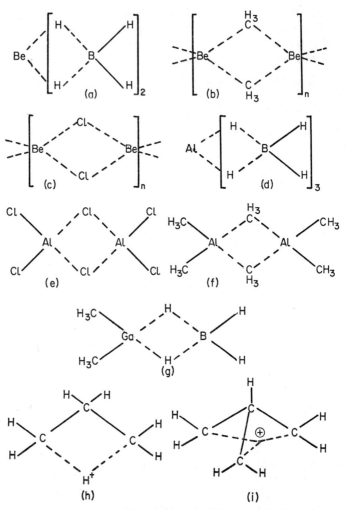

FIGURE 15.11   Some electron deficient molecules.

molecular orbital, leaving the non-bonding and antibonding orbitals vacant. (Non-bonding molecular orbitals are distinguished from lone-pair orbitals in that the electrons they contain are located between the atoms forming the molecule though, like lone-pair electrons, they are not directly involved in binding them together.)

Electron deficient molecules are not restricted to the boron hydrides. They can be formed by aluminium and gallium in the same group as boron and by beryllium and carbon from groups II and IV. In each case the most plausible of the simple descriptions involves two electron, three-centre bonds. Some examples are shown in Figure 15.11. Beryllium and aluminium borohydrides ((a) and (d)) are known but the corresponding lithium compound is ionic $Li^+[BH_4]^-$. The propyl cation (h) is thought to have a cyclic structure[21] and bridge structures have also been postulated for carbonium ions existing as intermediates in chemical reactions.[22–24]

From these few examples it is evident that the bridge can also be formed through the hybrid orbital of a carbon atom or through a halogen atom, though the compounds are then not necessarily electron deficient. In some cases the angles between the ring atoms are considerably less than 90°. In the $BeCl_2$ polymer (c) the B̂eClBe angle[25] is 82°, and if the chlorine atoms are replaced by methyls (b) the B̂eCBe angle[26] is reduced to 66°, due to the more favourable shape of an sp^3 hybrid orbital. At these angles the hybrids of the beryllium atoms must overlap with each other as well as with the hybrid of the bridge atom.

15.5. Solid Borides

Further interesting examples of electron deficient compounds are provided by the hexaborides such as $Ca^{2+}B_6^{2-}$. Crystallographic studies[27,28] have established that the boron atoms form regular octahedra, which are linked to six neighbouring octahedra. All the B—B distances are 1·72 Å and twenty valence electrons are available for each octahedron.

Longuet-Higgins and Roberts[29] suggested that the boron atoms were sp^1 hybridized and the octahedra linked by normal σ bonds formed from these hybrids (Figure 15.12). This would leave fourteen valence electrons to bind the six boron atoms in the octahedra. Each boron atom possesses the other sp^1 hybrid together with two

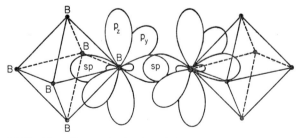

FIGURE 15.12   Two B_6 octahedra bonded by a σ bond formed from sp^1 hybrids.

p orbitals, and these eighteen atomic orbitals from the six atoms are thought to form an equal number of delocalized molecular orbitals. Only seven of these are bonding and contain the fourteen electrons.

The six sp^1 hybrid orbitals form one six-centre bonding molecular orbital, and two four-centre, and three two-centre antibonding orbitals (Figure 15.13). One simple way to consider the remaining

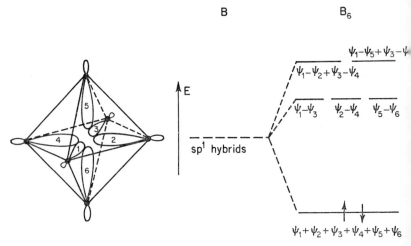

FIGURE 15.13   Molecular orbitals formed by an sp^1 hybrid from each boron atom in B_6 octahedra.

orbitals is as follows. Four of the p orbitals, on say B_1, B_2, B_3, and B_4, form one bonding, two non-bonding, and one antibonding σ-type molecular orbital (Figure 15.14a). These can now π bond with the two p orbitals of B_5 and with the two on B_6. The net result is the formation of two bonding and two antibonding molecular orbitals (Figure 15.14b). This happens in each of three directions round the octahedron so that each orbital is triply degenerate. The six orbitals of lowest energy are occupied.

Other examples of cages of boron atoms where the bonding is analogous occur in B_4Cl_4 and the carbide $B_{12}C_2$.[30]

15.6. Organic Complexes of Transition Metals

It is convenient to consider these complexes in the next chapter because, though it can be argued that some are electron deficient,

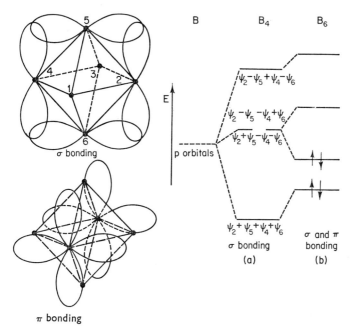

π bonding

FIGURE 15.14 Molecular orbitals formed from atomic p orbitals in B_6 octahedra.

the bonding involves the d orbitals of the transition element which are best considered by ligand-field theory.

BIBLIOGRAPHICAL REFERENCES

1. Marsden, R. J. B., and Sutton, L. E., *J. Chem. Soc.*, 1936, 1383.
2. Zahn, C. T., *Phys. Z.*, 1932, **33**, 730.
3. O'Gorman, J. M., Shand, W., and Schomaker, V., *J. Amer. Chem. Soc.*, 1950, **72**, 4222.
4. Mulligan, J. F., *J. Chem. Phys.*, 1951, **19**, 347, 1428.
5. Mulliken, R. S., *J. Chem. Phys.*, 1935, **3**, 720.
6. Hedberg, K., and Schomaker, V., *J. Amer. Chem. Soc.*, 1951, **73**, 1482.
7. Shoolery, J. N., *Disc. Faraday Soc.*, 1955, **19**, 215.
8. Price, W. C., *J. Chem. Phys.*, 1947, **15**, 614.
9. Price, W. C., *J. Chem. Phys.*, 1948, **16**, 895.
10. Pitzer, K. S., *J. Amer. Chem. Soc.*, 1945, **67**, 1126.
11. Ogg, R. A., *J. Chem. Phys.*, 1954, **22**, 1933.
12. Longuet-Higgins, H. C., *J. Chim. Phys.*, 1949, **46**, 268.
13. Longuet-Higgins, H. C., *Quart. Rev.*, 1957, **11**, 121.
14. Yamazaki, M., *J. Chem. Phys.*, 1957, **27**, 1401.

15. Hamilton, W. C., *Proc. Roy. Soc.*, 1956, A235, 395.
16. Hamilton, W. C., *J. Chem. Phys.*, 1958, 29, 460.
17. Eberhardt, W. H., Crawford, B., and Lipscomb, W. N., *J. Chem. Phys.*, 1954, 22, 989.
18. Lipscomb, W. N., *J. Chem. Phys.*, 1954, 22, 985.
19. Lipscomb, W. N., *J. Chem. Phys.*, 1956, 25, 38.
20. Lipscomb, W. N., *Advanc. Inorg. Chem. Radiochem.*, 1959, 1, 117.
21. Rylander, P. N., and Meyerson, S., *J. Amer. Chem. Soc.*, 1956, 78, 5799.
22. Roberts, J. D., and Mazur, R. H., *J. Amer. Chem. Soc.*, 1951, 73, 2509, 3542.
23. Roberts, J. D., and Chambers, V. C., *J. Amer. Chem. Soc.*, 1951, 73, 5034.
24. Winstein, S., Walborsky, H. M., and Schreiber, K. C., *J. Amer. Chem. Soc.*, 1950, 72, 5795.
25. Rundle, R. E., and Lewis, P. H., *J. Chem. Phys.*, 1952, 20, 132.
26. Snow, A. I., and Rundle, R. E., *Acta Cryst.*, 1951, 4, 348.
27. Pauling, L., and Weinbaum, S., *Z. Krist.*, 1934, 87, 181.
28. Stackelberg, M., and Neumann, F., *Z. Phys. Chem.*, 1932, B19, 314.
29. Longuet-Higgins, H. C., and Roberts, M. de V., *Proc. Roy. Soc.*, 1954, A224, 336.
30. Longuet-Higgins, H. C., and Roberts, M. de V., *Proc. Roy. Soc.*, 1955, A230, 110.

CHAPTER 16

TRANSITION ELEMENTS

Metals that form ions having partially filled d shells are known as transition elements, and ever since the classical work of Werner on the great variety of complexes formed by them a continuous interest has been maintained in this field. Their characteristic properties are naturally associated in large part with the presence of the d electrons in their valence shells. In recent years great advances have been made in the theoretical treatment of complexes and it is a brief account of these developments which is presented in this chapter. (For an excellent descriptive account see Orgel,[1] and for a mathematical treatment, Griffith.[2] There are also several good reviews, e.g. Griffith and Orgel,[3] Sutton,[4] and Orgel.[5])

The bonding in transition element complexes has been successfully described in terms of both covalent and ionic bonding! Pauling, in his initial theory, was primarily concerned with obtaining vacant (hybridized) orbitals on the metal which could then accept lone-pair electrons from each ligand to form coordinate bonds.† The logical development of this is a molecular orbital approach that considers all the bonding, non-bonding, and antibonding molecular orbitals formed by the metal and its surrounding atoms. Bethe and van Vleck on the other hand approached these compounds from the completely opposite point of view. They considered the purely electrostatic interaction between the central metal ion and the ionic charges or dipoles of the ligands. Their theory had many limitations but has recently been revived by Orgel and others, who considered specifically the energies of the d electrons of the metal atom. In this form it has been called the crystal-field theory. The most adequate approach at the present time is the ligand-field theory, which is essentially a combination of the molecular orbital and crystal-field

---

† This is naturally a formal description. Electrons could also be considered to have been transferred to the metal, thus giving ionic bonds, followed by the formation of electron pair bonds.

methods. The development of these theories is summarized below but before each one is described some features of d electrons will be considered.

Pauling theory   Electrostatic theory
        ↓   ↓
Molecular orbital theory   Crystal-field theory

Ligand-field theory

16.1. d Electrons

The shapes of the five d orbitals were considered in Section 7.4 and an indication of their energies given in Figure 9.2. The d_{z^2} orbital appears to differ from the remainder, but when it is realized that it is a combination of $d_{y^2-z^2}$ and $d_{z^2-x^2}$ it will be appreciated that it must behave as another of the d orbitals, $d_{x^2-y^2}$. These two, d_{z^2} and $d_{x^2-y^2}$, have their lobes directed along the cartesian axes; the remainder, d_{xy}, d_{yz}, and d_{zx}, have their lobes directed between pairs of axes. The five orbitals are degenerate in the isolated atom.

Consider the fourth group in the periodic table, potassium to krypton, containing the first series of transition elements. In the first two elements, potassium and calcium, the $4s$ orbital is more stable than the $3d$ orbital, but in the next element, scandium, an electron enters the $3d$ orbital for the first time. The greater nuclear charge in fact makes it more stable than the $4s$ electron so that Sc^+ has the electronic configuration $(\cdots 3d^14s^1)$. Proceeding along the series of transition elements, as additional electrons are added to the d shell they become progressively more stable relative to the $4s$ electrons† (cf. Figure 9.2). At the same time their radial distribution changes so that the $3d$ orbitals, which were initially much larger than the $4s$, become more compressed. Self-consistent field calculations show that by the end of the transition series the maximum in the radial curve of the $3d$ orbital is at nearly the same distance from the nucleus as that for the $3p$ electrons, and in their complexes the electrons are consequently more likely to be near the metal than the ligand atoms. This explains why they can be successfully described by an electrostatic crystal-field theory, particularly when discussing the more ionic compounds such as the oxides, halides, and hydrates. However, this approach is less reliable at the start of the transition series, and with ligands such as unsaturated hydrocarbons and the carbonyl group.

† Chromium and copper have the configurations $3d^54s^1$ and $3d^{10}4s^1$ respectively, instead of $3d^44s^2$ and $3d^94s^3$, thus demonstrating the special stability associated with a half-filled and a full d shell.

TABLE 16.1

Coordination number	Atomic orbitals	Arrangement	Angles between hybrid orbitals
2	dp ds	Linear Angular	180°
3	dp^2, ds^2 d^2p	Trigonal plane Trigonal pyramid	120° 90°
4	d^3s dsp^2, d^2p^2 d^2sp, dp^3, d^3p	Tetrahedral Tetragonal plane Irregular tetrahedron	109°28′ 90°
5†	dsp^3, d^3sp dsp^3, d^2sp^2, d^4s, d^4p, d^2p^3	Trigonal bipyramid Tetragonal pyramid	120°, 90°
6	d^2sp^3 d^4sp, d^5p d^3p^3	Octahedral Trigonal prism Trigonal antiprism	90° 90°, 60°
7	d^3sp^3, d^5sp d^4sp^2, d^4p^3, d^5p^2	ZrF_7^{3-} TaF_7^{2-}	
8	d^4sp^3 d^5p^3, d^5sp^2	Dodecahedron Prisms	

† dsp^3 hybridization gives a trigonal bipyramid with the d_{z^2} orbital but a tetragonal pyramid with the $d_{x^2-y^2}$ orbital.

In the following discussion attention will be focused upon octahedral complexes because of their widespread occurrence, but the theories may be equally well applied to any stereochemical arrangement†.

16.2. The Pauling Theory

Pauling showed that by hybridizing the $(n - 1)$ d orbitals of a transition metal with its $(n)s$ and $(n)p$ orbitals very strongly directed hybrids result. Many different hybridizations may occur, covering the known geometrical dispositions of ligand atoms and lone-pair electrons in transition metal complexes. Hybridization of s and p orbitals was considered in Chapter 11; in Table 16.1 the commonest

† See Gillespie and Nyholm[6] for a review of inorganic stereochemistry.

hybridizations involving d electrons are listed. Figure 16.1 illustrates the formation of typical dsp^2 and d^2sp^3 hybrids of analytical forms

$$dsp^2, \quad \psi = \frac{1}{2}\psi_s + \frac{1}{\sqrt{2}}\psi_{p_z} + \frac{1}{2}\psi_{d_{yz}}$$

and

$$d^2sp^3, \quad \psi = \frac{1}{\sqrt{6}}\psi_s + \frac{1}{\sqrt{2}}\psi_{p_z} + \frac{1}{\sqrt{3}}\psi_{d_{z^2}}$$

In this theory it is supposed that the necessary *unoccupied* hybrid orbitals can be made available on the metal to accept electrons from the ligands, thereby forming an equivalent number of co-ordinate bonds. To provide these vacant hybrid orbitals the electrons in the metal have frequently to be redistributed, thus changing the number of unpaired electrons. When this happens the paramagnetism of the complex and free ion often differ. Table 16.2 illustrates the change in electron arrangements during the formation of simple carbonyls by the neutral iron, chromium, and nickel atoms. The isolated atoms have parallel electron spins as

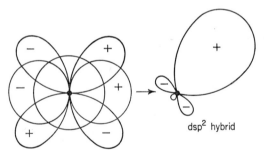

dsp² hybrid

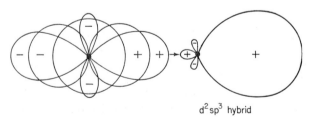

d² sp³ hybrid

FIGURE 16.1   Square planar dsp^2 and octahedral d^2sp^3 hybrids.

TABLE 16.2

	3d					4s	3p			S	μ_{calc}†
Cr atom	↑	↑	↑	↑	↑	↑				3	6·93
Cr(CO)₆	↑↓	↑↓	↑↓	0	0	0	0	0	0	0	0
Fe atom	↑↓	↑	↑	↑	↑	↑↓				2	4·90
Fe(CO)₅	↑↓	↑↓	↑↓	↑↓	0	0	0	0	0	0	0
Ni atom	↑↓	↑↓	↑↓	↑	↑	↑↓				1	2·83
Ni(CO)₄	↑↓	↑↓	↑↓	↑↓	↑↓	0	0	0	0	0	0

† μ is the magnetic moment in Bohr magnetons calculated from the 'spin-only' formula, $\mu = 2\sqrt{[S(S+1)]}$, where S is the resultant electron spin.

far as possible (Hund's rule), but considerable pairing occurs in forming the carbonyls. The orbitals utilized in forming the hybrids, denoted by circles in Table 16.2, show that in the chromium carbonyl the ligands are octahedrally distributed, in iron carbonyl as a trigonal bipyramid, and in nickel carbonyl tetrahedrally. Table 16.3 illustrates the possibilities for Ni^{2+} complexes.† With four coordination

TABLE 16.3

	3d					4s	4p			5s	S	μ_{calc}
Ni²⁺	↑↓	↑↓	↑↓	↑	↑						1	2·83
NiX₆	↑↓	↑↓	↑↓	0	0	0	0	0	0	↑↓	0	0
NiX₄	↑↓	↑↓	↑↓	↑↓	0	0	0	0			0	0
NiX₄	↑↓	↑↓	↑↓	↑	↑	0	0	0	0		1	2·83

two situations exist; either all the d electrons are paired and the dsp^2 orbitals hybridize to give a square planar arrangement, (e.g. $Ni(CN)_4{}^{2-}$), or two of the d orbitals are singly occupied and sp^3 hybridization occurs (e.g. $(Ph_3P)_2NiCl_2$).‡ The bonds would be stronger in the former case but, in the latter, the repulsion between the ligands would be reduced.

This situation should warn one against being too confident in predicting structures on this basis, a point which $Cu(H_2O)_4{}^{2+}$ demonstrates even more forcibly. A tetrahedral arrangement would probably be anticipated, corresponding to

3d	4s	4p
↑↓ ↑↓ ↑↓ ↑↓ ↑	0	0 0 0

† For further examples see Nyholm,[7] Selwood,[8] and Goodenough.[9]

‡ $Ni(NH_3)_2{}^{2+}$ and other ions are paramagnetic but it is possible that they have formed octahedral complexes with the solvent in solution.

The molecule however is planar which would suggest the distribution

	3d	4s	4p	4d
	↿⇂ ↿⇂ ↿⇂ ↿⇂ 0	0	0 0 ↑	
or	↿⇂ ↿⇂ ↿⇂ ↿⇂ ↑	0	0 0	0

This is still not entirely satisfactory as the first alternative implies that the unpaired electron might be removed fairly readily giving Cu^{3+}, whilst the second description involves the higher energy $4d$ orbitals.

If the metal atom is the acceptor for several coordinate bonds it would tend to have an unacceptably high negative charge. Pauling has suggested two reasons why this does not occur. Firstly, the bonds are polar and in his electroneutrality principle he showed one way in which the actual charges on the atoms could be estimated. The application of this principle to two octahedral aluminium complexes was illustrated on p. 233. Secondly, a reduction of the net charge on the central atom can be achieved through a back donation of some of the excess negative charge by double bond formation.[10] That this does occur in some cases is demonstrated by the shortness of their metal–ligand bonds and by electron-spin resonance studies.

An octahedral complex for example, with the six ligands situated along the coordinate axes, has its d_{z^2} and $d_{x^2-y^2}$ orbitals with the necessary symmetry to form d^2sp^3 hybrids. The three remaining d orbitals, which now hold the d electrons of the transition element, have the requisite symmetry to form delocalized π bonds with p or d orbitals of the ligands. This is illustrated in Figure 16.2 for the d_{xy} orbital, but equivalent orbital overlapping could also occur with d_{yz} and d_{zx}.

The wave function of the completely bonding π molecular orbital formed in this way with four identical ligands would be

$$\psi = \psi_{d_{xy}} + \lambda[(\psi_{p_y})_1 - (\psi_{p_y})_2 + (\psi_{p_x})_3 - (\psi_{p_x})_4]$$

Double bond character in carbonyls and cyanides is thought to be considerable, but it cannot occur at all if the ligands do not possess suitable vacant orbitals.

A problem which arises with this approach may be illustrated by reference to octahedral ferric complexes. The paramagnetism of $Fe(CN)_6^{3-}$ and many other iron (III) complexes corresponds to one unpaired electron. This is consistent with the following scheme:

	3d	4s	4p	S	μ
Fe^{3+}	↑ ↑ ↑ ↑ ↑			5/2	5·92
$Fe^{3+}X_6$	↿⇂ ↿⇂ ↑ 0 0	0	0 0 0	1/2	1·73

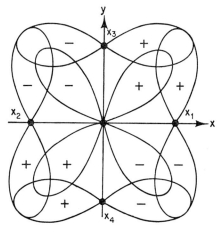

FIGURE 16.2 d–p, π bonding in octahedral complexes.

FeF_6^{3-}, $Fe(H_2O)_6^{3+}$ and others however have a paramagnetism corresponding to five unpaired electrons. These are termed ionic complexes on the supposition that to avoid pairing the d electrons the bonding must be ionic. This is not consistent with their chemistry. Another description involves a resonance between four coordinate bonds, involving the $4s$ and three $4p$ orbitals, and two ionic bonds. It is however still possible for d^2sp^3 hybridization to occur if the d orbitals are those of the fourth quantum shell.

	$3d$	$4s$	$4p$	$4d$	S	μ
$Fe^{3+}X_6$	↑ ↑ ↑ ↑ ↑	0	0 0 0	0 0	5/2	5·92

The use of *outer d orbitals* was initially thought unlikely because of their great size, but it has now been demonstrated that highly electronegative ligands can produce a considerable contraction.[11,12,13] If this occurred it would be possible for them to hybridize satisfactorily with s and p orbitals of the same shell. The maximum density of an electron in such an orbital would be found well away from the metal atom and close to the electronegative ligand. The electron distribution therefore is similar to that resulting from the previous concept of resonance between ionic and covalent bonds. It is worth while noting that a similar situation exists in SF_6, PF_6^-, and SiF_6^{2-}, only here the d orbitals can only be outer d orbitals.

The situation in $Fe(CN)_6^{3-}$, etc. has been variously described as a covalent complex, one involving inner d orbital hybridization, or as a low-spin complex. Conversely, FeF_6^{3-} has been called an ionic complex, one involving outer d orbital hybridization, or as a high-spin complex. The term 'ionic complex' is liable to be misleading.

We might note that outer orbital hybridization need not be postulated in the following theories.

16.3. The Molecular Orbital Theory

In the Pauling approach no mention is made of the orbitals of the ligand atoms. A logical development of this theory is to formulate the molecular orbitals formed between the ligands and the metal atom. Let us consider an octahedral complex with identical ligands 1 to 6, labelled as in Figure 16.3a.

σ bonding. Each ligand has an orbital, frequently hybridized, of σ symmetry directed towards the central metal atom and capable of interacting with its s, three p, and five d type orbitals. In the molecule

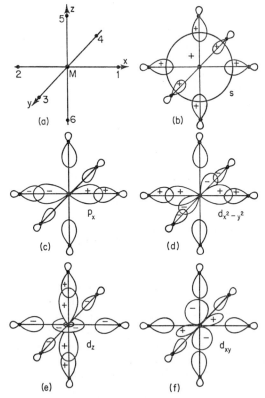

FIGURE 16.3   Interaction of the s, p, and d orbitals of a transition element with its six ligands in an octahedral complex.

these fifteen atomic orbitals form the same number of molecular orbitals—six are bonding, three non-bonding, and six antibonding. In formulating them it is first necessary to make composite orbitals for the ligands as a group, and then to consider the interaction of these group orbitals with the atomic orbitals of the metal. The manner in which this is done should be clear from Figures 16.3b, c, d, and e, in which the phases shown refer to the bonding orbitals.

Metal		*Ligands*

$$\psi_{1,2} = \psi_s \pm \lambda_a(\psi_1 + \psi_2 + \psi_3 + \psi_4 + \psi_5 + \psi_6)$$
$$\psi_{3,4} = \psi_{p_x} \pm \lambda_b(\psi_1 - \psi_2)$$
$$\psi_{5,6} = \psi_{p_y} \pm \lambda_c(\psi_3 - \psi_4)$$
$$\psi_{7,8} = \psi_{p_z} \pm \lambda_d(\psi_5 - \psi_6)$$
$$\psi_{9,10} = \psi_{d_{x^2-y^2}} \pm \lambda_e(\psi_1 + \psi_2 - \psi_3 - \psi_4)$$
$$\psi_{11,12} = \psi_{d_{z^2}} \pm \lambda_f[(\psi_5 + \psi_6) - \tfrac{1}{2}(\psi_1 + \psi_2 + \psi_3 + \psi_4)]$$
$$\psi_{13} = \psi_{d_{xy}}$$
$$\psi_{14} = \psi_{d_{yz}}$$
$$\psi_{15} = \psi_{d_{zx}}$$

It will be observed that the d orbitals behave in different ways. The two with their lobes directed towards the ligands interact with them forming degenerate pairs of bonding and antibonding molecular orbitals. They are known as the e_g orbitals. The other three d orbitals, termed the t_{2g} orbitals[†], have their lobes directed between the ligands so that their symmetry (i.e. the phases of their lobes) is not suitable for forming σ bonds. The energy of the $3d$ orbitals of an element in the first transition series is lower than that of the $4s$ and $4p$ orbitals, and because of their shape and smaller size they do not interact so strongly with the ligands. A schematic representation of the orbital energies is shown in Figure 16.4, but the order of the molecular orbitals is somewhat uncertain. The diagram has been drawn for the usual case in which the ligand orbitals are of lower energy than the metal orbitals; the bonding orbitals consequently have a large ligand character and the antibonding ones are centred mainly on the metal atom.

Each ligand contributes two electrons and these are just sufficient to fill the six bonding molecular orbitals. The valence electrons of the metal have still to be accommodated and are held in the non-bonding t_{2g} orbitals (ψ_{13}, ψ_{14}, and ψ_{15}) and in the antibonding

[†] The nomenclature arises from terminology used in group theory. The symbols a (or b), e, and t, denote singly, doubly, and triply degenerate states respectively. The subscript g denotes the symmetry property considered on p. 143. The e_g orbitals have also been called $d\gamma$ or γ_3 orbitals and the t_{2g} orbitals $d\xi$ or γ_5.

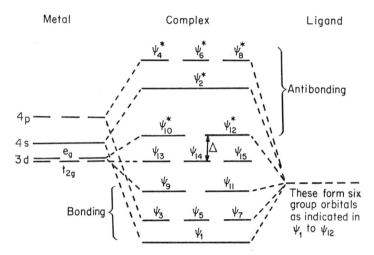

FIGURE 16.4   Molecular orbital energies in an octahedral complex of a transition metal.

e_g* molecular orbitals (ψ_{10}* and ψ_{12}*). The actual distribution of electrons between these energy levels depends upon two factors:

1. Electrons have a lower energy if their spins are parallel (Hund's rule).
2. Electrons prefer to occupy low energy orbitals first, up to a maximum of two electrons per orbital.

Atoms with one, two, or three d electrons (often written as d^1, d^2, and d^3 respectively) will therefore have them in the t_{2g} orbitals. With a fourth electron however, factor (1) would dictate that it enters an antibonding e_g* molecular orbital, whereas (2) would favour its pairing with one of the other electrons in the singly occupied t_{2g} orbitals. These possibilities correspond to high-spin and low-spin states respectively. Which one exists is largely controlled by the magnitude of the energy Δ in Figure 16.4. For a given complex, its paramagnetic moment shows unambiguously which has taken place. The possible distributions of d electrons in octahedral complexes is summarized in Table 16.4.

π *bonding.* So far only ligand orbitals which point towards the metal have been considered. With the exception of a hydrogen atom, ligands have one, or frequently two, orbitals capable of a π-type interaction with the metal atom. To be more specific they can form delocalized π molecular orbitals with the t_{2g} orbitals of the metal, as illustrated in Figure 16.2 for p ligand orbitals.

$$\psi = \psi_{d_{xy}} \pm \lambda[(\psi_{p_y})_1 - (\psi_{p_y})_2 + (\psi_{p_x})_3 - (\psi_{p_x})_4]$$

TABLE 16.4

Number of Electrons	Example	t_{2g}	e_g	S
1	$Ti(H_2O)_6{}^{3+}$	↑		$\frac{1}{2}$
2	$V(H_2O)_6{}^{3+}$	↑ ↑		1
3	$Cr(NH_3)_6{}^{3+}$	↑ ↑ ↑		$1\frac{1}{2}$

Number of Electrons	Example	High Spin State (Low Δ)			Example	Low Spin State (High Δ)		
		t_{2g}	e_g	S		t_{2g}	e_g	S
4	$CrCl_2 \cdot 4H_2O$	↑ ↑ ↑	↑	2	$Cr(CN)_6{}^{4-}$	↑↓ ↑ ↑		1
5	$FeF_6{}^{3-}$	↑ ↑ ↑	↑ ↑	$2\frac{1}{2}$	$Fe(CN)_6{}^{3-}$	↑↓ ↑↓ ↑		$\frac{1}{2}$
6	$Fe(H_2O)_6{}^{++}$	↑↓ ↑ ↑	↑ ↑	2	$Co(NH_3)_6{}^{3+}$	↑↓ ↑↓ ↑↓		0
7	$Co(H_2O)_6{}^{++}$	↑↓ ↑↓ ↑	↑ ↑	$1\frac{1}{2}$	$Co(NO_2)_6{}^{4-}$	↑↓ ↑↓ ↑↓	↑	$\frac{1}{2}$

Number of Electrons	Example	t_{2g}	e_g	S
8	$Ni(H_2O)_6{}^{++}$	↑↓ ↑↓ ↑↓	↑ ↑	1
9	$Cu(NH_3)_6{}^{++}$	↑↓ ↑↓ ↑↓	↑↓ ↑	$\frac{1}{2}$
10	$Zn(NH_3)_6{}^{++}$	↑↓ ↑↓ ↑↓	↑↓ ↑↓	0

These bonding and antibonding orbitals are formed from one of the three t_{2g} orbitals and four of the twelve p_x and p_y orbitals of the ligands. Two other equivalent sets are formed from the remaining atomic orbitals. Figure 16.4 could be completely redrawn to include these new orbitals, but rather than complicate this diagram Figure 16.5 shows the effect of the π orbitals of the ligands interacting with the t_{2g} orbitals in the complex.

Two cases are possible. In Figure 16.5a the π orbitals of the ligands are assumed to be occupied, (e.g. F^-, O^{2-}, H_2O), and consequently of comparatively low energy. Their repulsion by the electrons in the t_{2g} orbitals raises the energy of the latter and decreases the value of Δ. In the second case, (Figure 16.5b), the ligand π orbitals are unoccupied (e.g. the vacant d orbitals of P or As atoms) and are of higher energy. In this case the electrons in the t_{2g} orbitals enter the bonding π molecular orbitals and increase the Δ value. When this occurs, negative charge flows from the metal towards the ligands so that in addition to giving some double bond character the σ bonds are strengthened. Some ligands could function in either of the above ways but it is usually possible to predict whether the donor or acceptor tendency predominates, e.g. with CO and CN^- the acceptor action is normally the stronger, but in Cl^- the donor action of its $3p$ electrons is generally more important than any accepting power of its vacant $3d$ orbitals. There are exceptions.

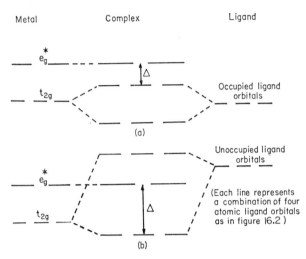

FIGURE 16.5   Interaction of t_{2g} metal orbitals with π ligand orbitals. (a) Occupied ligand orbitals, (b) unoccupied ligand orbitals.

16.4. The Electrostatic Theory

Having described the bonding in the compounds of transition elements in terms of covalent bonds, let us return to the beginning again and consider a description in terms of ionic bonding. This approach, due to Bethe[14] and van Vleck,[15,16] is of limited value but it has been developed into the crystal-field theory.

The cation of the transition element is considered to be surrounded by anions or by the negative ends of highly dipolar molecules. The electrostatic energy of such an arrangement may be estimated in a manner similar to that adopted for computing the energy of an ionic crystal lattice. In many cases reasonable agreement is obtained with experimental values, but in others the calculated energy is rather low.

The formation of a square planar complex is not explicable on this basis as the repulsions between four ligands should give a tetrahedral distribution around the metal. Neither can this theory explain the existence of complexes with virtually non-polar ligands (e.g. the carbonyls), the different stability of complexes formed by ions of nearly the same size (e.g. Fe^{3+} and Co^{3+}), nor how the larger ions of the elements in the second and third transition series can form more stable complexes than the corresponding element in the first series.

16.5. The Crystal-field Theory

A major oversight in the simple electrostatic theory is the failure to allow for the perturbation of the d orbitals of the metal ion by the ligands. In an octahedral complex, for example, the negative charge on the ligands does not repel the d electrons of the cation equally in all five orbitals. The coulombic repulsion of electrons occupying the e_g orbitals is greater than for those in the t_{2g} orbitals as, on the average, the former are nearer to the ligands. The de-

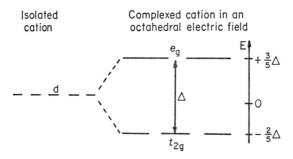

FIGURE 16.6   Crystal field splitting of d orbitals by an octahedral field.

generacy of the d orbitals is consequently removed by the electric field in the complex†. This is illustrated in Figure 16.6; the difference being that the e_g are now atomic orbitals.

The result is extremely similar to the formation of non-bonding t_{2g} orbitals and antibonding e_g* molecular orbitals. In particular, both this and the molecular orbital theory lead to low-spin and high-spin states for systems in which the transition element has 4, 5, 6, or 7 electrons in the d orbitals.

The absolute energies of these perturbed orbitals cannot be calculated, but fortunately many properties of complexes may be discussed entirely in terms of the energy separation Δ. This has been estimated theoretically in terms of the crystal-field model and has also been determined spectroscopically. In discussions it is convenient to take the mean energy of the five orbitals in each complex as an arbitrary zero, so that the two e_g orbitals have the energy $+\frac{3}{5}\Delta$ and the three t_g orbitals $-\frac{2}{5}\Delta$. Thus d^3 would have the energy $3[-\frac{2}{5}\Delta] = -1\frac{1}{5}\Delta$, and for d^8 the energy would be $6[-\frac{2}{5}\Delta] + 2[+\frac{3}{5}\Delta] = -1\frac{1}{5}\Delta$ also. When the altered energy, the crystal-field stabilization energy, of the d electrons in complexes is

† This effect was first discussed with ionic crystals—hence the name, crystal-field theory.

added to the other electrostatic interactions considered by the earlier theory, good agreement is often obtained with the experimentally determined values.

16.6. Ligand-field Theory

In the preceding sections the compounds formed by transition elements have been discussed in terms of covalent bonding and in terms of ionic bonding. Both predict the same low- and high-spin states for each type of complex. The crystal-field theory is the simpler and, with highly electronegative ligands is able to explain many experimental observations in a satisfactory manner. For less electronegative ligands, such as the carbonyls, the crystal-field theory is useless and the molecular orbital approach must be used. This theory is the only one which adequately considers the effect of π orbitals on the ligands. It also predicts electron delocalization; electrons from the ligands can be found near the metal as a result of forming σ bonds, and in some cases π bond delocalization can result in the t_{2g} electrons of the metal approaching close to the ligands. Both types have been confirmed experimentally, largely by electron-spin resonance.[17,18] However, for highly electronegative ligands and particularly with transition elements whose d shells are nearly complete and orbitals rather small, the value of Δ anticipated by the molecular orbital theory is less than that found experimentally. What is really required is a wave mechanical theory based upon the molecular orbital approach but including the electrostatic crystal-field effects in the calculation. This is not possible mathematically. The best compromise is a hybrid approach—the ligand-field theory—in which the energy splitting Δ is taken as the resultant effect of three factors:

1. The σ bond splitting, molecular orbital theory.
2. The π bonding perturbation of this situation, molecular orbital theory.
3. The purely electrostatic effect, crystal-field theory.

Δ *values.* To produce a quantitative theory the ligand-field splitting Δ must be known. It is obtained experimentally from the visible or ultraviolet spectrum of the complex. For a d^1 complex (e.g. $Ti(H_2O)_6^{3+}$) there is only one transition possible, $t_{2g} \rightarrow e_g{}^*$, and Δ is obtained directly from its frequency. If more electrons are present several absorption peaks are found, and though their interpretation and identification are difficult it has normally been achieved and the corresponding Δ value obtained.[19-21] For a given ligand Δ is generally found to be reasonably constant within each transition series for the same valency state, but to increase rapidly with higher valency and from the first to the later transition series†. The ligands themselves may be arranged in a spectrochemical series such that Δ for their complexes with any metal increases along the sequence.[22] For some common ligands this sequence is

$$I^- < Br^- < Cl^- < F^- < C_2H_5OH < H_2O < \text{pyridine} < NH_3$$
$$< \text{ethylene diamine} < NO_2^- < CN^-.$$

Finally, why do some complexes give a low-spin whilst others form a high-spin state? The ligand-field energy favours a low-spin

TABLE 16.5

	Loss of orbital energy in the high-spin state	Gain of exchange energy in the high-spin state	Ratio
d^4	Δ	$3J$	$\Delta/3J$
d^5	2Δ	$6J$	$\Delta/3J$
d^6	2Δ	$4J$	$\Delta/2J$
d^7	Δ	$2J$	$\Delta/2J$

state but this is opposed by a loss of exchange energy between electrons with parallel spins. The exchange energy J, between a pair of d electrons having the same spin, does not vary markedly through a given transition series and is also of the same order for each series. For octahedral complexes the position is summarized in Table 16.5. It is evident that d^6 would form a low-spin state at lower Δ values than the d^4 and d^5 configurations.

16.7. Complexes of Other Symmetries

Only octahedral complexes have so far been considered, but ligand-field theory naturally applies to complexes of all symmetries. Figure 16.7 summarizes the manner in which the ligands split the energies of d orbitals in other cases. In the absence of π bonding the lower orbitals contain the non-bonding electrons of the metal, whilst the highest energy orbitals are antibonding σ molecular orbitals. The relative energies of the orbitals are appreciated most easily in terms of the crystal-field approximation.

† For example, Δ values for hydrates of divalent metals of the first transition series are about 10,000 cm^{-1}, while those for the trivalent ions are about 18,000 cm^{-1}, and for elements in the other transition series roughly half as great again (8,000 cm$^{-1} \simeq 1$ eV).

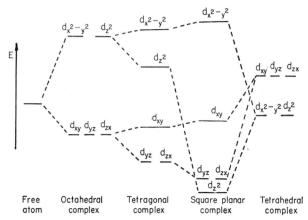

FIGURE 16.7 d orbital splitting in complexes of different symmetries.

A tetragonal prism resembles the octahedral complex very closely—the ligands situated along the z axis being at a different distance from the metal atom than are the other ligands. If they are further away then the d_{z^2}, d_{yz}, and d_{zx} orbitals will all have lower energies.

In the square-planar complex there are no ligands situated along the z axis. The $d_{x^2-y^2}$ and d_{xy} orbitals interact with the remaining ligands as in the octahedral complex, but the d_{z^2} and the degenerate d_{yz} and d_{zx} orbitals have their lobes further removed from the ligands and interact less strongly with them. Their relative energies are uncertain.

The position in tetrahedral complexes may be seen from Figure 16.8. No d orbital lobes point directly towards a ligand so the value of the splitting Δ is small. It is apparent that one lobe of

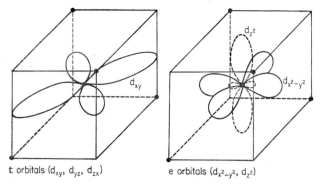

FIGURE 16.8   The orientation of d orbitals in a tetrahedral field.

each t orbital comes close to a ligand, whilst the lobes of the e orbitals bisect the angles made between pairs of ligands. The splitting is consequently the reverse of that for octahedral symmetry.

The reader is referred to the books by Orgel[1] and by Griffith,[2] or to those on inorganic chemistry, for a fuller treatment of these systems.

16.8. Further d Orbital Splitting

In addition to the factors considered under ligand-field theory, an electrostatic field can split the energies of d orbitals in two further ways. The first is a minor effect, except for heavy atoms,[23] which arises from a magnetic interaction of the spin and orbital motions of the electrons. For a single electron in the t_{2g} orbitals of an octahedral complex for example, the d_{yz} and d_{zx} orbitals have $m_l = 1$, whereas for the d_{xy} orbital m_l is twice as great and has a slightly different energy.

The second factor, known as the Jahn–Teller effect,[24] can be more important and is more interesting. One, two, four, or five electrons in the t_{2g} orbitals of an octahedral complex do not constitute a uniform electron distribution. If the single electron of a d^1 complex is in the d_{xy} orbital it would repel the four ligands in the xy plane more strongly that the two situated along the z axis. As a result the latter would form slightly shorter and stronger bonds; the perfect octahedral symmetry is lost and the degeneracy of the t_{2g} orbitals removed.

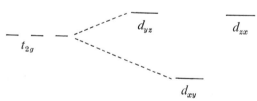

A much larger effect occurs when the two e_g orbitals hold different numbers of electrons as these have their lobes pointing directly towards the ligands. If there are more electrons in the d_{z^2} orbital than in the $d_{x^2-y^2}$, then the two ligands on the z axis are repelled more strongly than the others. The complex distorts, giving two long and four short bonds. Conversely, excess electrons in the $d_{x^2-y^2}$ orbital would result in the complex possessing four long and two short bonds. With few exceptions the experimental evidence on bond lengths indicates that four short and two long bonds are obtained, i.e. the first and third e_g electrons enter the d_{z^2} orbital.

The Jahn–Teller effect also explains small distortions in tetrahedral complexes. The t orbitals interact most strongly with the ligands (Figure 16.8), and distortions would only be expected when the distribution of their electrons is unsymmetrical, that is for 1, 2, 4, or 5, t electrons. This corresponds to d^3 and d^4 (high-spin) and to d^8 and d^9 complexes (cf. Figure 16.7). With one or four t electrons the ligands move away from the orbital possessing the odd electron, giving an elongated tetrahedron. In the other cases the tetrahedron is flattened so that the ligands are closer to the t orbital with fewer electrons than are in the other two. Both cases have been confirmed experimentally.

16.9. Unsaturated Hydrocarbon Ligands

In recent years a large number of compounds between metals, usually the transition elements, and unsaturated hydrocarbons have been prepared and characterized. The latter include ethylene, acetylene, butadiene, carbon rings of four to eight atoms, and heterocyclic systems†. In many cases, but not all, the bond lengths and absorption spectra of the hydrocarbon are not changed dramatically in forming the complex. A few typical examples will be discussed.

Olefine, Acetylene, and Butadiene Complexes

Besides being the simplest, the complexes formed with olefines were the first to be recognized, but before discussing them let us remind ourselves of the structure of ethylene (Figure 11.10). In addition to the σ bond there are two π-type molecular orbitals, a bonding one holding two electrons, and a vacant antibonding orbital. Compared with the complexes we have just been considering the occupied π orbital has a similar symmetry, with respect to the metal, as has the σ orbital of the ligands, whilst the antibonding orbital bears a strong resemblance to the unoccupied ligand π orbital. It was therefore suggested[28-30] that the bonding π electrons of the olefine form a three-centre bond with a vacant metal orbital, whilst the unoccupied π molecular orbital interacts with one of the occupied metal d orbitals. This is illustrated in Figure 16.9 for Ag^+, C_2H_4 and $[Pt\ Cl_3 \cdot C_2H_4]^-$.

In the silver complex its $5s$ orbital accepts the electrons of the bonding π molecular orbital of ethylene. This resembles a σ bond

† For summaries of their chemistry and properties see Bennett,[25] Fischer and Fritz,[26] and Guy and Shaw.[27]

but has a different symmetry and so is termed a μ orbital. Electronic charge is donated from the ethylene molecule to the metal, but much of this is thought to be returned by a second three-centre orbital formed from an occupied $4d$ orbital of Ag^+ and the vacant anti-bonding π molecular orbital of ethylene. Raman spectra and proton magnetic resonance studies[31,32] show that the double bond character

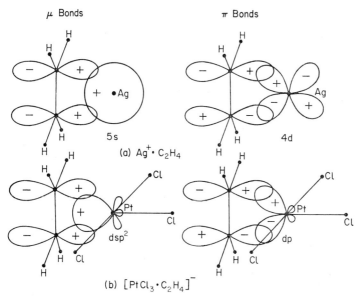

FIGURE 16.9 μ and π bonds in two ethylene complexes. (a) $Ag^+ \cdot C_2H_4$, (b) $[PtCl_3 \cdot C_2H_4]^-$.

of the olefine is not greatly changed on complexing with the Ag^+ ion. The formation of a similar complex with Br^+ has also been suggested. The most stable complexes of this form have metal ions with ten d electrons, which is consistent with the postulate of d electron donation from the ion to the olefine.

This description can be extended to $[PtCl_3 \cdot C_2H_4]^-$ and similar complexes.[33] The ion is a square complex of platinum, the mid-point of the carbon double bond occupying one of the sites but with the bond perpendicular to the $PtCl_3$ plane.[34,35] The μ bond is formed with a vacant dsp^2 hybrid orbital of the platinum, and the π bond by a d or, rather more likely, a dp hybrid as indicated in Figure 16.9b.

Acetylene forms analogous complexes but because of the de-generacy in its π orbitals (Figure 11.11) it can bond with two metal atoms, the bonds being roughly perpendicular[36] (Figure 16.10a). The C—C bond is longer than in the isolated acetylene molecule which is no longer linear. The structure of the butadiene molecule in the complex $Fe(CO)_3 \cdot C_4H_6$ also differs from that of the isolated hydrocarbon. The molecule is *cisoid*, the three C—C bond lengths being nearly equal[37] at 1·45 Å, corresponding to single bonds between sp^2 hybridized carbon atoms (Table 14.8). The carbon atoms are nearly equidistant from the iron atom. In the complex a square pyramid is formed about the iron atom by the three carbonyls

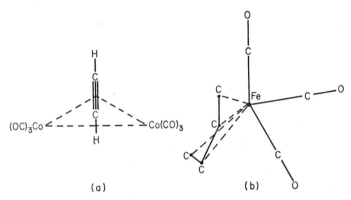

(a)   (b)

FIGURE 16.10   Structure of (a) an acetylene complex $[Co(CO)_3]_2 \cdot C_2H_2$, (b) a butadiene complex $Fe(CO)_3 \cdot C_4H_6$.

and the terminal atoms of the diene chain. It seems probable that the four π electrons of the diene complete the valence shell of the iron atom, giving the krypton structure, and that some of its $3d$ electrons back donate to the vacant antibonding π molecular orbitals of the diene.

Complexes with Cyclic Hydrocarbons

Many complexes have been made between metals and cyclic polyenes; the best known example is ferrocene, an iron atom sandwiched between two cyclopentadienyl rings, but analogous molecules involving a great range of metal atoms and unsaturated rings of many sizes have been described.

The cyclopentadienyl radical has a vacancy in its bonding π molecular orbitals and therefore has a strong tendency to form the anion $C_5H_5^-$. Electropositive elements such as the alkali, alkaline earth, and rare earth metals do in fact form essentially salt-like complexes with cyclopentadiene. Transition elements, however, form covalent complexes.

Let us consider ferrocene, dicyclopentadienyl iron, in detail. X-ray investigations[38] have proved that its configuration is a pentagonal antiprism with the iron atom equidistant from the ten carbons. The rings are staggered, but since they rotate freely at about 300°C and in $Ru(C_5H_5)_2$ are eclipsed, the staggering is unlikely to be an essential feature. There are two main concepts of the bonding.

(a) Fischer and Pfab[39] suggested that the bonding resembled that of octahedral ferrous compounds. Each cyclopentadienyl anion has three pairs of π electrons which form six coordinate bonds

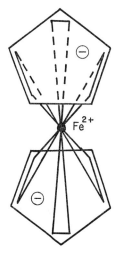

FIGURE 16.11 A description of the bonding in ferrocene, $Fe(C_5H_5)_2$.

with the central Fe^{2+} ion, distributed around it as a trigonal antiprism, Figure 16.11. This idea has been presented in terms of molecular and equivalent orbitals.[40,41]

(b) In the alternative theoretical approach[42–45] the interactions of the $3d$ and $4s$ orbitals of the iron atom with the π orbitals of the two rings are considered to give six bonding and three non-bonding molecular orbitals, all being occupied, and three unoccupied antibonding molecular orbitals. The cyclopentadienyl radical has three bonding π molecular orbitals, two of which are degenerate (Figure 17.2), and when their phases are correct, corresponding orbitals for each ring can bond with each other and with three of the d orbitals of the central metal atom. These three bonding eleven-centred orbitals, which hold six electrons between them, are illustrated in Figure 16.12. The first (Figure 16.12a) probably does not involve the d_{z^2} orbital alone but a $(3d_{z^2} + 4s)$ hybrid which

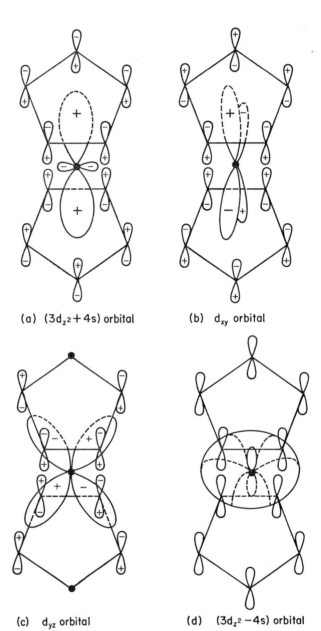

(a) $(3d_{z^2} + 4s)$ orbital

(b) d_{xy} orbital

(c) d_{yz} orbital

(d) $(3d_{z^2} - 4s)$ orbital

FIGURE 16.12 Formation of molecular orbitals in ferrocene. The orbitals of the iron atom are (a) $3d_{z^2} + 4s$ hybrid, (b) d_{xy}, (c) d_{yz}. A nodal plane passes through one carbon atom in each ring. (d) $3d_{z^2} - 4s$ hybrid. This contains a lone-pair which does not interact strongly with either carbon ring. The d_{xy} orbital (not shown) has its principle axes parallel to the rings and holds a lone-pair.

would have an even higher density close to the rings. The other hybrid ($3d_{z^2} - 4s$) is a ring-like orbital containing a lone pair of electrons well removed from the organic residues (Figure 16.12d). In addition there would be three occupied orbitals in which the phases of the wave functions of one of the two carbon rings in Figures 16.12a, b, and c are reversed. No orbitals of the central metal atom have a symmetry suitable for bonding with these, and the rings themselves are too far apart to interact strongly with each other. Their electrons simply bond the carbon atoms in the individual rings. Another three orbitals will differ from those in Figures 16.12a, b, and c in that the phases of the metal atom orbitals are reversed, giving unoccupied antibonding molecular orbitals of high energy. The remaining two d orbitals of the metal, $d_{x^2-y^2}$ and d_{xy}, have their lobes parallel to the organic rings and hold non-bonding lone-pairs.

Similar theoretical treatments apply to other mono- and di-cyclopentadienyl complexes, and both approaches may be applied to analogous compounds containing benzene rings. It is interesting to note that the C—C bonds in dibenzene chromium $Cr(C_6H_6)_2$ apparently alternate in length[46] as in a Kekulé structure. In the cyclobutadiene complex, $Ph_4C_4 \cdot Fe(CO)_3$, the C—C bonds seem to be of equal length.[47] A seven-membered cyclic polyene has an electron in an antibonding molecular orbital (Figure 17.2), so that the complex $(C_7H_7)Mo(CO)_3^+$ almost certainly contains the tropylium cation $C_7H_7^+$.

BIBLIOGRAPHICAL REFERENCES

1. Orgel, L. E., *An Introduction to Transition Metal Chemistry*, Methuen, London, 1960.
2. Griffith, J. S., *The Theory of Transition Metal Ions*, Cambridge University Press, London, 1961.
3. Griffith, J. S., and Orgel, L. E., *Quart. Rev.*, 1957, **11**, 381.
4. Sutton, L. E., *J. Chem. Educ.*, 1960, **37**, 498.
5. Orgel, L. E., *Endeavour*, 1963, **22**, 42.
6. Gillespie, R. J., and Nyholm, R. S., *Quart. Rev.*, 1957, **11**, 339.
7. Nyholm, R. S., *Quart. Rev.*, 1953, **7**, 377.
8. Selwood, P. W., *Magnetochemistry*, Interscience, New York, 1956.
9. Goodenough, J. B., *Magnetism and the Chemical Bond*, John Wiley, New York, 1963.
10. Pauling, L., *Victor Henri Memorial Volume*, Étude de la Structure Moléculaire, Desoer, Liège, 1948, p. 1.
11. Craig, D. P., Maccoll, A., Nyholm, R. S., Orgel, L. E., and Sutton, L. E., *J. Chem. Soc.*, 1954, 332.

12. Craig, D. P., and Magnusson, E. A., *J. Chem. Soc.*, 1956, 4895.
13. Cruickshank, D. J. W., Webster, B. C., and Mayers, D. F., *J. Chem. Phys.*, 1964, **40**, 3733.
14. Bethe, H., *Ann. Phys.*, 1929, **3**, 133.
15. Van Vleck, J. H., *The Theory of Electric and Magnetic Suscepti-bilities*, Oxford University Press, London, 1932.
16. Van Vleck, J. H., *Phys. Rev.*, 1932, **41**, 208.
17. Carrington, A., and Longuet-Huggins, H. C., *Quart. Rev.*, 1960, **14**, 427.
18. Owen, J., *J. Inorg. Nuclear Chem.*, 1958, **8**, 430.
19. McClure, D. S., *Solid State Phys.*, 1959, **9**, 399.
20. Hartmann, H., *J. Inorg. Nuclear Chem.*, 1958, **8**, 64.
21. Jørgensen, C. K., *Energy Levels of Complexes and Gaseous Ions*, Gjellerups Foolag, Copenhagen, 1957.
22. Tsuchida, R., *Bull. Chem. Soc. Japan*, 1938, **13**, 388, 436, 471.
23. Condon, E. U., and Shortley, G. H., *Theory of Atomic Spectra*, Cambridge University Press, London, 1951.
24. Jahn, H. A., and Teller, E., *Proc. Roy. Soc.*, 1937, A**161**, 220.
25. Bennett, M. A., *Chem. Rev.*, 1962, **62**, 611.
26. Fischer, E. O., and Fritz, H. P., *Advanc. Inorg. Chem. Radiochem.*, 1959, **1**, 55.
27. Guy, R. G., and Shaw, B. L., *Advanc. Inorg. Chem. Radiochem.*, 1962, **4**, 78.
28. Dewar, M. J. S., *Bull. Soc. Chim.*, France, 1951, **18**, C71.
29. Cotton, F. A., *J. Chem. Soc.*, 1960, 400.
30. Brown, D. A., *J. Inorg. Nuclear Chem.*, 1959, **10**, 39, 49.
31. Taufen, H. J., Murray, M. J., and Cleveland, F. F., *J. Amer. Chem. Soc.*, 1941, **63**, 3500.
32. Powell, D. B., and Sheppard, N., *J. Chem. Soc.*, 1960, 2519.
33. Chatt, J., and Duncanson, L. A., *J. Chem. Soc.*, 1953, 2939.
34. Wunderlich, J. A., and Mellor, D. P., *Acta Cryst.*, 1954, **7**, 130.
35. Wunderlich, J. A., and Mellor, D. P., *Acta Cryst.*, 1955, **8**, 57.
36. Sly, W. G., *J. Amer. Chem. Soc.*, 1959, **81**, 18.
37. Mills, O. S., and Robinson, G., *Proc. Chem. Soc.*, 1960, 421.
38. Dunitz, J. D., Orgel, L. E., and Rich, A., *Acta Cryst.*, 1956, **9**, 373.
39. Fischer, E. O., and Pfab, W., *Z. Naturf.*, 1952, **7B**, 377.
40. Ruch, E., *Z. Phys. Chem.*, Frankfurt, 1956, **6**, 356.
41. Ruch, E., *Rec. Trav. Chim.*, 1956, **75**, 638.
42. Moffit, W., *J. Amer. Chem. Soc.*, 1954, **76**, 3386.
43. Liehr, A. D., and Ballhausen, C. J., *Acta Chem. Scand.*, 1957, **11**, 207.
44. Robertson, R. E., and McConnell, H. M., *J. Phys. Chem.*, 1960, **64**, 70.
45. Dunitz, J. D., and Orgel, L. E., *J. Chem. Phys.*, 1955, **23**, 954.
46. Jellinek, F., *Nature*, 1960, **187**, 871.
47. Dodge, R. P., and Schomaker, V., *Nature*, 1960, **186**, 798.

CHAPTER 17

CONJUGATED AND AROMATIC MOLECULES

The properties which are characteristic of unsaturated systems have been ascribed to the presence of electrons in π-type orbitals. If these electrons approach close to three or more nuclei in the molecule they are said to be mobile, and if they help in bonding separate pairs of atoms the system is a conjugated one. A substantial part of the application of wave mechanics to chemistry has been devoted to describing the molecular properties associated with the presence of mobile electrons. The comparatively simple techniques of the valence bond method of perfect pairs and the Hückel molecular orbital approximation have been described in previous chapters, it is now proposed to discuss the results of calculations on some selected conjugated systems. Space, unfortunately, dictates that the treatment must be cursory, but it is hoped that the examples included will indicate both the power and the limitations of the theoretical methods.

The results are normally presented in the form of comparisons between related molecules, and naturally in doing this, the same mathematical approximations and fundamental assumptions must be made for each molecule. The approximations mentioned above, or simple elaborations of them, have been applied to an extensive range of molecules but relatively few have been considered by each of the most refined theoretical procedures available so these results will not be included.

ORGANIC MOLECULES

It might not be amiss to remind ourselves of a discussion on p. 194 where it was suggested that the molecular orbital method, because it neglects electron correlation, seriously overemphasizes conjugation in molecules which can only be represented by a single, unexcited, covalent canonical structure. Fortunately this is not so important for those compounds which possess aromatic character as the impossibility of representing them adequately by a single structure minimizes the effects of neglecting electron correlation.

17.1. Resonance and Delocalization Energies

Resonance energy, in valence bond theory, was defined as the extra stability of the molecule which arises from the most stable of the canonical structures entering into resonance with alternative structures. It is expressed in terms of the quantity J. The corresponding delocalization energy of molecular orbital theory was defined as the additional bonding energy of the molecule compared to a hypothetical state in which the π electrons are constrained to remain in isolated double bonds. It is expressed in terms of the parameter β.

For aromatic hydrocarbons the correlation between these two approaches is good with $J \simeq 1 \cdot 80 \, \beta$. There is also an excellent correlation with the empirical resonance energies obtained from heats of hydrogenation and atomization. A selection of the results[1,2] are demonstrated graphically in Figure 17.1, from which $\beta = -16$ kcal.[2]† The experimental energies have not been corrected for the distortion energy required to change the bond length or for the effects of changes in hybridization, (see p. 223). The energy is seen to be roughly proportional to the number of rings in the molecule, though a staggered arrangement is slightly more stable than a linear one (e.g. phenanthrene and anthracene). Hydrocarbons such as biphenyl have a very small conjugation energy between the rings because of their non-planar conformation; they can only be fitted into the above schemes by associating a small weight with structures in which the bond linking the rings has a double bond character, or in molecular orbital theory when a small resonance integral is assigned to this bond.

In comparison with the experimental resonance energies of aromatic molecules those of substituted olefines and polyenes are small requiring a β value of only about -6 kcal. This is in spite of the virtual absence of any distortion energy and indicates that there is little conjugation in such systems.

For non-benzenoid aromatic hydrocarbons the experimental resonance energies are again less than the values calculated with

† Somewhat greater numerical values have also been suggested (see Wheland,[3] Huckel,[4] and Magnus, Hartmann and Becker.[5]

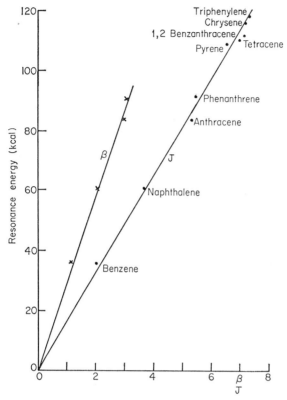

FIGURE 17.1   Resonance energies of hydrocarbons.

$\beta = -16$ kcal (Table 17.1). The discrepancy must be due to the effects of ring strain and to the small double bond character of some bonds in these molecules; a partial bond fixation is present. If a heteroatom is present the situation is further complicated by its different electronegativity and size.

The question of ring strain merits further consideration. Cyclopropane and tetraphosphorus are stable, yet have bond angles of only 60° (p. 183). In discussing orbital hybridization we saw that sp hybrids could subtend any angle from 90° to 180°, C—C bonds being stronger the greater the angle. Although planar hexagons occur in the majority of aromatic and many heterocyclic compounds, there is nothing magical associated with a bond angle close to 120°. The really fundamental feature is the stability associated with six π electrons. The cyclopentadienyl anion I with six π electrons is relatively stable for example, whereas the corresponding cation II

TABLE 17.1

Molecule		Calculated Resonance Energy (kcal)	Experimental Resonance Energy (kcal)	Difference (kcal)
Fulvene	$1 \cdot 47\beta$	23	11	12
Heptafulvene	$1 \cdot 99$	32	14	18
Fulvalene	$2 \cdot 78$	44	20	24
Heptafulvalene	$4 \cdot 00$	64	29	35
Cyclo-octatetraene	$1 \cdot 66$	27	4	23
Azulene	$3 \cdot 36$	54	31	23

which has only four π electrons is not. Likewise the cyclohepta-trienyl anion III is unstable compared with its cation IV. These facts are summarized and extended by the $4N + 2$ rule of Hückel

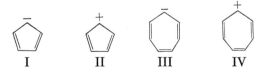

$$\text{I} \qquad \text{II} \qquad \text{III} \qquad \text{IV}$$

who concluded that coplanar single ring systems with $(4N + 2)\pi$ electrons ($N = 0, 1, 2 \ldots$) possess relative electronic stability.[6-9]

Molecular orbital theory proves that $4N + 2$ electrons are required to fill all the bonding π orbitals in the molecule. This is of greater importance than the numerical value of the delocalization energy. To illustrate this, some systems will be considered very briefly. The energies of the Hückel molecular orbitals for *planar* monocyclic rings of sp^2 hybridized carbon atoms are given by $\xi_k = 2\beta \cos 2k\pi/N$, where N is the number of atoms and $k = 0, 1, 2 \ldots N - 1$. The distribution of π electrons amongst the orbitals in the cation, radical, and anion for the first seven rings are shown in Figure 17.2.

Ethylene satisfies the $4N + 2$ rule with $N = 0$ and should be stable, showing little tendency to form either cation or anion.

The cyclopropenyl cation also satisfies the $4N + 2$ rule; the cyclopropenyl radical and anion however have electrons in anti-bonding molecular orbitals and should be progressively less stable. The parent cation has not been isolated but its triphenyl derivative V is relatively stable.[10] Diphenylcyclopropenone VIa is also remark-ably stable[11,12] and its dipole moment ($5 \cdot 08$ D) is so high for a ketone that structure VIb must make a substantial contribution to the resonance description of the molecule; it does in fact form a

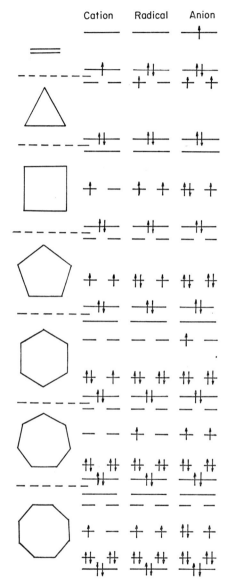

FIGURE 17.2   Hückel energies for planar rings of two to eight carbon p orbitals and the electron distribution in their cations, radicals, and anions.

stable hydrobromide salt. In contrast the triphenylcyclopropenyl

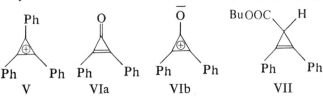

V   VIa   VIb   VII

radical has not been detected and its dimer shows no tendency to dissociate.[13] Also the ester VII exchanges its α-hydrogen for deuterium much more slowly than does a corresponding cyclopropane[14,15] ester thus demonstrating the relative instability of a cyclopropenyl anion.

Cyclobutadiene[16] has not been isolated, though it probably has a transient existence; its four π electrons do not satisfy the $4N + 2$ rule, the square conformation having two electrons in a bonding orbital and one in each of the degenerate pair of non-bonding molecular orbitals. A bent or rectangular structure would remove this degeneracy, giving two doubly occupied bonding orbitals and a lower delocalization energy, but even this system appears to be too unstable for it to be isolated.

In the cyclopentadienyl system the anion satisfies the $4N + 2$ rule, and its chemistry[17] shows it to be more stable than either the radical or cation which have unpaired bonding π electrons. Pyrrole, on the other hand, is also a five-membered ring system but with six π electrons; experiment proves that the molecule is planar[18–19] and the nitrogen therefore trigonally hybridized with two electrons in the p orbital perpendicular to the plane of the ring. It should be electronically stable. A p orbital cannot accept more than two electrons and so, although the nitrogen atom is highly electronegative, it actually donates some π electronic charge to the remainder of the ring and itself carries a partial positive charge. This is confirmed by the direction of its dipole moment.[20] This unfavourable situation would be reflected in small contributions from the ionic structures in Figure 17.3. The diagram to the right of the figure shows the charge distribution calculated by molecular orbital theory from the parameters in Table 12.3. Considering the series furan, pyrrole, and thiophen, Pauling[21] suggested that the ionic structures contribute 8, 24, and 28% respectively, the contribution increasing as the electronegativity of the heteroatom decreases.

The six-membered carbon ring in benzene typifies aromatic chemistry and is a very stable system. The situation is very similar in pyridine, quinoline, etc. (Figure 12.7), where in contrast to pyrrole the nitrogen atom supplies only one p electron to the delocalized π molecular orbitals and is able to attract electronic

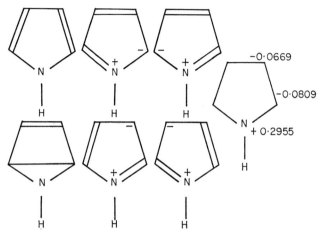

FIGURE 17.3   Canonical forms and charge distribution in pyrrole.

charge from the carbon atoms, particularly those in the *ortho* and *para* positions. In the eight π electron compounds VIII, IX, and X, two of the π electrons would be forced into antibonding molecular orbitals so that these systems should not be particularly stable.

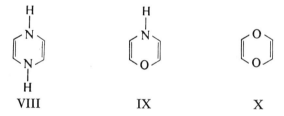

Since oxygen is more electronegative than nitrogen the antibonding tendency should be least in dioxadiene X, which does exist but behaves as an unsaturated aliphatic ether with little aromatic character. The 1,4-oxazine IX only occurs as its dibenzo-derivative, phenoxazine, and this readily loses an electron to form a radical. Alkyl and phenyl substituted 1,4-dihydropyrazines VIII are known but are readily hydrolyzed and oxidized.

With the cycloheptatrienyl or tropylium system the cation satisfies the $4N + 2$ rule, and its stability is confirmed by the ionic character of tropylium bromide $C_7H_7^+Br^-$ and by the general chemistry associated with this system.[22]

Finally cyclo-octatetraene with eight π electrons does not satisfy the $4N + 2$ rule; a planar molecule would have one electron in each of two degenerate non-bonding molecular orbitals. The

Jahn–Teller effect[23, 24] states that such a system would distort to remove this degeneracy. The hydrocarbon actually has a non-planar 'tub' conformation XI, typical olefinic character associated with isolated double bonds, and a small delocalization energy. This was

XI

originally ascribed to the strain which would be present in a planar molecule with bond angles of 135°. The radical anion and dianion formed with alkali metals in ethers, however, appear to be planar,[25,26] which indicates that cyclo-octatetraene is non-planar because of π electron instability and not because of steric strain.

Fused rings and larger non-planar ring systems do not necessarily obey the $4N + 2$ rule, but they have a strong tendency to fill each bonding π molecular orbital.

Substituents in cyclic systems, for which the attached atom has an occupied or unoccupied orbital of suitable symmetry, can participate in π electron conjugation. Let us discuss chlorobenzene, aniline, and nitrobenzene as typical examples.

The eigenvalues of chlorobenzene and of planar aniline and nitrobenzene molecules, computed from the parameters in Table 12.3, are displayed in Figure 17.4. Chlorine has a pair of electrons in an orbital perpendicular to the benzene ring, so that chlorobenzene has a total of eight electrons in π molecular orbitals. Their distribution is such that charge flows from the chlorine atom into the ring, primarily to the *ortho* and *para* positions. This is confirmed by the *ortho* and *para* directing character of the substituent, and by its dipole moment (1·59 D) being smaller than that of alkyl chlorides (1·94 D). This flow of π electron charge is small because of the high electronegativity of a chlorine atom; the carbon–chlorine σ bond is of course polar with excess electronic charge near the chlorine atom.[27,28] The corresponding valence bond description involves resonance between the structures.

Aliphatic amines are pyramidal and require something like 8 kcal/mole to produce the planar distribution of bonds about the

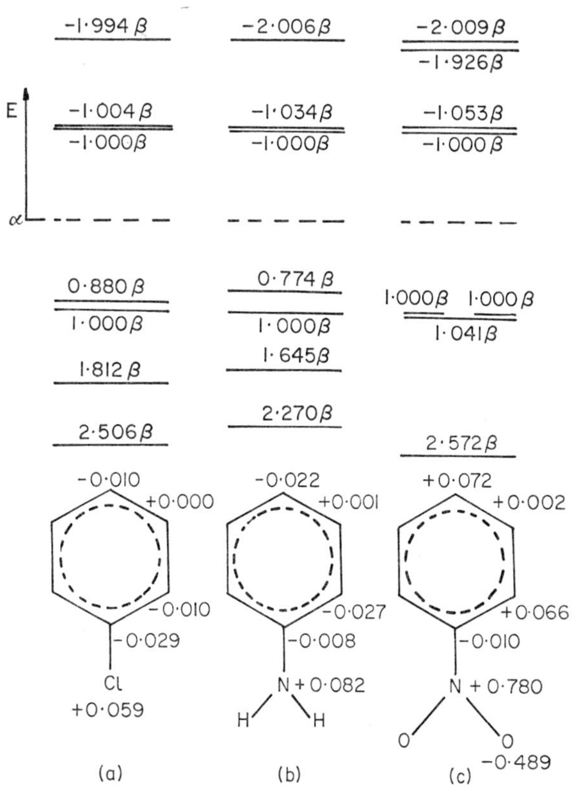

$$-1\cdot994\,\beta \qquad -2\cdot006\beta \qquad -2\cdot009\,\beta$$
$$\qquad\qquad\qquad\qquad\qquad\qquad -1\cdot926\beta$$

E

$$-1\cdot004\,\beta \qquad -1\cdot034\beta \qquad -1\cdot053\beta$$
$$-1\cdot000\beta \qquad -1\cdot000\beta \qquad -1\cdot000\,\beta$$

α

$$0\cdot880\,\beta \qquad 0\cdot774\,\beta$$
$$1\cdot000\beta \qquad 1\cdot000\beta \qquad 1\cdot000\beta \quad 1\cdot000\,\beta$$
$$1\cdot812\,\beta \qquad 1\cdot645\beta \qquad\qquad 1\cdot041\beta$$
$$2\cdot506\,\beta \qquad 2\cdot270\,\beta$$
$$\qquad\qquad\qquad\qquad\qquad 2\cdot572\,\beta$$

FIGURE 17.4 Hückel energy levels and charge distribution in (a) chloro-benzene, (b) aniline, and (c) nitrobenzene.

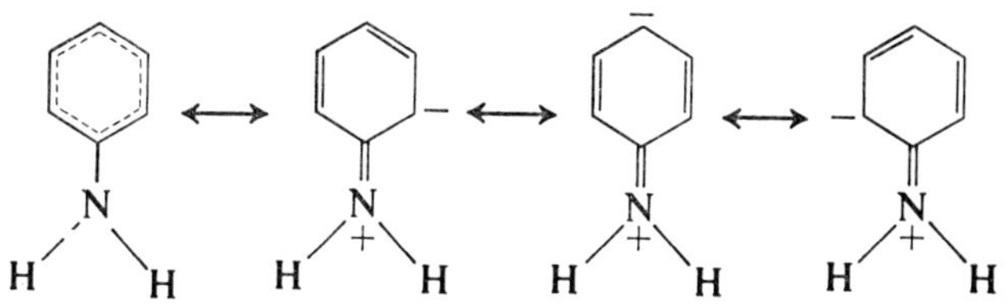

nitrogen atom,[29] which is necessary if its lone-pair electrons are to occupy a pure p orbital and thereby conjugate most efficiently with the delocalized electrons of the benzene ring. For this to occur the resulting additional delocalization energy would have to provide this 8 kcal but this is rather unlikely as it would confer a substantial positive charge on the nitrogen atom. This is clearly shown by a valence bond formulation. A compromise is reached; the nitrogen is rather flatter than in alkylamines, and the lone-pair electrons occupy a hybridized orbital which is not quite perpendicular to the plane of the ring and which therefore has a reduced overlap with its π orbitals. That some conjugation is present is demonstrated by the chemical reactivity of the molecule, by its weak basic character as some delocalization energy has to be sacrificed in forming $C_6H_5NH_3^+$, and by its electric dipole moment. In urea the oxygen atom increases the electronegativity of the carbon and the conjugation is then apparently sufficiently great to produce a planar molecule.[30-32]

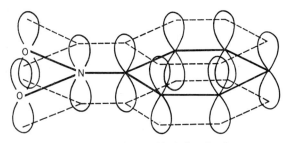

FIGURE 17.5   Atomic p orbitals in nitrobenzene.

The nitro-group is taken as a typical *meta* directing substituent. Nitrobenzene is planar and both the nitrogen and the oxygen atoms enter into conjugation with the benzene ring giving ten π electrons (Figure 17.5). The nitro-group is sometimes represented as involving a double and a coordinate bond, (cf. p. 224). The charge distribution calculated by the Hückel method is such that there is almost a unit negative charge distributed equally between the two oxygen atoms, but the corresponding positive charge on the nitrogen atom is relieved by an electron flow from the ring. This occurs particularly from the *ortho* and *para* atoms. In confirmation of this the dipole moment of nitrobenzene (4·01 D) is greater than that of alkyl nitrates (3·35 D) and the *ortho* and *para* positions react with anions.

17.2. Ultraviolet Spectra

Ultraviolet or electronic absorption spectra arise through the acquisition of just sufficient energy by the molecule to promote one of its electrons into an unoccupied higher energy orbital. In its ground electronic state the π electrons in a molecule possess the greatest energy and are consequently the most easily excited, giving the $\pi \to \pi^*$ transitions. Those involving the σ electrons ($\sigma \to \sigma^*$)

are normally of much greater energy and are only observed in the far ultraviolet. These transitions from the normal or valence state have been called $N \rightarrow V$ transitions.[33] Transitions involving the promotion of lone-pair electrons from the normal state are also usually of low energy, occurring in the visible and near ultraviolet regions. When the upper energy level is an antibonding π level the transition is termed an $N \rightarrow A$ one; if it is an antibonding σ level then the transition is classified as an $N \rightarrow B$ type. Finally, when the principal quantum number changes, the transitions are of the $N \rightarrow R$ or Rydberg type and can be of great energy, converging to a limit that gives the ionization potential of the molecule. (The ionization potentials of paraffinic hydrocarbons were mentioned in Chapter 13.)

The frequencies or energy changes associated with these electronic transitions may be correlated with wave mechanical calculations. We shall confine our discussion to $\pi \rightarrow \pi^*$ transitions. It is found that electrons cannot be promoted directly to each of the higher energy orbitals—the permitted transitions depend upon the symmetry of the molecular wave functions associated with these states—but this topic will not be considered further.

$\pi \rightarrow \pi^*$ Transitions in Polyenes

Conjugated linear polyenes with N atoms have Hückel molecular orbital energies[34,35] of

$$\xi = \alpha + 2\beta \cos \frac{k\pi}{N+1} \qquad k = 1, 2, 3 \ldots N$$

The transition frequency ν between the highest occupied molecular orbital and the lowest antibonding π^* orbital is therefore given by

$$h\nu = \Delta\xi = 2\beta \left[\cos \frac{(\frac{1}{2}N + 1)\pi}{N+1} - \cos \frac{\frac{1}{2}N\pi}{N+1} \right]$$

$$= -4\beta \sin \frac{\pi}{2(N+1)}$$

Experimentally it is found that a plot of ν against $\Delta\xi$ is reasonably linear but does not pass through the origin. This is mainly due to the neglect of electron correlation in the two states which would tend to increase their energy separation. Table 17.2 shows the frequencies calculated with $\beta = -60.5$ kcal/mole and with 54.9 kcal/mole added to allow for the origin shift.

TABLE 17.2

	λ_{max} (nm)	ν_{obs} (cm^{-1})	$\Delta \xi$	ν_{calc} (cm^{-1})
Ethylene	162·5	61,500	2·000β	62,900
Butadiene	217·0	46,080	1·236β	45,360
Hexatriene	251	39,750	0·890β	38,040
Octatriene	304	32,900	0·695β	33,920

Similar results are obtained for the carotenoids, and also for the polyene aldehydes with $\beta = -71$ kcal/mole. α,ω-Diphenylpolyenes, however, require a lower β value, probably because the different value of β for single and double bonds has been ignored. Indeed the agreement within these series is surprisingly good when it is remembered that no allowance has been made for electron correlation or for the altered geometry of the molecules in their excited states (cf. butadiene).

$\pi \to \pi^*$ *Transitions in Aromatic Hydrocarbons*

Polycyclic benzenoid hydrocarbons generally have three main absorptions which have been termed the α, β, and *para* or p bands.[36] (For transition energies see also Layton.[37]) The p band is associated with a transition from the highest occupied, to the lowest unoccupied, molecular orbital, and for many aromatic hydrocarbons

$$\nu(\text{cm}^{-1}) = 10,520 + 19,020 \, \Delta\xi \pm 300 \qquad (\beta = -54\cdot4 \text{ kcal})$$

where $\Delta\xi$ is the energy difference calculated from the Hückel approximation and expressed in terms of β. Likewise the α band involves promotion of the highest energy π electron to the second antibonding level, and the β band represents a transition between the levels on either side of the highest occupied π orbital. According to the Hückel approximation these should be degenerate, but this would be removed by a configuration interaction.[38] The approximate correlations between the experimental and theoretical results are, for the α bands,

$$\nu = 10,250 + 13,300 \, \Delta\xi \pm 500$$

and for the β bands,

$$\nu = 17,790 + 13,950 \, \Delta\xi \pm 700$$

Experimental and calculated values of the frequencies for a few hydrocarbons are given in Table 17.3.

Naturally there are exceptions to the above correlations. For example, molecules of high symmetry (e.g. benzene, triphenylene,

and coronene) do not fit in very well because of electronic interactions between nominally degenerate levels; neither do they apply
to non-benzenoid hydrocarbons. Better agreement is obtained if
the overlap integral is included in the calculations, and if explicit
allowance is made for electronic interactions a reasonable correlation
is obtained even for non-benzenoid hydrocarbons.[39]

TABLE 17.3

Hydrocarbon	Frequency (10^{-2} cm^{-1})					
	p Band		α Band		β Band	
	Obs.	Calc.	Obs.	Calc.	Obs.	Calc.
Benzene	484	486	379	368	559	457
Naphthalene	347	337	318	318	452	404
Phenanthrene	340	336	290	285	392	370
3,4 benzphenanthrene	317	321	269	266	356	350
Triphenylene	349	365	292	288	385	379
Anthracene	264	251	—	—	397	375
Tetraphene	278	277	260	257	345	341
Pentaphene	279	272	237	230	316	312
Tetracene	212	217	—	—	365	328
Pentacene	174	188	234	242	323	295
Coronene	293	310	234	246	328	328
Pyrene	297	275	269	278	365	363
1,2 benzpyrene	260	246	248	258	337	341
4,5 benzpyrene	302	294	258	263	346	347
Fluoranthene	279	293	—	—	349	333
1,2 benzfluoranthrene	234	239	276	275	325	313
2,3 benzfluoranthene	286	291	271	280	332	326
Chrysene	313	303	278	277	375	363
1,2 benzchrysene	299	308	270	268	350	351
5,6 benzchrysene	312	314	259	256	342	339

Sufficient evidence has now been quoted to show that the N → V
electronic spectra of hydrocarbons may be correlated with the
calculated energies of the π molecular orbitals in molecules; the
correlations are naturally improved by more elaborate computations,
but they always require an empirical value for the resonance integral
β. Because of the approximations made in the analysis the numerical
value of β differs somewhat from one series of molecules to another,
and it is not surprising that there is no agreement with the value
obtained from delocalization energies, since this involves some
completely different assumptions.

From Figure 17.2 it will be observed that carbonium ions,

carbanions, and radicals of the same system do not always have their highest energy π electrons in the same molecular orbital, so that their transition frequencies may differ considerably.

In principle the ultraviolet $N \rightarrow V$ transitions in molecules containing heteroatoms can also be calculated from the orbital energies obtained by the Hückel method, provided the parameters for the coulombic integrals of heteroatoms (Table 12.3) are employed. Conversely, the observed frequencies may be used to obtain these parameters. No extensive correlation has been attempted along these lines.

For more detail the reader is referred to books on ultraviolet spectra and to the relevant chapters in the books by Pullman and Pullman[1] and by Streitwieser.[17] Before concluding, we might note that the infrared stretching frequencies of carbonyl compounds have been correlated with their bond order,[40–44] and N—H frequencies with the electron density on the nitrogen atom.[45]

17.3. Electric Dipole Moments

In compounds which possess a conjugated system of π electrons it is customary to dissect their total electric dipole moment into components from these electrons and those from the σ bonds and lone-pair electrons. This procedure ignores interactions between the different components. The σ bond moments of molecules were considered in Section 14.2. The contribution from the π electrons may be estimated from the net charges associated with individual atoms in the molecule, assuming that these are situated at the actual nuclei of the respective atoms.

The Hückel molecular orbital approximation shows that each carbon atom in an alternant hydrocarbon is uncharged and there can be no π electron contribution to their total dipole moment. This is not the case with non-alternant hydrocarbons and their calculated π moments are generally in the range 3–7 D. Since their σ bond moments are small and the experimental values of the dipole moments of hydrocarbons are generally less than 1·5 D, the simple Hückel theory seriously overemphasizes π moments. Various elaborations of this theory reduce the calculated π moments but not to the extent of making them consistent with experimental results. There are two main reasons for this. Firstly, the variation procedure adopted in the Hückel approach minimizes the energy of the molecule and thereby gives reasonable eigenvalues. The charge densities of the carbon atoms however depend upon the eigenfunctions which are not obtained with the same accuracy.

Secondly, the representation of the π electron charge density distribution by a series of point charges at the atomic nuclei is inadequate.

Many calculations of the π electron contribution to the dipole moments of heteroatom compounds are available. Naturally they depend upon the parameters chosen for the coulombic integrals of the heteroatoms, and unless values smaller than those suggested in Table 12.3 are utilized the π moment is again normally too large. It may be worth while pointing out that in some compounds, such as the nitrogen heterocyclics, the contribution of the σ bonds and lone-pair electrons to the resultant dipole moment is far from being firmly established.

In spite of the unreliability of theoretical values they can be helpful when comparing the dipole moments of different compounds.

17.4. Polarographic Potentials

Many organic compounds give a reproducible half-wave potential at a dropping mercury electrode, corresponding to the reduction $R + e \rightarrow R^-$. They are given by the expression

$$\varepsilon_{1/2} = \frac{\Delta F^\circ}{\mathscr{F}} - \frac{RT}{\mathscr{F}} \ln \frac{D_R}{D_{R^-}}$$

where $\mathscr{F}$ is the faraday and D_R and D_{R^-} the diffusion constants of R and R^- respectively. For a series of hydrocarbons the last term is usually small. ΔF° is the free energy change in the above reaction.

$$\Delta F^\circ = (F_R{}^\circ)_{aq} - (F_{R^-}{}^\circ)_{aq} + (F_{electron})_{Hg}$$

The free energy difference between R and R^- will be largely dependent upon the electron affinity of R and the relative solvation energies of R and R^-. The former should be proportional to the energy of the first unoccupied π molecular orbital in the molecule, and though the solvation term probably decreases as the hydrocarbon becomes larger, a proportionality between the energy of the orbital and the half-wave reduction potential would be anticipated. An excellent correlation has in fact been found for a number of essentially planar hydrocarbons,[46,47] the effective value of the resonance integral β being about -55 kcal/mole. Similar correlations have been observed for carbonyl compounds,[48] substituted styrenes, and ethylenes. Hoijtink[49] has also found an analogous relationship for polarographic oxidation potentials at a rotating platinum electrode, employing in this case the calculated energy for the highest occupied molecular orbital.

Sufficient has been said to demonstrate that many physical properties of unsaturated compounds can be correlated with the results of relatively simple molecular orbital calculations. Other properties, such as bond lengths (Section 14.3), ionization potentials, electron spin resonance, and pure quadrupole resonance could be added to the list. The majority of these semi-empirical results apply to hydrocarbons, partly because heteroatom compounds require additional parameters. In view of the differing assumptions which have to be made to interpret the various physical properties, the values of these parameters, including that of the integral β, would not be expected to be universally applicable to each phenomenon.

17.5. A Simple Molecular Orbital Treatment of Alternant Hydrocarbons

We shall conclude this discussion of conjugation in organic molecules with an outline (without proof) of a very simple molecular orbital approximation†. It is less accurate than a Hückel-type calculation but is included because of its extreme simplicity and the speed with which the necessary calculations may be made.

It is evident from the examples already considered that when overlap integrals are neglected, the energies of the π molecular orbitals in an *alternant* hydrocarbon are symmetrically disposed about the energy $\xi = \alpha$. For an even number of carbon atoms the orbitals occur in pairs with energies $\xi = \alpha \pm k\beta$. Exactly half of them (the bonding molecular orbitals) contain two electrons each and the net charge on each atom is unity. With an odd number of atoms there is also a single non-bonding orbital with energy α. In a radical this would hold a single electron and there is again a uniform charge distribution over all the conjugated atoms. The energy levels for these systems are illustrated in Figure 17.6. The above statements have been proved in the general case.[51]

A uniform charge distribution means that the molecules are non-polar, unlike non-alternant hydrocarbons which have finite dipole moments. If one electron is lost from an alternant system the charge distribution in the resulting cation would correspond to the distribution of the missing electron. In fact the charge on each atom would be

$$q_i = 1 - c_i^2 \qquad \text{(cf. Section 12.2)}$$

where c_i is the coefficient for this atom in the molecular wave function of the orbital from which the electron has been removed. Likewise,

---

† For a summary of some applications of this method see Dewar.[50]

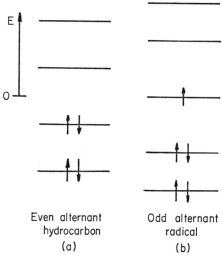

Even alternant
hydrocarbon
(a)

Odd alternant
radical
(b)

FIGURE 17.6 Energy levels in hydrocarbons. (a) An even alternant of four carbon atoms and (b) an odd alternant of five carbon atoms.

when an electron is gained to form an anion

$$q_i = 1 + c_i^2$$

In the case of the odd-alternant system, whether the electron is lost or gained the coefficient would be for the same orbital—the non-bonding molecular orbital. These coefficients may be obtained with great ease as Longuet-Higgins has shown[52] that for the non-bonding orbital

$$\sum c_i \beta_{ij} = 0$$

the summation being taken over all the atoms j directly bonded to one particular atom i. If all the resonance integrals with this atom β_{ij} are the same, as is reasonable in an aromatic system, then

$$\sum c_i = 0 \qquad (17.1)$$

Consequently for this one orbital in an odd-alternant hydrocarbon, the coefficients of either the starred or the unstarred atoms must be zero. The more numerous, or active, set has the non-vanishing coefficients. For example, in Figure 17.7a the active atoms in the 1-naphthylmethyl system are starred. If the coefficient of C_6 in the non-bonding molecular orbital is $+a$, then from equation (17.1) the corresponding coefficients of the other atoms must be as in Figure 17.7b. Normalization gives

$$(a)^2 + (-a)^2 + (2a)^2 + (-2a)^2 + (3a)^2 + (-a)^2 = 1 \text{ or } a = 1/\sqrt{20}$$

and the charge distribution in its anion or cation must therefore
be as in Figure 17.7c. The final structure (Figure 17.7d) shows the
corresponding charge distribution for the other isomer. Naturally
these charges are positive in the cation and negative in the anion.

The great merits of this approach are not apparent until it is
extended to estimate the change in π electron energy when two

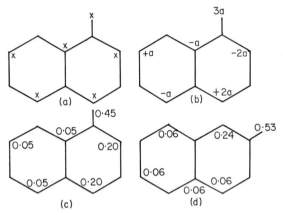

FIGURE 17.7   Naphthylmethyl systems (see text).

separate systems R and S unite to form R—S, e.g.

$$CH_3\bullet + \quad \rightarrow \quad + 2H_2$$

R   S   R—S

Dewar[53,54] employed a perturbation method for this calculation.
Normally a second-order perturbation has to be employed and it
leads to several important qualitative generalizations which could
provide a basis for theoretical organic chemistry; such as the
charge distribution and energy of unsaturated hydrocarbons and the
effects upon these of introducing substituents or heteroatoms. One
result which might be quoted is the *approximate* charge distribution
which results when a heteroatom is introduced into an even alternant
hydrocarbon. If the heteroatom were removed an odd alternant
hydrocarbon would be left; the relative charges on its atoms from
an electron in its non-bonding molecular orbital can be obtained as
indicated above and these relative charges are approximately the
same as in the parent hetero-molecule. The actual relationship
between them is

$$q_i \simeq 1 - \frac{c_i^2 \alpha}{|\sum c_j| \beta}$$

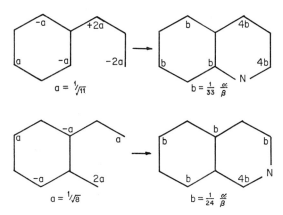

FIGURE 17.8   Charge distribution in quinoline and isoquinoline.

where the summation is over the atoms originally attached to the heteroatom. This is illustrated in Figure 17.8.

When R and S each have an orbital of the same energy, a first order splitting of this level occurs in forming R—S. Consider the combination of a methyl radical ($\xi = \alpha$) with the non-bonding orbital ($\xi = \alpha$) of an odd-alternant hydrocarbon (Figure 17.9). The change in energy of the two electrons in these degenerate orbitals is

$$\Delta\xi = 2\beta(\sum c_j) \tag{17.2}$$

where the summation is of the coefficients of the atoms to which the methyl radical becomes linked. Consider the formation of

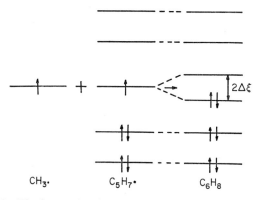

FIGURE 17.9   The interaction between a methyl radical and an alternant hydrocarbon.

benzene from the pentadiene radical.

The energy change when the open-chain hexatriene is converted into benzene is

$$4\beta a - 2\beta a = 2\beta a = 2\beta/\sqrt{3}$$

and this may be regarded as the delocalization energy of benzene. Likewise for naphthalene

The delocalization energy is $4\beta a = 4\beta/\sqrt{5}$, which is greater than for benzene but is not twice as great. The nonatetraenyl radical could also give rise to azulene as follows

but the delocalization energy of $2\beta a = 2\beta/\sqrt{5}$ is only half that of naphthalene. Finally we might consider cyclo-öctatetraene.

The 'delocalization energy' is negative! The planar cyclo-octatetraene molecule does not exist, and the puckered molecule displays little conjugation.

An important application of this method is to the rates of chemical reactions, these will be considered in the next chapter.

INORGANIC MOLECULES

Conjugation is not a prerogative of organic molecules, though there are many fewer examples amongst purely inorganic compounds. The best known case is borazole in which there is π bonding closely similar to that in benzene. It is interesting to compare this molecule with the phosphonitrilic and 'thiazyl' groups of compounds, in which alternate atoms have p and d atomic orbitals with which to form delocalized molecular orbitals. Unsaturated, cyclic inorganic molecules are known containing B, N, P, O, and S atoms. Borazole and the phosphonitrilic chlorides will be discussed to illustrate the wave mechanical approach to conjugation in inorganic chemistry.

17.6. Borazole $B_3N_3H_3$

Borazole, also known as 'inorganic benzene', is a planar hexagonal molecule XII, isoelectronic with benzene and possessing a constant

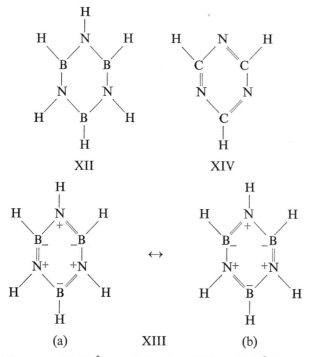

B—N distance of 1·44 Å round the ring. This is 0·14 Å less than for a normal B—N single bond. Each ring atom has sp^2 hybridized

orbitals which are employed in forming the σ bond skeleton of the molecule. In addition, each nitrogen has two electrons in a pure p orbital perpendicular to the plane of the ring, whilst each boron atom has a similar vacant p orbital. These six atomic p orbitals form six delocalized molecular orbitals analogous to those of benzene (p. 200), but differing in detail since the boron and nitrogen atoms have different electronegativities and coulombic integrals.[55] The π electrons which fill the three orbitals of lowest energy are more likely to be found near nitrogen than boron atoms, but some charge does flow from nitrogen to boron. This is very apparent from the valence bond description of borazole, which involves a resonance between XII and the Kekulé forms XIII (a) and (b).

Boron–nitrogen bonds also occur in other cyclic compounds,[56] an extreme example being boron nitride $(BN)_n$, which exists in both graphitic and diamond forms.[57,58] $(BMe)_3O_3$ is similar to borazole, an oxygen atom replacing each N—H group, but in triazine $(CH)_3N_3$ (XIV) each ring atom supplies one electron for the delocalized molecular orbitals so that its structural resemblance to benzene is even closer.

17.7. Phosphonitrilic Chlorides $(PCl_2N)_n$

The best known phosphonitrilic chloride is the trimer XV, but phosphorus–nitrogen rings of up to thirty four atoms are known, and so are polycyclic and linear molecules. The trimer has a constant

XV

P—N bond length of 1·59 Å but the ring is not quite planar in the solid state, though it probably is in the vapour phase.[59–61] The corresponding fluoride and also the tetrameric fluoride have been reported to be planar, whereas analogous nitrogen–sulphur rings in $(NSCl)_3$, $(NSOCl)_3$, and $(NSF)_4$ are slightly puckered,[62–64] and in the last-named molecule, the N—S bonds alternate in length. Larger rings are naturally non-planar. There is evidently variation in the extent and the strength of the delocalized orbitals present in these molecules.

Consider the trimeric chloride XV. X-ray analysis shows that the phosphorus atoms undergo tetrahedral sp^3 hybridization, leaving one electron in a $3d$ orbital. The sp^2 hybridized nitrogen has a pair

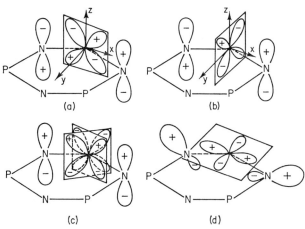

FIGURE 17.10   N($2p$)—P($3d$) bonding in a phosphonitrilic chloride (see text).

of electrons in one of its hybrids in the plane of the ring, and one electron in a pure p orbital perpendicular to the ring. There are, therefore, six electrons not involved in forming the σ bond skeleton of the molecule which are held in π molecular orbitals constructed from the phosphorus $3d$ and nitrogen $2p$ orbitals. Normally $3d$ orbitals are considered too large and diffuse to form satisfactory π bonds with $2p$ orbitals of neighbouring atoms but if highly electronegative ligands are attached to the atom (the chlorines in the above case) these orbitals contract and a $3d$–$2p$ bond with π symmetry is then possible.

Craig[65,66] considered the d_{xz} and d_{yz} orbitals to be orientated as in Figure 17.10a and b respectively. These would be affected differently by the ligands, and Craig concluded that the interaction of the d_{yz} orbital of the phosphorus with the p_z orbital on the adjacent nitrogens may be neglected. The d_{xz} orbital can only form a bonding orbital with both its adjacent nitrogens if their p_z orbitals are of opposite phase (Figure 17.10a). This delocalization could be extended round the ring, but the requirement of alternating phase on the nitrogen atoms precludes the formation of a completely bonding molecular orbital unless there are an even number of nitrogen and of phosphorus atoms in the ring. In the trimer, the lowest energy level would be doubly degenerate, followed by a single level—each occupied by two electrons in the ground electronic state, (cf. benzene). According to this description the ring would have to be planar, or nearly planar, for maximum overlapping in the π orbitals.

Dewar et al.[67] did not consider it justifiable to ignore the d_{yz} orbital and suggested that if they were orientated as in Figure 17.10c three-centre delocalized orbitals, each containing two electrons, could be formed by one d orbital from two phosphorus atoms and the intervening nitrogen p_z orbital. The other phosphorus d orbital would then form a three-centre orbital with the nitrogen and phosphorus atoms on its other side, giving delocalized orbitals extending over P_1—N_2—P_3, P_3—N_4—P_5, and P_5—N_6—P_1. The interaction between these orbitals would be slight and there would be little conjugation and no aromatic character in the molecule. Further, provided the P—N—P groups remain planar, the ring could be bent slightly at the phsophorus atoms and, by analogy with the cycloparaffins, this would be expected to occur.

In a reconsideration of the bonding in the whole group of phosphonitrilic and 'thiazyl' compounds, Craig and Paddock[68] suggested that four d orbitals could enter into π bonding—d_{xz} and d_{yz} as before, and d_{xy} and $d_{x^2-y^2}$ in the plane of the ring with the lone-pair electrons of the nitrogen, (Figure 17.10d). The extent to which each is involved is sensitive to the nature of the atoms forming the ring, their ligands, and the size of the ring; localized π bonds between d and p orbitals may be formed as in $(NSF)_4$ with its alternating N—S bond lengths, three-centre orbitals, or a more extensive delocalization as must occur in the planar hexagonal rings. The strength of the π bonding in turn controls the flexibility, planarity, conjugation, and aromatic character of the molecule. (The d_{z^2} orbital is not thought to participate in bonding in these systems because its main lobes are not directed towards the p orbital of the nitrogen and the symmetry of its 'smoke-ring' is unsuitable.)

BIBLIOGRAPHICAL REFERENCES

1. Pullman, B., and Pullman, A., Les Théories Electroniques de la Chimie Organique, Masson, Paris, 1952, p. 226.
2. Wheland, G. W., Resonance in Organic Chemistry, John Wiley, New York, 1955, p. 98.
3. Wheland, G. W., J. Chem. Phys., 1934, 2, 474.

4. Hückel, E., *Z. Elektrochem.*, 1937, **43**, 752.
5. Magnus, A., Hartmann, H., and Becker, F., *Z. Phys. Chem.*, 1951, **197**, 75.
6. Hückel, E., *Z. Phys.*, 1931, **70**, 204.
7. Hückel, E., *Z. Phys.*, 1932, **76**, 628.
8. Hückel, E., *Z. Elektrochem.*, 1937, **43**, 752.
9. Frost, A. A., and Musulin, B., *J. Chem. Phys.*, 1953, **21**, 572.
10. Breslow, R., and Yuan, C., *J. Amer. Chem. Soc.*, 1958, **80**, 5991.
11. Breslow, R., Haynie, R., and Mirra, J., *J. Amer. Chem. Soc.*, 1959, **81**, 247.
12. Vol'pin, M. E., Koreshkov, Y. D., and Kursanov, D. N., *Izvest. Akad. Nauk, S.S.S.R., Otdel Khim. Nauk*, 1959, 560.
13. Breslow, R., and Gal, P., *J. Amer. Chem. Soc.*, 1959, **81**, 4747.
14. Roberts, J. D., Streitwieser, A., and Regan, C. M., *J. Amer. Chem. Soc.*, 1952, **74**, 4579.
15. Breslow, R., and Battiste, C. M., *Chem. and Ind.*, 1958, 1143.
16. Baker, W., and McOmie, J. F. W., *Non-benzenoid Aromatic Compounds* (Ed. Ginsburg, D.), Interscience, New York, 1959, p. 43.
17. Streitwieser, A., *Molecular Orbital Theory for Organic Chemists*, John Wiley, 1961, p. 269.
18. Wilcox, W. S., and Goldstein, J. H., *J. Chem. Phys.*, 1952, **20**, 1656.
19. Bak, B., Christensen, D., Hansen, L., and Rastrup-Anderson, J., *J. Chem. Phys.*, 1956, **24**, 720.
20. Kofod, H., Sutton, L. E., and Jackson, J., *J. Chem. Soc.*, 1952, 1467.
21. Pauling, L., *The Nature of the Chemical Bond*, Cornell University Press, Ithaca, N.Y., 1960.
22. Nozoe, T., *Non-benzenoid Aromatic Compounds* (Ed. Ginsburg, D.), Interscience, New York, 1959, p. 339.
23. Jahn, H. A., and Teller, E., *Proc. Roy. Soc.*, 1937, A**161**, 220.
24. Clinton, W. L., and Rice, B., *J. Chem. Phys.*, 1959, **30**, 542.
25. Katz, T. J., and Strauss, H. L., *J. Chem. Phys.*, 1960, **32**, 1873.
26. Katz, T. J., *J. Amer. Chem. Soc.*, 1960, **82**, 3784.
27. Coulson, C. A., and Longuet-Higgins, H. C., *Proc. Roy. Soc.*, 1947, A**191**, 39.
28. Matsen, F. A., *J. Amer. Chem. Soc.*, 1950, **72**, 5243.
29. Kincaird, J. F., and Henriques, F. C., *J. Amer. Chem. Soc.*, 1940, **62**, 1474.
30. Waldron, R. D., and Badger, R. M., *J. Chem. Phys.*, 1950, **18**, 566.
31. Vaughan, P., Donohue, J., *Acta Cryst.*, 1952, **5**, 530.
32. Andrew, E. R., and Hyndman, D., *Disc. Faraday Soc.*, 1955, **19**, 195.
33. Mulliken, R. S., *J. Chem. Phys.*, 1955, **23**, 397.
34. Coulson, C. A., and Longuet-Higgins, H. C., *Proc. Roy. Soc.*, 1947, A**192**, 16.
35. Frost, A. A., and Musulin, B., *J. Chem. Phys.*, 1953, **21**, 572.
36. Clar, E., *Aromatische Kohlenwasserstoffe*, Springer-Verlag, Berlin, 1952.
37. Layton, E. M., *J. Mol. Spectrosc.*, 1960, **5**, 181.
38. Moffitt, W. E., *J. Chem. Phys.*, 1954, **22**, 320.
39. Pariser, R., *J. Chem. Phys.*, 1956, **25**, 1112.

40. Coulson, C. A., and Longuet-Higgins, H. C., *Proc. Roy. Soc.*, 1948, A**193**, 456.
41. Berthier, G., Pullman, B., and Poutis, J., *J. Chim. Phys.*, 1952, **49**, 367.
42. Estellés, I., and Alonso, J. I. F., *Anal. Real. Soc. Espan. de Fis. y Quim.*, 1954, B**50**, 151.
43. Josien, M. L., and Deschamps, J., *J. Chim. Phys.*, 1955, **52**, 213.
44. Baudet, J., Berthier, G., and Pullman, B., *J. Chim. Phys.*, 1957, **54**, 282.
45. Mason, S. F., *J. Chem. Soc.*, 1958, 3619.
46. Hoijtink, G. J., *Rec. Trav. Chim.*, 1955, **74**, 1525.
47. Balk, P., de Bruijn, S., and Hoijtink, G. J., *Rec. Trav. Chim.*, 1957, **76**, 860.
48. Schmid, R. W., and Heilbronner, E., *Helv. Chim. Acta*, 1954, **37**, 1453.
49. Hoijtink, G. J., *Rec. Trav. Chim.*, 1958, **77**, 555.
50. Dewar, M. J. S., *Progress in Organic Chemistry* (Ed. Cook, J. W.), Butterworths, London, 1953, **2**, 1.
51. Coulson, C. A., and Rushbrooke, G. S., *Proc. Camb. Phil. Soc.*, 1940, **36**, 193.
52. Longuet-Higgins, H. C., *J. Chem. Phys.*, 1950, **18**, 265, 275, 283.
53. Dewar, M. J. S., *J. Chem. Soc.*, 1950, 2329.
54. Dewar, M. J. S., *J. Amer. Chem. Soc.*, 1952, **74**, 3341–3363.
55. Davies, D. W., *Trans. Faraday Soc.*, 1960, **56**, 1713.
56. Dewar, M. J. S., Kubba, V. P., and Pettit, R., *J. Chem. Soc.*, 1958, 3073.
57. Taylor, R., and Coulson, C. A., *Proc. Phys. Soc.*, 1952, A**65**, 834.
58. Kleinman, L., and Phillips, J. C., *Phys. Rev.*, 1960, **117**, 460.
59. Liquori, A. M., Pompa, F., and Ripamonti, A., *XVIIth Int. Congr. Pure Appl. Chem.*, Munich, 1959.
60. Pompa, F., and Ripamonti, A., *Ric. Sci.*, 1959, 29, 1516.
61. Chapman, A. C., and Paddock, N. L., *J. Chem. Soc.*, 1962, 635.
62. Becher, H. J., and Seel, F., *Z. Anorg. Chem.*, 1960, 305, 148.
63. McGeachin, H. McD., and Tromans, F. R., *J. Chem. Soc.*, 1961, 4777.
64. Wiegers, G. A., and Vos, A., *Proc. Chem. Soc.*, 1962, 387.
65. Craig, D. P., *Chem. Soc. Special Publ.* No. 12, 1958, p. 343.
66. Craig, D. P., *J. Chem. Soc.*, 1959, 997.
67. Dewar, M. J. S., Lucken, E. A. C., and Whitehead, M. A., *J. Chem. Soc.*, 1960, 2423.
68. Craig, D. P., and Paddock, N. L., *J. Chem. Soc.*, 1962, 4118.

CHAPTER 18

THE RATES OF CHEMICAL REACTIONS

Two prime objectives in theoretical chemistry are to explain why a chemical reaction takes place, and then to predict its rate. The former problem involves the application of thermodynamics to the ground state energies of molecules; we have seen already how wave mechanics approaches the tasks of first predicting their structures and then calculating their energies. The speed of a chemical reaction, however, involves the energy difference between the ground and activated states of molecules. This problem is discussed in the present chapter.

Two aspects will be considered. Firstly, the wave mechanical contribution to the calculation of the absolute rate of a reaction will be discussed, and then how the relative rates of similar organic reactions depend upon the exact nature of the organic molecules.

ABSOLUTE RATE THEORY

18.1. Basic Postulates

In the absolute rate theory of chemical reaction[1] it is postulated that the reactants A and B exist in equilibrium with an activated complex AB* of greater energy. The complex can either break down to produce the products P, or revert to the original reactants.

$$A + B \overset{K}{\rightleftharpoons} AB^* \longrightarrow P$$

It is further postulated that the formation of the products is slow compared with the rate at which the complex is formed. Consequently the equilibrium can be considered to be maintained at all times.

The rate of reaction may be expressed in any of the following ways.

$$\text{Rate} = \frac{dn_P}{dt} = -\frac{dn_A}{dt} = -\frac{dn_B}{dt}$$

$$= kn_A n_B$$

$$= \nu n_{AB}{}^*,$$

$$= \nu K n_A n_B$$

$$= \nu n_A n_B \frac{Q_{AB}{}^*}{Q_A Q_B} \exp\left(-\frac{\Delta E_0}{RT}\right)$$

$$= n_A n_B \frac{k_0 T}{h} \frac{Q^\dagger}{Q_A Q_B} \exp\left(-\frac{\Delta E_0}{RT}\right)$$

The first line gives the experimental measurement of the rate of reaction in terms of the changes in number of molecules n with time t. The quantity k is the velocity, or specific rate, constant expressing the proportionality between the measured rate of reaction and the product of the reactant concentrations. In the third line the rate is expressed as the product of the frequency ν at which the activated complex breaks down to give the products and the number of these complexes present at any time. The latter cannot be measured experimentally but may be written as the product of a thermo-dynamic equilibrium constant K and the reactant concentrations. This assumes that the complexes break down slowly compared with the rate at which the equilibrium is established. This restriction is satisfied in most reactions between organic molecules but, in some instances, a steady state treatment is more appropriate. Statistical theory shows that K can be calculated from the partition functions Q of the complex and reactants, and the energy ΔE_0 of the complex relative to that of the reactants when all are in their ground states. One factor in the partition function of the complex involves the vibration frequency of a very weak bond, corresponding to transla-tion along the reaction coordinate (see below) leading to formation of the product. It gives rise to the factor $k_0 T/h\nu$, where k_0 is the Boltzmann gas constant and ν has been identified as the frequency of breakdown of the complexes into product. When this is extracted from $Q_{AB}{}^*$ the remaining terms in the partition function will be denoted by $Q^\dagger$. In principle, partition functions can be computed from spectroscopic and other data, but this requires a detailed model of the structure of the activated complex. In practice, numerical values of this factor are less reliable for large molecules and in condensed phases.

The above equations may be rearranged to give expressions for the velocity constant k.

$$k = \nu K = \frac{k_0 T}{h} \frac{Q^\dagger}{Q_A Q_B} \exp\left(-\frac{\Delta E_0}{RT}\right)$$

The equilibrium constant K can also be related to the free energy of formation ΔF of the complex, and hence to the associated changes in entropy and heat content.

$$k = \nu K = \nu \exp\left(-\frac{\Delta F}{RT}\right)$$

$$= \nu \exp\left(\frac{\Delta S}{R}\right) \exp\left(-\frac{\Delta H}{RT}\right)$$

$$= \frac{k_0 T}{h} \exp\left(\frac{\Delta S^\dagger}{R}\right) \exp\left(-\frac{\Delta H}{RT}\right)$$

Where $\Delta S^\dagger$ differs from the entropy of activation ΔS by the extraction of one vibrational factor. Comparing these expressions for k it is evident that the ratio of the partition functions may be identified with an entropy change in forming the activated complex.

The equations are formally similar to the famous expression of Arrhenius,[2]

$$k = A \exp\left(-\frac{\Delta E}{RT}\right)$$

The factor A, known as the frequency factor, is not markedly dependent upon temperature, but the exponential term changes rapidly as the temperature is altered. The energy of activation ΔE may also change slowly with temperature, like ΔH but unlike ΔE_0.

18.2. The Frequency Factor A

The classical collision theory of reaction rates maintained that the Arrhenius factor A should not vary greatly from one bimolecular reaction to another. This was contrary to experiment and to the subsequent treatment in terms of partition functions or entropy changes, both of which indicated that it could alter by several orders of magnitude. Normally the larger the reactant species the smaller the value of A. In elementary gas phase reactions considerable success has been achieved in calculating the value of A from partition functions, but generally this is not possible for more complex species in solution. The *change* in the frequency factor between two similar reactions can still be analyzed in terms of

11

changes in the component factors which make up the complete expression for the partition function factor.

In organic chemistry most interest is attached to the relative rates of very similar reactions rather than to the absolute rate of a particular reaction. Why does a particular reagent attack one carbon atom in a molecule more rapidly than it attacks all the other atoms and why does it attack one molecule more readily than an analogous molecule? In discussing these problems it is generally assumed that for similar reactions the relationship between the structure of the complex and those of the reactants is similar in each case, so that the frequency factors for the different reactions are almost identical. This is the same as saying that the partition function factor or the entropy of activation is the same in each case. Making this assumption for two similar reactions

$$\frac{k}{k'} = \exp\left(-\frac{\Delta E - \Delta E'}{RT}\right)$$

or

$$\ln\frac{k}{k'} = \frac{\Delta E' - \Delta E}{RT}$$

If the frequency terms differed by a factor of 10, the natural logarithm of the ratio of the rate constants would be in error by about 2·3 units. It is unrealistic to expect this equation to be completely reliable. Nevertheless it does emphasize the overriding importance of changes in the energy of activation. Virtually all theoretical discussions of the relative rates of similar organic reactions involve estimating $\Delta E' - \Delta E$, the difference between the activation energies of the two reactions. The methods will be considered in the second part of this chapter. First, the absolute calculation of the energy of activation of an elementary reaction will be discussed.

18.3. The Energy of Activation

For simplicity the reaction between an atom X and a diatomic molecule YZ will be considered, though the broad principles of the following account apply to reactions of any complexity.†

$$X\cdot + Y{-}Z \rightarrow X\cdots Y\cdots Z \rightarrow X{-}Y + \cdot Z$$

As X approaches Y the Y—Z bond lengthens and, in the activated state, all three atoms are bound together in a metastable complex. This can either revert to the reactants or the $X\cdots Y$ distance

---

† For more detailed treatments see Glasstone *et al.;* and Moelwyn-Hughes. [3,4]

continues to decrease and $Y \cdots Z$ to increase until the products are formed. The overall change in energy during the reaction can be found from the dissociation energies of the appropriate diatomic molecules.

$$\Delta U = [D(X—Y) + \tfrac{1}{2}D(Z—Z)] — [D(Y—Z) + \tfrac{1}{2}D(X—X)]$$

But how does the energy of the three atoms vary during the course of the reaction?

The bond energy of a diatomic molecule may, by the Heitler–London method, be written as $Q + J$ if the overlap integral is

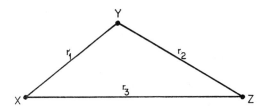

FIGURE 18.1 $X \cdots Y \cdots Z$ activated complex.

neglected. Both the coulombic energy Q and the exchange energy J depend upon the internuclear distance. For three atoms, arranged as in Figure 18.1, London[5,6] proved that to a good approximation the corresponding relationship is

$$E = (Q_1 + Q_2 + Q_3) - \frac{1}{\sqrt{2}} [(J_1 - J_2)^2 + (J_2 - J_3)^2] + (J_3 - J_1)^2]^{1/2}$$

$$= (Q_1 + Q_2 + Q_3) - [(J_1^2 + J_2^2 + J_3^2) - (J_1 J_2 + J_2 J_3 + J_3 J_1)]^{1/2} \tag{18.1}$$

where the subscripts 1, 2, and 3 refer to the atoms taken in pairs, XY, YZ, and XZ respectively. For given values of J_1 and J_2 this energy will be smaller, and the activated complex more stable, the lower the value of J_3. If only s orbitals are employed, equation (10.10) for the approximation of perfect pairing shows that this occurs for a linear complex (maximum value of r_3), and it is normally also true in other cases (cf. Figure 18.6). The values of the six factors contributing to the energy E are not known, but Eyring and Polyani[7–9] argued that $Q_1 + J_1$ may be identified with the potential energy of the diatomic molecule X—Y. This is conveniently summarized, as a function of the internuclear distance r_1, by the Morse equation (5.6)

$$Q_1 + J_1 = D(X—Y)\{1 - \exp[-a(r_1 - r_0)]\}^2$$

Similar expressions may be written for $Q_2 + J_2$ and $Q_3 + J_3$. The remaining problem is to know the individual contributions of Q and J to their sum $Q + J$, and here one can do little more than guess. For hydrogen, Q is about 15% of $Q + J$ but this percentage increases with larger atoms and for hybridized orbitals (see p. 174). Assuming a fixed percentage and employing the Morse potential functions, the total energy of the three atoms may be computed from equation (18.1) for any values of r_1 and r_2.

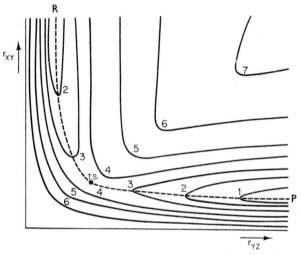

FIGURE 18.2   Energy contours for X · · · Y · · · Z.

The most convenient way to express the full results is in the form of an energy contour diagram such as the one shown diagrammatically in Figure 18.2. In this diagram the numbers correspond to contours of increasing energy. The initial system with the atom X far away from the molecule Y—Z is represented by a point R near the top left-hand side of the diagram. As the atom X approaches the molecule the representative point moves downwards whilst the energy of the system increases; as the atom Z breaks away the point moves to the right until at P the reaction is complete. The diagram has been likened to two steep-sided valleys meeting at a col. The dotted line shows the path of minimum energy through these valleys, the col corresponding to the minimum energy which the system must possess if it is to pass over from X + Y—Z to the products X—Y + Z. The comparatively flat col represents the activated transition complex X · · · Y · · · Z. This path of minimum energy is termed the *reaction coordinate*, and in Figure 18.3 the energy of the system is plotted along this reaction coordinate. Both the reactant molecule Y—Z and the transition complex have zero-point vibrational energies; that of the reactant may be obtained from spectroscopic data, whilst for the complex it has to be computed from the energy profile at the col. The energy of the complex relative to that of the reactants, and corrected for the zero-point energies, is the theoretical activation energy ΔE_0 for the reaction.

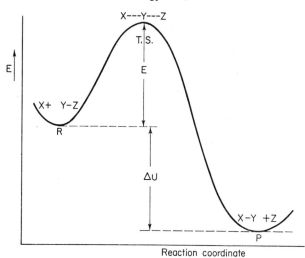

FIGURE 18.3   Energy profile along the reaction coordinate for
$$X + Y—Z \rightarrow X \cdot \cdot Y \cdot \cdot Z \rightarrow X—Y + Z.$$

The first calculations along these lines were for the reaction between hydrogen atoms and molecules, but the method has since been applied to many more complex systems. Unfortunately, the numerical results are sensitive to the precise way the Morse function is split into the individual coulombic and exchange energies. Hence, though the method can explain why the *ortho-para* hydrogen conversion occurs through the reaction of an atom with a molecule and not by a reaction between two molecules or between two atoms, the results are not generally sufficiently reliable to permit a comparison between two similar reactions whose activation energies differ by only a few kcal/mole.

If instead of computing the energy of activation for a reaction the difference between the activation energies of two similar reactions could be estimated directly, then the *relative* rates of these reactions would be known with some reliability. This is the procedure which will now be adopted in discussing the rates of organic reactions between similar reactants. In making these comparisons it must be remembered that the rates of reaction also depend upon an entropy factor, and if these differed significantly for the two reactions the comparison would be invalidated. When comparing similar reactions this arises most frequently from steric hindrance to the formation of the transition state.

THE RATES OF ORGANIC REACTIONS

18.4. The Reaction Coordinate

The reaction coordinate† illustrated in Figure 18.3 must be modified if the reaction proceeds in two consecutive steps with the

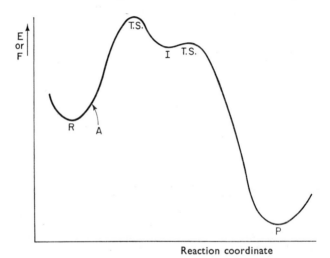

FIGURE 18.4　Free energy profile for a reaction proceeding through an intermediate. $R \rightleftharpoons I \rightleftharpoons P$.

formation of an unstable intermediate I.

$$R \rightleftharpoons I \rightleftharpoons P$$

The appropriate free energy profile for this situation is shown in Figure 18.4. Each reaction has its own transition state (T.S.) and energy of activation, but the first reaction would constitute the rate-determining step. In aromatic substitution, for example, a σ complex has been postulated as an intermediate;[11] in it the attacked carbon atom has an approximately tetrahedral configuration and is not conjugated to the remaining atoms in the ring. In a few cases, $ArH_2^+AlBr_4^-$, $ArH_2^+BF_4^-$, etc, complexes of this form have

† A valuable collection of papers is to be found in *The Transition State*.[10]

actually been isolated, but this is exceptional. In contrast to

σ bonding in the intermediate, π complexes, or charge transfer complexes, have also been postulated.[12,13] They are considered to involve a perturbation of the π electrons in an aromatic molecule. Hydrogen chloride and silver ions (I) for example are known to

I

form these complexes but it seems probable that in a substitution reaction they would only exist as a prelude to forming a σ complex. In other words they would normally only give rise to small humps (transition states) along the reaction coordinate, close to the reactants and products in Figure 18.4, and would not materially affect the overall picture.

The structure of the transition state will not coincide with that of the intermediate because, as the hybridization of the attacked carbon atom changes from sp^2 to sp^3, (a) the energy of the π electrons in the system increases, and (b) the energy of the σ electrons, together with the solvation energy, probably first increases slightly before becoming negative. All that can be said of the transition state, the state with maximum energy along the reaction coordinate, is that it lies somewhere between the extremes marked R and I in Figure 18.4.

Qualitatively the rates of chemical reactions and positions of chemical equilibria have been discussed in terms of both molecular orbital and valence bond approaches, but only the former has been extensively employed in semi-quantitative discussions so our remarks will be restricted to this method.

18.5. Substitution at an Unsaturated Carbon Atom

In an unsaturated organic molecule the π electrons have the greatest energy, are most easily polarized by an attacking reagent, and their distribution is one of the main factors differentiating between the properties of different carbons in the same molecule. As a reasonable approximation the difference in the activation energy and in the reaction rates for a series of similar reactions may be discussed solely in terms of their π electrons. To do so however requires an exact knowledge of the nature of the transition state. In practice we can only discuss either the nature of the σ complex (intermediate) or how the energy of the molecule starts to change as it moves along the reaction coordinate—say to the point A in Figure 18.4. If the structure of the transition state resembles that of the intermediate, then the reaction rates should correlate with the energy of formation of the intermediate. This has been called the localization approximation, as electrons which were delocalized have now become localized on the one carbon. On the other hand, if the transition complex bears a resemblance to the reactant molecule the reaction rates would correlate better with the initial energy change along the reaction coordinates—the isolated molecule approximation.

It is not always easy to predict which approximation should be closest to the true transition state. In some cases the reaction coordinates for similar reactions are nearly parallel over the whole of the reaction path and it does not matter which approximation is employed. In other cases the curves cross, and then the two approximations lead to contrary predictions.

Most theoretical discussions do not consider the specific nature of the attacking reagent, but discuss only the susceptibility to attack by a given reagent of different carbon atoms in a series of aromatic molecules. Benzene is the natural reference standard, but for experimental reasons the α-carbon in naphthalene is often employed. Following Hammett[14,15] it is found that for many reactions†

$$\log (k_i/k_8) = \sigma_i \rho$$

where k_i is the velocity constant for attack on carbon atom i in the aromatic molecule, and k_8 refers to that for the standard reference atom. The substitution or reactivity constant σ_i depends upon the attacked atom, but to a good approximation is independent of the reagent. The reagent controls the reaction constant ρ—its value is a measure of the degree to which the transition state resembles the σ complex. In interpreting the experimental data allowance must naturally be made for the number of carbon atoms in corresponding situations. In a monosubstituted benzene compound, for example, reaction could take place at two *ortho*, two *meta*, but only at one *para* carbon atom.

† For a quantitative treatment of directive effects in aromatic substitution see Stock and Brown.[16]

18.6. The Isolated Molecule Approximation

There are three categories of reagent—radicals which seek an unpaired electron, electrophilic reagents which seek a pair of electrons, and nucleophilic reagents which seek an atom deficient in electrons.

Free Radicals

Thiele suggested there was a residual affinity associated with an unsaturated atom. In modern terminology this is expressed by the free valence[17-19] F of the atom where

$$F_i = C - \sum p$$

In this equation C is a constant, the maximum valency of the atom, and $\sum p$ the sum of the π bond orders of all the bonds to this atom. The value of C is often taken to be $\sqrt{3}$, but values of $\sqrt{2}$ and 1 have been used for secondary and primary carbon atoms respectively.[20] In comparing similar molecules the exact value of C is irrelevant.

Residual valency has been successfully employed as a measure of the ease of attack by free radicals and a reasonable correlation exists with the experimental σ_i values. From the Hückel treatment of butadiene, for example (Section 12.2), the free valence of its terminal carbons is $F = \sqrt{3} - 0.894 = 0.838$, whilst for the inside carbons it is only $\sqrt{3} - 1.341 = 0.391$. The terminal atoms are preferentially attacked by free radicals.

Heterolytic Reactions

When the reagent is charged its point of attack is determined not so much by the free valence as by how the electron distribution in the molecule is perturbed by the close approach of the charge. This problem may be discussed in terms of molecular orbital theory.

It is usual to ignore the overlap integrals, which greatly simplifies the calculations without altering the general conclusions. When this is done the energy of a single electron in a π orbital may be expressed in terms of coulombic and resonance integrals by

$$\xi = \sum c_i^2 \alpha_i + 2 \sum_{i>j} c_i c_j \beta_{ij} \qquad \text{(see p. 191)}$$

the summations being taken over all the conjugated atoms. The total energy of all the π electrons will be the sum of the individual energies ξ of each electron in its particular molecular orbital. The first term makes a contribution of $\sum c_a^2 \alpha_a$ from atom a, where the summation is now over all the π electrons; it is equivalent to $q_a \alpha_a$

12

where q_a is the net π electron charge on the atom (Section 12.2). Likewise $\Sigma\, c_a c_b \beta_{ab}$, summed over all the electrons for a single bond in the conjugated system, is $p_{ab}\beta_{ab}$ where p_{ab} is the π bond order of the bond between atoms a and b. This holds true for each atom and each bond in the molecule so that the total π electron energy may be written as

$$E = \sum q_i \alpha_i + 2 \sum p_{ij}\beta_{ij}$$

the summation in this equation being over each atom and each bond in the molecule. An approaching reagent is considered to alter the coulombic energy of the attacked atom and the resonance energies of the bonds to this atom. If the changes are small, first order perturbation theory gives the change in π electron energy as

$$\delta E = \frac{\partial E}{\partial \alpha_i}\, \delta\alpha_i + \frac{\partial E}{\partial \beta_{ij}}\, \delta\beta_{ij}$$

$$= \sum q_i\, \delta\alpha_i + 2 \sum p_{ij}\, \delta\beta_{ij} \qquad (18.2)$$

the last term being summed over the bonds to the attacked atom i. An alternant hydrocarbon possessing an even number of conjugated atoms however has a unit charge, $(q_i = 1)$, on each atom (Sections 12.2 and 17.5). To differentiate between the atoms in these cases it is necessary to include a second order term of the form

$$\frac{1}{2} \frac{\partial^2 E}{\partial \alpha_i^2} (\delta\alpha_i)^2 = \frac{1}{2} \Pi_i (\delta\alpha_i)^2$$

where Π_i is the atom polarizability. The resultant equation is due to Coulson and Longuet-Higgins.[21]

If the reagent is a positive ion (electrophilic substitution) or presents the positive end of a dipole, it will attract electrons from the atom being attacked. This is simulated in the isolated molecule approach by taking $\delta\alpha_i$ as a negative quantity, thereby increasing the magnitude of α_i. The smallest initial increase in the π electron energy will occur where the charge density q_i is greatest and this atom will have the greatest electrophilic reactivity. Conversely, a nucleophilic attack is simulated by a positive value for $\delta\alpha_i$ and the initial attack occurs preferentially where the charge is least. If several atoms of the substrate possess the same charge then both electrophilic and nucleophilic attack occur preferentially at the atom with the most negative value for the atom polarizability Π_i (self-polarizabilities are always negative).

If the transition state is a little further along the reaction co-ordinate, delocalized electrons in the molecule become partially localized on the attacked atom. In this case the changes in the β values become more important, and in the limit, when the changes in α_i are neglected

$$\delta E = 2 \sum p_{ij} \delta \beta_{ij}$$
$$= 2(\sqrt{3} - F_i) \delta \beta_{ij}$$

The smallest increase in energy and fastest heterolytic attack occurs where the free valence is greatest.

Summarizing these conclusions. For reactions in which the attacking reagent is neutral, such as homolytic substitutions, the rate of attack is determined by the localization effect and the free valence F_i; in heterolytic substitution the values of q_i are normally more important. However, when these charges are the same on each atom, the rate of heterolytic attack depends upon the relative values of Π_i and F_i for each atom and the position of the transition state. For an early transition state the Π_i values are the more important, but if it occurs further along the reaction coordinate the F_i values are of greater importance; if these factors act in opposition little can be predicted about the reaction.

Many series of chemical reactions have now been investigated and the correlation between the reaction rates or substitution constants, and the theoretical values of F_i, q_i, or Π_i† as appropriate, is generally satisfactory.[24]

These however are not the only features of the reactant molecules to be correlated with reaction rates. In the frontier electron theory[25] the electron density of the highest energy electron only is considered. This does not enable the reactivity of different molecules to be compared, but the same workers later defined a superdelocalizability value which overcame this snag.[26,27] In this method the reagent was considered to form a weak π bond to a carbon atom of the aromatic molecule. Several other approaches assume the formation of a π or charge-transfer complex. Brown,[28] for example, obtained a reactivity index by considering the transfer of electronic charge from the molecular orbital of highest energy (frontier orbital) to an electrophilic reagent.

Considering a large number of different reactions each theory is better than the others for some reactions but inferior for others; no single approach is really adequate for all reacting systems.

18.7. The Localization Approximation

Wheland[29] suggested that in the transition state the reagent was covalently bonded to the substrate molecule, so that the attacked atom could no longer participate in forming the delocalized π

---

† The values of these quantities for many molecules are available from Coulson and Daudel,[22] and Streitwieser and Brauman.[23]

molecular orbitals. The smaller the resultant loss of π electron energy, known as the localization energy, the faster the reaction.

Consider benzene. According to the Hückel theory the energy of its π electrons (p. 200) is $6\alpha + 8.000\beta$. The isolation of one carbon atom leaves five conjugated together, as in the pentadienyl system, with orbital energies

$$\alpha + 1.732\beta; \quad \alpha + \beta; \quad \alpha; \quad \alpha - \beta; \quad \alpha - 1.732\beta$$

In a nucleophilic attack two electrons are required to bind the reagent to the benzene ring, leaving four π electrons to be accommodated in these orbitals, and their combined energy would be

$$2(\alpha + 1.732\beta) + 2(\alpha + \beta) = 4\alpha + 5.464\beta$$

Hence in this case the localization energy l is

$$l = 6\alpha + 8.000\beta - (4\alpha + 5.464\beta)$$
$$= 2\alpha + 2.536\beta$$

For attack by a radical five π electrons would be left in the pentadienyl system and the localization energy is then $\alpha + 2.536\beta$, and for an electrophilic reagent which supplies both electrons needed to bond it to the benzene ring the localization energy is 2.536β. In general $l = a\alpha + b\beta$, where a depends on the class of reagent and b on the aromatic carbon atom which is being attacked. In comparing reactions with the same reagent the coulombic contribution to the localization energy (2α, α, and 0 respectively in the above cases) is immaterial and the reactivity is decided by the different coefficients of β for localization energies at the various carbon atoms. With even alternant hydrocarbons there must, of necessity, be an odd number of carbons participating in the conjugation of the transition complex, so that its highest occupied orbital must be non-bonding (energy α). This orbital is unoccupied in nucleophilic attack and holds one and two electrons respectively in radical and electrophilic reactions. In each case the coefficient of β is the same so that the reactivity constant of the carbon atoms in these hydrocarbons should be independent of the nature of the reagent. In contrast, the transition complex of non-alternant hydrocarbons does not possess a non-bonding molecular orbital, so that the localization energies and reactivity constants differ in nucleophilic, radical, and electrophilic attack.

We have just seen that when the molecule is an even alternant, the removal of the attacked carbon atom from the conjugated system leaves an odd alternant hydrocarbon. When this is the case, localization energies can be obtained in a very quick and simple way by the methods of Dewar outlined in the previous chapter— equation (17.2). Attack on the α and β-carbon atoms of naphthalene, for example, is shown in Figure 18.5; electrophilic and nucleophilic reactions occur more readily at the α position. The coefficient of β obtained in this way has been termed the *reactivity number*—it correlates well with the more sophisticated calculations of localization energies.

$$\Delta\epsilon_\pi = l = 2\beta(a + 2a)$$
$$= 6\beta a$$
$$= 6\beta/\sqrt{11}$$
$$= 1\cdot81\beta$$

$$a = \frac{1}{\sqrt{11}}$$

$$\Delta\epsilon_\pi = l = 2\beta(a+2a)$$
$$= 6\beta a$$
$$= 6\beta/\sqrt{8}$$
$$= 2\cdot12\beta$$

$$a = \frac{1}{\sqrt{8}}$$

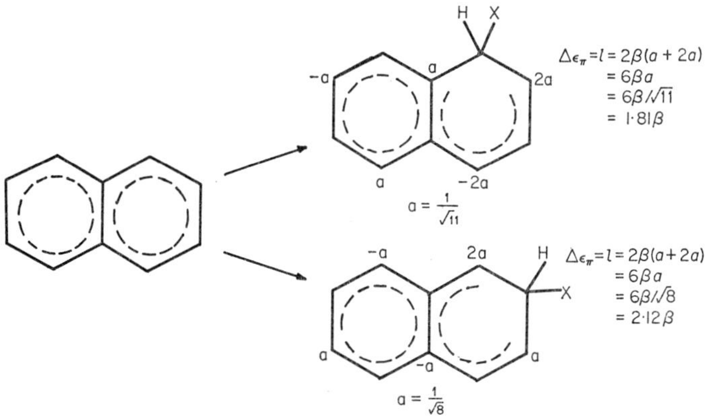

FIGURE 18.5 Localization energies for the α and β carbon atoms in naphthalene.

Naturally, by whatever theoretical method the reactivity of atoms in aromatic molecules is estimated, none takes into account steric effects. Attack at C_9 in anthracene for example is considerably hindered by the hydrogen atoms on either side of it—to a lesser extent this also occurs at the α position in naphthalene.

18.8. Addition Reactions

Addition reactions to an unsaturated system follow the general pattern just discussed. If the reagent is AB then it can either,

1. Dissociate into radicals A· and B·.
2. Dissociate into ions A⁻: and B⁺.
3. Attack two points in the molecule simultaneously.

In the first two cases the radical B· or the electrophilic cation B⁺ first attacks the molecule at the point indicated by the isolated molecule approximation. A· or A⁻: then attacks preferentially at the most susceptible atom in the resulting system.

Consider the addition of HBr to styrene. In the absence of peroxides the reagent is thought to ionize, either before or during the reaction, and the very reactive proton attacks the styrene molecule. The charge on each atom in the hydrocarbon is unity, but the terminal carbon of the chain has the greatest free valence

TABLE 18.1. FREE VALENCE F, LOCALIZATION ENERGIES l, AND CHARGES q FOR SOME HYDROCARBONS

Hydrocarbon		Atom					
		1	2	3	4	5	6
(structure, atoms 5,4,1,6,3,2,7,8)	F	0·821	0·415	0·106	0·443	0·394	0·414
	l	1·704	2·424	2·906	2·369	2·546	2·424
	q	0	0	0	0	0	0
(structure, atoms 5,4,1,6,3,2,7,8)	F		1·097	0·052	0·504	0·392	0·462
	l		0·720	3·256	1·732	2·564	1·820
	q (ion)		±0·571	0	±0·143	0	±0·143
	q (radical)		0	0	0	0	0
(structure, atoms 4,3,2,1)	F	0·838	0·391				
	l	1·644	2·472				
	q	0	0				
(structure, atoms 3,2,1)	F	1·025	0·318				
	l	0·828	2·828				
	q (ion)	±0·500	0				
	q (radical)	0	0				

and smallest localization energy (Table 18.1). The initial attack therefore takes place here giving (cf. Markownikoff's rule)

Calculation shows that the greatest positive charge and free valence but least localization energy, is now associated with the atom next to the ring. The product is consequently 1-bromethyl benzene, $C_6H_5CHBr·CH_3$. In the presence of peroxides, however, it is thought that bromine atoms (radicals) are formed

$$HBr + \text{'peroxide'} \rightarrow HO_2· + Br·$$

These attack where the free valence is greatest giving

The carbon atoms are now uncharged to a first approximation and free valence and localization energy values show that in reacting with the hydrogen of another HBr molecule, 2-bromoethyl benzene, $C_6H_5CH_2CH_2Br$ is formed—the liberated bromine atom continuing the chain reaction.

In additions to butadiene, if the reagent (e.g. Br_2) dissociates during or prior to the reaction the first product is

$$\underset{4}{CH_2}{=\!=}\underset{3}{CH}{=\!=}\underset{2}{CH}{-}\underset{1}{CH_2X}$$

with two, three, or four electrons in the π molecular orbitals formed by the three conjugated carbon atoms. The charge distribution, free valence, and localization energy of the second and fourth carbon atoms in this intermediate would be the same, to a first approximation, so that 1,2 and 1,4 addition occurs. The composition of the mixture depends upon the relative effects (e.g. inductive effect), of the —CH_2X and —H at the ends of the three atom chain participating in the delocalized orbitals. Addition of bromine for example first gives $CH_2{=\!=}CH{=\!=}CH{-}CH_2Br$ and then about 20% of 1,2 and 80% of 1,4 dibromobutene.

In the Diels–Alder type of reaction the reagent does not dissociate and thus provides an example of case (3) above. The reaction of maleic anhydride (A $\cdots$ B) with anthracene could proceed in either one or two steps.

It is generally agreed that the mechanism of this diene synthesis is the one step process. The delocalization energy, termed the *para-localization energy*, is the π electron energy difference between anthracene and two isolated benzene rings. Brown[30,31] has shown that the experimental hydrocarbon reactivity in diene synthesis is greater, the smaller the *para*-localization energy, or the greater the sum of the free valencies of the attacked carbon atoms.

18.9. Heteroatom Compounds

The theories already outlined have been applied to hydrocarbons. What is the effect of heteroatoms? Free valence and atom polarizabilities have been employed as reactivity indices for heteroatom systems,[32] but the use of electron densities and localization energies seem the more popular.

If any group, methyl, amino, nitro, etc. is attached to a carbon atom in a conjugated system it will give rise to an inductive effect. This may be incorporated in molecular orbital calculations by suitably changing the coulombic integral of the carbon atom. If the carbon is replaced by a heteroatom which participates in the delocalized orbitals, then again, the coulombic integral for this position has to be changed (see p. 202), and in addition the resonance integral to neighbouring atoms is altered. In both cases the coulombic integrals of neighbouring atoms might change by a smaller amount. On the other hand, if a carbon is substituted with a group which can participate in the π bonding, then the delocalized molecular orbitals must be extended to incorporate these atoms (cf. Figure 18.4).

This might sound simple, but in practice it is not so easy to guess at the changes in the values of the Hückel parameters so as to obtain not only the correct relative changes in electron density at other atoms in the same molecule, but also the correct reactivities in a series of analogous molecules. Predicted reactivities are not always reliable.

The charge densities and localization energies are best calculated by a Hückel, or a more elaborate, molecular orbital method, but the rapid treatment of Dewar can be applied if desired. An approximate method of obtaining the relative charges on the carbon atoms in a heterocyclic molecule was given in the previous chapter (see Figure 17.8). To obtain the localization energy $\Delta \xi_\pi{}'$ for a heterocyclic, it is related to the corresponding value $\Delta \xi_\pi$ for the hydrocarbon analogue. For an even alternant system the equation is

$$\Delta \xi_\pi{}' \simeq \Delta \xi_\pi + \sum (q_i - 1)\, \delta \alpha_i$$

This follows if equation (18.2) is applied to both the transition state and the initial state of the reaction. In the transition state the charge on each atom is q_i (found by the Hückel or the approximate Dewar method) but it is unity in the ground state for an even alternant hydrocarbon. The main change in the localization energy arises from the heteroatom itself, for which $\delta\alpha_i$ is appreciable, but smaller effects will also be produced by the adjacent carbons whose electronegativities are changed slightly by inductive effects.

For radical reactions, q_i at each atom in the transition state is unity and introduction of the heteroatom should have little effect as $\Delta\xi_\pi' \simeq \Delta\xi_\pi$. In electrophilic substitution $q_i = 1$ at the inactive positions but is less than one at the active positions; hence $q_i - 1$ is negative at active positions and when one of them is replaced by an electronegative heteroatom, such as nitrogen, $\delta\alpha_i$ at this position is also negative and $\Delta\xi_\pi' > \Delta\xi_\pi$. The reaction rate would thus be reduced. A heteroatom in an inactive position would have only a second-order effect, due to the slightly increased electronegativity of the neighbouring carbons arising from the inductive effect. The converse applies in nucleophilic substitution. For example, substitution at the α or γ positions in pyridine would mean that the

nitrogen atom was in an active position. Reaction would be very slow with electrophilic reagents, but fast with nucleophilic reagents. The nitrogen, however, occupies an inactive position with respect to substitution at the β carbons, so that electrophilic substitution would be only slightly retarded compared with benzene, but nucleophilic attack would be slow. The inductive effect of the nitrogen confers a greater electronegativity (negative $\delta\alpha$) on the α than on the β or γ atoms, thereby somewhat increasing the susceptibility to electrophilic attack and decreasing it for nucleophilic attack. In quinoline and isoquinoline the atoms in the benzene ring for which the nitrogen occupies an active position resemble the β carbon in pyridine, and so should be particularly susceptible to electrophilic attack; nucleophilic reaction occurs primarily at the inactive atoms in the heterocyclic ring (cf. Figure 18.5). This effect upon the atoms in the benzene ring is normally subsidiary to the marked difference observed between the α and β carbons (p. 323).

18.10. Equilibrium Constants

Equilibrium constants are the ratio of two rate constants and, as such, they may be discussed by the methods of this chapter. The equilibrium constant for the reaction $A \rightleftharpoons B$ is

$$K = \exp\left(-\frac{\Delta F}{RT}\right) = \exp\left(\frac{\Delta S}{R}\right)\exp\left(-\frac{\Delta E}{RT}\right)$$

$$= \frac{Q_B}{Q_A}\exp\left(-\frac{\Delta E_0}{RT}\right)$$

If for similar equilibria the entropy changes ΔS, or the ratio of the partition functions Q_A/Q_B, are the same, then

$$RT \ln K/K' = \Delta E_0' - \Delta E_0$$

In equilibria involving conjugated systems it is normally legitimate to consider only the differences of π electron energy.

One example will suffice. The base strength of nitrogen heterocyclics is determined by the equilibrium

$$\left[\begin{array}{c} \diagup \\ \diagdown \end{array} N{-}H\right]^{+} \rightleftharpoons \begin{array}{c} \diagup \\ \diagdown \end{array} N{:} + H^{+}$$

The delocalized system has the same structure in the ion and the neutral molecule, the difference being the greater electronegativity of NH^+ compared to the lone-pair on the nitrogen. Hence

$$\Delta \xi_{\pi} \simeq q_N \delta \alpha_N$$

and there should be a linear relation between q_N and the pK_b value of the base.[33,34] This has been verified in many cases and those deviations which have been observed can be ascribed to the entropy factor.

Tautomerism, reduction of quinones, and the dimerization of radicals are a few equilibrium problems which have also been correlated with theoretical parameters.

18.11. Substitution at a Saturated Carbon Atom

In an S_{N^2} reaction the reagent X and the displaced group Z are both covalently bonded to the same carbon atom in the intermediate state. The formation of three-centre σ molecular orbitals from the three atomic orbitals, illustrated in Figure 18.6, must be of importance in the transition state. (This situation is the converse of the one just discussed in that the reactant carbon is sp^3 hybridized, and this becomes sp^2 in the intermediate state.) Of the three delocalized orbitals one would be bonding and hold two electrons, another would be essentially non-bonding and hold the same number of electrons as are contributed by the reagent X, whilst the third orbital is antibonding and unoccupied. This differs from the stable three-centre bonds in electron deficient molecules by having electrons in the second molecular orbital.

To a first approximation the energy of the second molecular orbital will depend upon the electronegativity of the displaced group

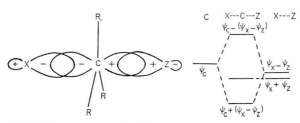

FIGURE 18.6   Three-centre molecular orbitals formed during substitution at a saturated carbon atom.

Z, but be independent of the nature of the R groups; the energy of the bonding molecular orbital, and hence of the transition state, will be lower the greater the combined electronegativity of the R groups (inductive effect). The position may be complicated by steric factors and solvation.

The bonding three-centre orbital has π symmetry with respect to the R_3C plane, and if one of the R groups can conjugate with it the effect on the reaction rate may be appreciable. Halogen exchange between benzyl chloride and the iodide ion furnishes an example.[35] The transition state is

$$\left[\langle \rangle - \underset{I}{\overset{Cl}{\underset{|}{C}}} {\Large <} \overset{H}{\underset{H}{}} \right]^{-}$$

with the three-centre $Cl \cdots C \cdots I$ bonding orbital capable of conjugating with π electrons in the phenyl ring. The *ortho* and *para* carbons will carry partial negative charges (cf. benzyl radical in Table 18.1) and substitutents in these positions will affect the localization energy and rate of substitution. For calculation purposes the $Cl \cdots C \cdots I$ group may be treated as a pseudo-atom with p electrons. Daudel and Chalvet calculated localization energies on this basis and found them to vary linearly with respect to the logarithm of the measured rate constants.

Free valence arguments may also be employed. In the methyl-naphthalene radicals

the π bond order of the C_α—$CH_2\cdot$ bond is greater than the corresponding bond in the β isomer because of the greater free valence of the α carbon atom. Hence the activated complex

(Cl $\cdots$ C $\cdots$ I is perpendicular to the plane of the naphthalene residue.)

is the more stable, and the rate of the exchange of the α-chloromethyl derivative greater than for the β-isomer. In general, halogen exchange occurs more rapidly the greater the free valence of the carbon to which the CH_2Cl group is attached.

The same arguments explain why, for example, displacement reactions of allyl compounds occur more rapidly than in the corresponding saturated derivative.

In this brief theoretical treatment of reaction kinetics only an outline of the current theories has been given and examples included where they are necessary to assist in the explanation. The results and correlations achieved by these methods are to be found in books dealing with theoretical organic chemistry and in the scientific literature.

BIBLIOGRAPHICAL REFERENCES

1. Glasstone, S., Laider, K. J., and Eyring, H., *The Theory of Rate Processes*, McGraw-Hill, New York, 1941.
2. Arrhenius, S., *Z. Phys. Chem.*, 1889, **4**, 226.
3. Moelwyn-Hughes, E. A., *Ann. Rep.*, 1935, **32**, 89.
4. Moelwyn-Hughes, E. A., *Ann. Rep.*, 1936, 33, 86.
5. London, F., *Probleme der Modernen Physik* (Sommerfeld Festschrift), S. Hirzel, Liepzig, 1928.
6. London, F., *Z. Elektrochem.*, 1929, 35, 552.

7. Eyring, H., and Polanyi, M., *Z. Phys. Chem.*, 1931, **B12**, 279.
8. Eyring, H., *J. Amer. Chem. Soc.*, 1931, **53**, 2537.
9. Eyring, H., *Chem. Rev.*, 1932, **10**, 103.
10. *The Transition State*, Chem. Soc. Special Publ. No. 16, 1962.
11. Wheland, G. W., *J. Amer. Chem. Soc.*, 1942, **64**, 900.
12. Brown, R. D., *J. Chem. Soc.*, 1959, 2224.
13. Nagakura, S., and Tanaka, J., *Bull. Chem. Soc. Japan*, 1959, **32**, 734.
14. Hammett, L. P., *Physical Organic Chemistry*, McGraw-Hill, New York, 1940.
15. Jaffé, H. H., *Chem. Rev.*, 1953, **53**, 191.
16. Stock, L. M., and Brown, H. C., *Advanc. Phys. Organ. Chem.*, 1963, **1**, 35.
17. Coulson, C. A., *Trans. Faraday Soc.*, 1946, **42**, 106, 265.
18. Coulson, C. A., *Disc. Faraday Soc.*, 1947, **2**, 9.
19. Coulson, C. A., *J. Chim. Phys.*, 1948, **45**, 243.
20. Moffitt, W. E., *Trans. Faraday Soc.*, 1949, **45**, 373.
21. Coulson, C. A., and Longuet-Higgins, H. C., *Proc. Roy. Soc.*, 1947, A**191**, 39.
22. Coulson, C. A., and Duadel, R., *Dictionary of Values of Molecular Constants*, Centre de Chemie Théoriqué de France, Paris.
23. (a) Streitwieser, A., and Brauman, J. I., *Supplemental Tables of Molecular Orbital Calculations*, (b) Coulson, C. A., and Streitwieser, A., *Dictionary of Pi-Electron Calculations*, Pergamon Press, New York, 1964.
24. Streitwieser, A., *Molecular Orbital Theory for Organic Chemists*, John Wiley, New York, 1961.
25. Fukui, K., Yonezawa, T., Nagata, C., and Shingu, H., *J. Chem. Phys.*, 1954, **22**, 1433.
26. Fukui, K., Yonezawa, T., and Nagata, C., *Bull. Chem. Soc. Japan*, 1954, **27**, 423.
27. Fukui, K., Yonezawa, T., and Nagata, C., *J. Chem. Phys.*, 1957, **27**, 1247.
28. Brown, R. D., *J. Chem. Soc.*, 1959, 2232.
29. Wheland, G. W., *J. Amer. Chem. Soc.*, 1942, **64**, 900.
30. Brown, R. D., *J. Chem. Soc.*, 1950, 2730.
31. Brown, R. D., *J. Chem. Soc.*, 1951, 1612, 3129.
32. Sándorfy, C., Vroelant, C., Yvan, P., Chalvet, O., and Dandel, R., *Bull. Soc. Chim. France*, 1950, 304.
33. Longuet-Higgins, H. C., *J. Chem. Phys.*, 1950, **18**, 275.
34. Chalvet, O., Dandel, R., Pagès, M., Roux, M., Ng. Ph. Buu-Hoï, and Royer, R., *J. Chim. Phys.*, 1954, **51**, 548.
35. Dandel, R., and Chalvet, O., *J. Chim. Phys.*, 1956, **53**, 943.

CHAPTER 19

THE HYDROGEN BOND AND HYPERCONJUGATION

In this chapter two properties specifically associated with hydrogen atoms are discussed. The first of these, the hydrogen bond, is a weak bond formed by a hydrogen atom which is already covalently bonded to another atom. It is of tremendous physical importance, being largely responsible for many properties of water and other solvents, for holding the polypeptide chains of proteins together in their uniquely folded conformations, and for a multitude of other properties of solids and liquids. Its energy is low but this is the very cause of much of its importance as hydrogen bonds can be readily formed and broken.

On the other hand the second topic, hyperconjugation, is introduced to explain certain features associated with the presence of methyl, and to a lesser extent other alkyl groups in molecules. Recently the evidence for the existence of this phenomenon has been greatly weakened, so that its importance has diminished rather dramatically.

THE HYDROGEN BOND

The hydrogen bond† may be represented by

$$X—H \cdots Y$$

Hydrogen, covalently bonded to atom X, is also attracted by Y to an appreciable extent. This can occur both inter- and intramolecularly. It has been termed a hydrogen bond and has only been detected when both X and Y are highly electronegative atoms. Atom X is frequently oxygen as it occurs more often in molecules than other electronegative atoms such as fluorine, nitrogen, chlorine,

† For an excellent review see Coulson.[1]

or sulphur. More information is consequently available for the —O—H $\cdots$ O< system. Very weak hydrogen bonds may be formed with other atoms, such as when X is carbon, but they are often too weak to be detected experimentally.

19.1. Evidence for Hydrogen Bonding

The attraction between hydrogen and the atom Y confers an abnormal melting point, boiling point, latent heat, vapour pressure, solubility, dielectric constant, etc. upon the molecules which possess these bonds. That is abnormal by comparison with analogous non-hydrogen bonded systems.

The most obvious direct measurements which can be made on a system thought to possess hydrogen bonds is the X $\cdots$ Y distance. It is shorter than the non-bonded (van der Waals) distance between these atoms—sometimes very considerably shorter. The O $\cdots$ O distance in ice, for example, is 2·76 Å, compared with about 3·5 Å for non-bonded oxygen atoms. Further, methods capable of locating a hydrogen atom such as neutron diffraction, very accurate X-ray measurements, and nuclear magnetic resonance measurements on solids show that, with rare exceptions, the hydrogen is not situated symmetrically between the two atoms. The X—H distance, however, is slightly longer than when hydrogen bonding does not occur.

The simplest direct evidence for the presence of a hydrogen bond follows from this lengthening of the X—H distance. The covalent bond is weakened slightly and its characteristic infrared stretching frequency is consequently reduced. The actual decrease in frequency is small, but occurs in both the fundamental and overtone absorptions. Sometimes two peaks are observed due to some molecules entering into hydrogen bonding, whilst in others the X—H group is free. The change in X—H distance may be estimated from the frequency shift either empirically, or by employing the Badger[2,3] or similar equation. Another difference in the spectroscopic absorption is a large increase in intensity when hydrogen bonding occurs.

19.2. Properties of the Hydrogen Bond

Any satisfactory theoretical description of hydrogen bonding must explain certain features which for convenience are listed below.

1. The X $\cdots$ Y distance is very variable[4] and in the case of the —O—H $\cdots$ O< system, for which the evidence is most

extensive, as the $O \cdots O$ distance is decreased the covalent O—H length increases!

2. There is a strong preference for a linear arrangement of the $X—H \cdots Y$ atoms but this is not obligatory and a very wide range of bond angles is found in different molecules. Non-linear arrangements occur with intramolecular bonding, such as in *cis-ortho*-chlorophenol (I), and in crystals where a compromise is struck between straight and strong bonds and close-packing of the molecules to reduce the 'PV term' in the free energy of the system. Urea (II) is an example.

I   II

3. The $H \cdots Y$ bond energies are small,[5,6] their maximum value being about 10 kcal/mole, about a tenth the energy of normal covalent and ionic bonds. Furthermore, their energy varies greatly from one molecule to another even for the same atoms X and Y. Generally the greater the electronegativities of X and Y the stronger is the hydrogen bond.
4. The intensity of the X—H absorption band increases by tenfold, or even more, when hydrogen bonding occurs.
5. Dipole moment evidence[7-9] indicates that electronic charge flows from Y to X.
6. Finally hydrogen, or deuterium, is the only central atom and both X and Y must be electronegative atoms.

19.3. Theoretical Description of the Hydrogen Bond

It was suggested at one time that hydrogen could display a covalency of two, but this is impossible in view of the high energy of its $2s$ and $2p$ orbitals. Neither can proton resonance be involved.

$$-X—H \cdots Y— \leftrightarrow -X \cdots H—Y—$$

Experimental evidence does not confirm this postulated oscillation of the hydrogen atom and the calculated resonance energy is too small. Since both X and Y must be electronegative a purely electrostatic description was popular at one time, but it is now realized that at least five factors contribute to the energy of hydrogen bonds. Ice will be taken as an example.

Electrostatic Energy. In their calculations for ice, Bernal and Fowler[10] (see also Verwey[11,12]) located negative charges at the oxygen nuclei and positive charges at the hydrogen nuclei such that these charges gave the observed dipole moment of an isolated water molecule. Then they evaluated the total electrostatic energy from this distribution of point charges. The satisfactory agreement obtained with the experimental intermolecular energy of ice led them to suggest that the hydrogen bond was primarily an electrostatic bond.

We now realize that this electrostatic calculation is inadequate. Firstly, the charge distribution in the water molecule is such that its lone-pair electrons make the greatest contribution to its dipole moment (Section 14.2). (Incidentally they also explain the tetrahedral distribution of four hydrogen atoms round each oxygen in ice.) This probably does not materially alter the calculated electrostatic energy.[13,14] Secondly, in ice there is a large electrostatic field which will polarize each water molecule, thus appreciably increasing their dipole moment. Electrostatic energy is evidently a major factor in hydrogen bonding but reliable values for its contribution to the bond energy are not available.

Delocalization Energy. A valence bond description of the covalent bonds in ice involves resonance between two canonical forms.

$$\diagdown O{-}H \quad O\diagup \quad \leftrightarrow \quad \diagdown \overset{-}{O} \quad \overset{+}{H} \quad O\diagup$$

Dipole moment evidence however indicates that charge flows from atom Y towards X. Polarization of the lone-pair electrons of Y is not sufficient to account for this, so resonance with a third structure is indicated, viz.

$$\diagdown \overset{-}{O} \quad H{-}\overset{+}{O}\diagup$$

It involves a longer and weaker covalent bond. The extra resonance energy contributed by this structure may be termed a delocalization energy. Coulson and Danielsson[15] estimated the relative weights of these three structures, and found that the contribution of the last form was always significant and increased rapidly as the $O \cdots O$ distance was decreased. The contribution to the energy of the hydrogen bond could be as great as, or even greater than, the electrostatic energy. Tsubomura[16] included additional canonical forms in a subsequent analysis of this factor and confirmed the importance of delocalization energy.

Dispersion Energy. The neighbouring oxygen atoms in ice are so close together that the London-type (van der Waals) dispersion energy of attraction could well be considerable. Unfortunately it is rather more difficult to calculate.

Repulsive Forces. A more important consequence of bringing the oxygen atoms close together is that the charge clouds of the lone-pair electrons of the non-bonded oxygen atom overlap and repel those of the covalent O—H bond. This exchange repulsion, which must be substantial, offsets a considerable part of the stabilizing energy from the preceding three factors. With a larger central atom, such as lithium, its inner electrons would greatly increase the repulsion. This is the main reason why hydrogen and deuterium are the only atoms to form this type of bond.

Zero-Point Energy. This last factor is a minor one tending to stabilize the hydrogen bonded system. It arises from the difference between the zero-point vibrational energy of an isolated O—H bond and one that has entered into hydrogen bonding.

It is evident that at least three attractive and one repulsive force determine the energy of a hydrogen bond. Both the absolute and the relative magnitudes of the factors change as the atoms X and Y are changed and as the X $\cdots$ Y distance is altered. The actual nature or description of a hydrogen bond consequently differs from one molecule to another.

How does the above description explain the high intensity of infrared absorption? Infrared radiation interacts with a fluctuating dipole in the molecule. Now, as the hydrogen atom vibrates between the X and Y atoms the weight of the canonical form $\overset{-}{X}$ H—$\overset{+}{Y}$— changes (see delocalization energy above) to a greater extent than is normal from atom vibrations. This implies that the partial charges on X and Y alter during the vibration, and since they are far apart it gives rise to a larger fluctuating dipole and intense absorption.

19.4. Potential Energy of the Hydrogen Atom

For an isolated O—H bond the potential energy curve has the form of curve (a) in Figure 19.1. In O—H $\cdots$ O< the curve cannot flatten off at larger bond lengths because of the presence of the second, non-bonded, oxygen atom. Curves (b), (c), and (d)

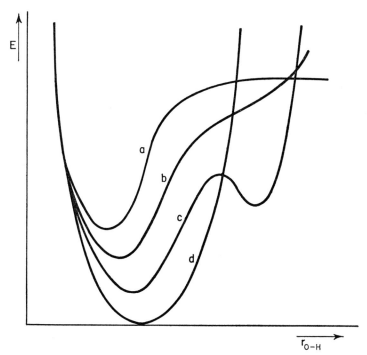

FIGURE 19.1   Potential energy curves of O—H $\cdots\cdot$ O for four fixed
O $\cdots\cdots$ O distances.

show three possibilities as the O $\cdots$ O distance is progressively
decreased.

In curve (b) the O $\cdots$ O distance is long and the hydrogen bond
weak. At shorter O $\cdots$ O distances, (curve (c)), it is suggested that
a second minimum can occur in the potential energy curve. Experimental evidence[17] for this is afforded by analysis of fundamental
and overtone infrared absorption frequencies. Curve (d) is perfectly
symmetrical with a single minimum mid-way between the two
oxygen atoms. This arises when the oxygen atoms are about 2·43 Å
apart and in this situation the amplitude of vibration of the hydrogen
atom is abnormally great. The O $\cdots$ O distance in maleic acid (III)
is 2·46 Å and the hydrogen is slightly nearer the one oxygen atom,
but in the anion (IV) it is thought to be centrally situated. It is also
probably central in the nickel dimethylglyoxime complex and might
be so in some other molecules.[11,18,19]

In formula IV below, the OHO bonding has been represented
as being purely electrostatic. This must make a major contribution
to the energy of the system, but it is still possible to represent it as

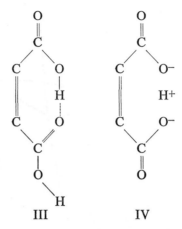

III   IV

being in resonance with two covalent structures of equal weights. Alternatively, three-centre orbitals could be formulated. These abnormally short hydrogen bonds are naturally stronger than usual and their O—H stretching frequency is greatly different from that of the isolated bond. A similar situation exists in the (FHF)⁻ ion, but polymeric HF is normal, the hydrogen being closer to one fluorine than to the other.

HYPERCONJUGATION

19.5. Evidence for Hyperconjugation

Baker and Nathan[20] investigated the kinetics of reactions which involved the bromine atom in various alkylbenzyl bromides, $R \cdot C_6H_4 \cdot CH_2Br$. They concluded that the ability of alkyl groups to donate electronic charge to the benzene ring was in the order

$$Me > Et > Pr^i \backsimeq Bu^t$$

This is not the order expected for a purely inductive effect. The methyl group behaved, in fact, as if it possessed a triple bond $H_3{\equiv}C{-}$, rather like $N{\equiv}C{-}$ but with very much weaker powers of conjugation. Mulliken[21] called the phenomenon *hyperconjugation*. In his book[22] Baker gives a comprehensive review of the experimental evidence (see also Crawford[23]), largely kinetic, for hyperconjugation of the methyl group linked directly to atoms or systems possessing π electrons, and to a smaller extent, for hyperconjugation involving the methylene group $-CH_2-$.

A subsequent analysis of this problem by Dewar[24,25] has cast doubt on the reality of hyperconjugation and the case for and against has been argued in *Tetrahedron*.[26] (See also Dewar[27].)

Dewar and Schmeising list five lines of experimental evidence which have been advanced to indicate the existence of electron delocalization in general and hyperconjugation in particular. They are:

1. Changes in bond lengths.
2. A greater heat of formation, and smaller heats of combustion and hydrogenation.
3. A shift of ultraviolet absorption lines to lower frequencies.
4. Altered chemical reactivity and equilibrium constants.
5. Altered polarity, as indicated by dipole moment measurements.

To this list we might add nuclear magnetic resonance and electron spin resonance measurements.

It is argued that the observed phenomena can, in many cases, be equally well explained by the well-established inductive effect and by the consequences of bonding between differently hybridized carbon atoms. Before considering this reappraisal of hyperconjugation is it convenient to present the wave mechanical description of how the electron delocalization can arise.

19.6. Theoretical Description of Hyperconjugation

Both valence bond and molecular orbital methods have been employed to describe hyperconjugation. Let us consider toluene.

The Valence Bond Method

The usual valence bond description of toluene involves resonance between the Dewar and Kekulé structures of the aromatic ring and may be summarized by structure (i) below. It is possible to formulate additional canonical forms however, and, from the variation principle, we know that even if the weighting of these structures is small they must confer a little extra stability upon the system. One possibility is a diradical structure such as (ii). If desired, the electron

(i)   (ii)   (iii)

of the methyl hydrogen can be paired with the one on the aromatic carbon, but this long covalent bond has little significance. Alternatively, ionic structures such as (iii) may be written. Structures (ii) and (iii) can also be drawn with the unpaired electron or negative charge situated in the *para* or second *ortho* position of benzene. It might be worth noting that the π bond from the methyl carbon to the aromatic ring would involve a tetrahedral sp^3 hybrid of the former atom as in (i).

These additional structures show how it is possible for charge to flow from the alkyl group to an unsaturated system. Unfortunately there is no satisfactory way of deciding the relative weights of the various structures so this must remain a purely formal description of a possible phenomenon.

The Molecular Orbital Method

In discussing electron-deficient molecules and the bonding between certain ligands and a transition metal atom we employed group orbitals—that is, a combined orbital extending over several atoms was considered to interact with the orbitals of another atom. The properties of determinantal wave functions (Sections 11.2 and 13.1) actually tell us that it is always possible to describe a system of localized two-electron bonds by delocalized molecular orbitals. Let us apply these ideas to the three hydrogen atoms of a methyl group.

From the three $1s$ hydrogen wave functions, labelled ψ_a, ψ_b, and ψ_c, group orbitals may be formulated with wave functions of the form

$$\psi_1 = \sqrt{\tfrac{1}{3}}(\psi_a + \psi_b + \psi_c)$$

$$\left.\begin{aligned}
\psi_2 &= \sqrt{\tfrac{1}{6}}(2\psi_a - \psi_b - \psi_c) \\
\psi_3 &= \sqrt{\tfrac{1}{6}}(-\psi_a + 2\psi_b - \psi_c) \\
\psi_4 &= \sqrt{\tfrac{1}{6}}(-\psi_a - \psi_b + 2\psi_c)
\end{aligned}\right\} \text{degenerate}$$

The wave functions ψ_2, ψ_3, and ψ_4 are degenerate but not independent as their sum is zero. Rather than drop one of them it is desirable to combine them so as to produce two orthogonal wave functions. The ones chosen are ψ_2 and $\psi_3 - \psi_4 = \sqrt{\tfrac{1}{2}}(\psi_b - \psi_c)$. Electron density contour diagrams for the three orbitals ψ_1, ψ_2, and $(\psi_3 - \psi_4)$ are shown schematically in Figure 19.2. In these diagrams the hydrogens are viewed from the fourth orbital of the carbon atom.

In CH_3—X the group wave function ψ_1 has the same σ symmetry as the C—X single bond and can overlap with it. In other words the wave function of the C—X bond should be written as

$$\psi = N[\psi_X + \lambda\psi_C + \mu(\psi_a + \psi_b + \psi_c)]$$

This has been termed σ-type hyperconjugation; its existence was discussed earlier (cf. equation (13.1)). This situation arises whenever the localized molecular orbitals formed by a hybridized carbon atom are not completely orthogonal. The consequences of this type of delocalization are implicitly included in tables of bond lengths, atomic radii, and bond energies.

Now consider the two degenerate group orbitals. They have π symmetry and could interact with any orbitals of similar symmetry

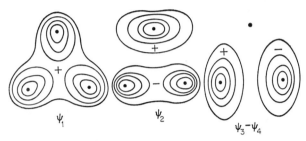

FIGURE 19.2 Group molecular orbitals formed by the three hydrogen atoms in a methyl group.

on the atom or group X. It is the possibility of this π-type conjugation which is the molecular orbital description of hyperconjugation. In toluene only one of the π group orbitals could enter into conjugation with the delocalized electrons of the benzene ring; in methylacetylene CH_3—$C\equiv C$—H however, the triple bond has two orthogonal sets of π orbitals and each could conjugate with one of the π group orbitals of the methyl. The extent of hyperconjugation should therefore be greater in methylacetylene than in toluene.

Hyperconjugation can be incorporated in molecular orbital calculations in three ways. The coulombic integral of the atom to which the methyl is attached can be increased, the carbon and the H_3 group can be separately treated as atoms possessing π symmetry, or the methyl group as a whole can be replaced by a hypothetical atom possessing π electrons. In each case parameters have to be assigned to the coulombic and exchange integrals (Table 12.3) and there is no unambiguous way of doing this. They are chosen to be consistent, as far as is possible, with the experimental observations attributed to hyperconjugation.

Hence both major wave mechanical approaches to chemical bonding can account for the phenomenon of hyperconjugation, but neither can indicate the magnitude of the delocalization. The molecular orbital approach is possibly the more convincing of the two.

19.7. Analysis of the Evidence for Hyperconjugation

The experimental evidence for the effects of hyperconjugation will now be analyzed. Space does not allow for discussion of all the experimental evidence, but the criticisms made of each line of evidence apply to all molecules, not just to the isolated examples quoted.

Bond Lengths

Conjugation is known to produce alterations in bond lengths.[†] One calculation[30] indicated that the C—H bonds which donate electronic charge in hyperconjugation should be longer by 0·001 Å. This of course cannot be verified experimentally. The C—C bond which accepts the electrons on the other hand should be shorter than in a non-conjugated system. Great importance was attached to the observation that the C—C single bond length[31] in methyl acetylene, 1·458 Å, is 0·084 Å less than for a paraffinic C—C bond. It is now realized, however, that the radius of an sp^1 hybridized carbon is much less than that of an sp^3 carbon, so that the bond in methyl acetylene should be short on this count. It is, in fact, virtually the same as in methyl cyanide and methyl cyanoacetylene[32] and the sum of the atomic radii in Table 14.8. It can be argued that this is the characteristic length of a C—C bond between sp^3 and sp^1 hybridized carbons subjected to hyperconjugation. At the same time it is evident that any effect of hyperconjugation must be small and the experimentally measured bond lengths could be completely understood without invoking hyperconjugation. Methyl acetylene should be a particularly favourable molecule in which to observe hyperconjugation as the interaction occurs with the π orbitals in two planes. Any effect would be smaller in toluene, or in any molecule in which the C—C bond was between sp^3 and sp^2 hybridized carbons. In fact, as mentioned in Section 14.3, it is difficult to obtain unambiguous evidence for conjugation in butadiene from the length of its central C—C bond so what hope is there of recognizing hyperconjugation in this way?

Thermal Stability

Hyperconjugation would lower the energy of the ground state of a molecule and thereby give rise to larger heats of formation and

[†] For a discussion of bond lengths and hyperconjugation see Sutton[28] and Wilson.[29]

smaller heats of combustion and hydrogenation. Mulliken, Rieke, and Brown,[30] for example, found that they could only correlate the heats of combustion of a large number of hydrocarbons by including an additional 1·5 kcal/mole for each methyl group adjacent to a double bond. But they assumed that all the C—C and all the C—H bond energies were the same, independent of the hybridization of the carbon. Bond lengths, force constants, etc. depend upon the hybridization. So also must bond energies, and if the values suggested in Table 14.4 are employed no 'hyperconjugation energy' has to be included for methylated double bonds. The position with respect to heats of formation and hydrogenation is similar.

Absorption Spectra and Ionization Potentials

Consider the progressive replacement of the hydrogen atoms in ethylene by methyls. Donation of electrons to the carbon double bond would increase its energy and reduce the ionization potential. This is observed for both the ground and the first electronically excited state. But some, if not all, of this change has to be attributed to an inductive effect. An sp^2 hybridized carbon is more electronegative than an sp^3 carbon. Consequently, charge passes from the methyl to the ethylenic carbon atom and this will repel the π electrons of the double bond. Their ionization potential is consequently reduced.

The difference between the first and second ionization potentials gives the energy of an absorption band in the ultraviolet spectrum; it can be observed directly if desired. Progressive substitution of the hydrogen atoms by methyls shifts the absorption to lower frequencies and could be attributed to hyperconjugation. The inductive effect on its own, however, would cause a change in the same direction, and even if there is hyperconjugation, is it occurring in the ground state, in the excited state, or in both? One consequence of the concept of electron correlation is that delocalization is more pronounced when orbitals are singly occupied. Unpaired electrons are present in electronically excited states, and so it seems probable that hyperconjugation would be more important in excited than in ground states.

Chemical Reactivity

The original postulation of hyperconjugation arose from the interpretation of kinetic data; a methyl group seemed to be capable of donating electronic charge to an unsaturated system by conjugation. Let us re-examine this.

It is actually very similar to the position with respect to the preceding line of evidence. The inductive effect of a methyl group attached to a more electronegative sp^2 or sp^1 hybridized carbon would affect the kinetics of reactions in the same manner as hyperconjugation. Again, in reaction rates we are also studying an energy difference between two states—the ground state and an activated complex. And, as with light absorption, hyperconjugation would probably be more effective in the higher energy activated state.

The same arguments apply to evidence from equilibrium constants, such as the dissociation constants of alkylbenzoic acids. An equilibrium constant can be regarded as the ratio of two rate constants.

Dipole Moments

Toluene has a dipole moment of 0·39 D, the methyl group being at the positive end of the dipole. This has been attributed to hyperconjugation, but again other factors must be considered.

The moment of the *para* C—H bond in the benzene ring has been assumed to cancel the resultant moment of the three methyl C—H bonds. The carbons, however, are differently hybridized and this will alter the atomic, homopolar, and ionic contributions to the C—H bond moments (see Section 14.2). The opposing C—H moments cannot cancel. The available evidence[33,34] would suggest that their resultant moment is in the reverse direction to the observed moment. The C—C single bond from the methyl group to the ring is also between differently hybridized carbons but this time the contributing factors would produce a bond moment in the same direction as the observed moment. Not until the magnitudes of these bond moments is known in a variety of molecules can dipole moment measurements unambiguously provide evidence for or against hyperconjugation.

Magnetic Resonance Methods

The chemical shift in proton magnetic resonance measurements provides evidence of the electron density round the proton. In toluene the chemical shifts of protons in the *ortho*, *meta*, and *para* positions are almost the same.[35] The altered coulombic integral of the substituted carbon atom due to the inductive effect of the methyl group could explain the small changes without invoking hyperconjugation.

Finally, in electron spin resonance there is another tool for investigating the distribution of an electron in a molecule. In a recent review[36] Carrington concludes that the hyperfine splitting observed in aromatic radicals and ions does provide evidence for hypercon-jugation. It must be remembered, however, that in order to observe electron spin resonance, unpaired electrons must be present, and so there is not necessarily hyperconjugation in the parent hydrocarbon.

The evidence for and against hyperconjugation is confusing. Lines of evidence which were originally thought to provide concrete evidence for hyperconjugation are now known to involve other factors, particularly the inductive effect and other consequences of changes in hybridization. Kinetic and spectroscopic data are concerned with two energy states and what happens in the excited state may not occur in the ground state. There does not appear to be any really conclusive experimental evidence for hyperconjuga-tion in the ground state of a molecule. Hyperconjugation is more likely to arise when unpaired electrons are present—i.e. in radicals, carbonium ions, and carbanions, and in electronically excited states and transition complexes—and there is some experimental evidence that it does then occur.

BIBLIOGRAPHICAL REFERENCES

1. Coulson, C. A., *Research*, 1957, **10**, 149.
2. Badger, R. M., *J. Chem. Phys.*, 1934, **2**, 128.
3. Badger, R. M., *J. Chem. Phys.*, 1935, **3**, 710.
4. Nakamoto, K., Margoshes, M., and Rundle, R. E., *J. Amer. Chem. Soc.*, 1955, **77**, 6480.
5. Davies, M. M., *Ann. Rep. Progr. Chem.*, 1946, **43**, 1.
6. Pimentel, G. C., and McClellan, A. L., *The Hydrogen Bond*, Freeman, San Francisco, 1960.
7. Eda, B., and Ito, K., *Bull. Chem. Soc. Japan*, 1956, **29**, 524.
8. Eda, B., and Ito, K., *Bull. Chem. Soc. Japan*, 1957, **30**, 164.
9. Hullett, J. R., Pegg, L. E., and Sutton, L. E., *J. Chem. Soc.*, 1955, 3901.
10. Bernal, J. D., and Fowler, R. H., *J. Chem. Phys.*, 1933, **1**, 515.
11. Verwey, E. J. W., *Rec. Trav. Chim.*, 1941, **60**, 887.
12. Verwey, E. J. W., *Rec. Trav. Chim.*, 1942, **61**, 127.
13. Lennard-Jones, J. E., and Pople, J. A., *Proc. Roy. Soc.*, 1951, A**205**, 155
14. Pople, J. A., *Proc. Roy. Soc.*, 1951, A**205**, 163.
15. Coulson, C. A., and Danielsson, U., *Ark. Fys.*, 1954, **8**, 239, 245.
16. Tsubomura, T. H., *Bull. Chem. Soc. Japan*, 1954, **27**, 445.
17. Bell, C. L., and Barrow, G. M., *J. Chem. Phys.*, 1959, **31**, 300.
18. Cardwell, H. M. E., Dunitz, J. D., and Orgel, L. E., *J. Chem. Soc.*, 1953, 3740.
19. Godycki, L. E., and Rundle, R. E., *Acta Cryst.*, 1953, **6**, 487.
20. Baker, J. W., and Nathan, W. S., *J. Chem. Soc.*, 1935, 1844.
21. Mulliken, R. S., *J. Chem. Phys.*, 1939, **7**, 339.

22. Baker, J. W., *Hyperconjugation*, Oxford University Press, London, 1952.
23. Crawford, V. A., *Quart. Rev.*, 1949, **3**, 226.
24. Dewar, M. J. S., and Schmeising, H. N., *Tetrahedron*, 1959, **5**, 166.
25. Dewar, M. J. S., and Schmeising, N. N., *Tetrahedron*, 1960, **11**, 96.
26. *Tetrahedron*, 1959, **5**, 105–274.
27. Dewar, M. J. S., *Hyperconjugation*, Ronald Press, New York, 1962.
28. Sutton, L. E., *Tetrahedron*, 1959, **5**, 118.
29. Wilson, E. B., *Tetrahedron*, 1962, **17**, 191.
30. Mulliken, R. S., Rieke, C. A., and Brown, W. G., *J. Amer. Chem. Soc.*, 1941, **63**, 41.
31. Heath, G. A., Thomas, L. F., and Sheridan, J., *Trans. Faraday Soc.*, 1955, **50**, 779.
32. Costain, C. C., and Stoicheff, B. P., *J. Chem. Phys.*, 1959, **30**, 777.
33. Smith, J. W., *Electric Dipole Moments*, Butterworths, London, 1955.
34. Petro, A. J., *J. Amer. Chem. Soc.*, 1958, **80**, 4230.
35. Pople, J. A., Schneider, W. G., and Bernstein, H. J., *High Resolution Nuclear Magnetic Resonance*, McGraw-Hill, New York, 1959.
36. Carrington, A., *Quart. Rev.*, 1963, **17**, 67.

APPENDIX 1

ATOMIC UNITS

Units are generally chosen so that the quantities measured have convenient magnitudes. For calculations on atoms and molecules atomic units (a.u.) are frequently employed. These are given below.

Unit of mass, the mass of the electron, m_e.

Unit of charge, the charge of the electron, e.

Unit of distance. Atomic distances are most conveniently expressed in terms of the Bohr radius of the hydrogen atom in its ground state. That is in terms of $a = h^2/4\pi^2\mu e^2 = 0.52942$ Å, or for infinite nuclear mass 0.529166 Å.

Unit of energy. This is taken as the coulombic repulsion between two unit charges at unit distance apart. That is in terms of $e^2/a = 27.209$ eV. It is twice the ionization potential of the hydrogen atom.

In terms of these units, Planck's constant h has the value 2π and the velocity of light c becomes 137.037. The Schrödinger equation is also considerably simplified to

$$\nabla^2\psi + 2(E - V)\psi = 0$$

and the wave function for the $1s$ orbital of hydrogen is $\psi = \pi^{-1/2}\,e^{-r}$ with an energy $E = -\frac{1}{2}$.

Apart from simplifying the mathematical expressions, an advantage of working in atomic units is that the results are not affected by revisions of the values of the constants m_e, e, c, and h.

ILLUSTRATIONS OF THE HEISENBERG UNCERTAINTY PRINCIPLE

A2.1. Diffraction of a de Broglie Wave

Consider the diffraction of a de Broglie wave by a slit of width Δq (Figure A2.1). When the particle passes through this slit its position is known with an accuracy of Δq. If the diffracted particle strikes the screen at the point A it must have acquired a transverse momentum of $\Delta p = p \sin \alpha$ in addition to its original momentum.

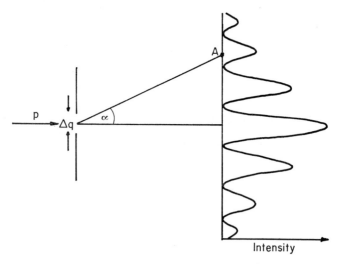

FIGURE A2.1   Diffraction of a de Broglie wave.

Now according to diffraction theory the first-order diffraction angle α is roughly equal to $\lambda/\Delta q$ and so

$$\Delta p = p \sin \frac{\lambda}{\Delta q} \simeq \frac{p\lambda}{\Delta q}$$

Or since $p\lambda = h$ from the de Broglie equation

$$\Delta p \, \Delta q \sim h$$

In other words, when the position of the particle is restricted to passing through a small slit the momentum parallel to the slit is uncertain to the extent $\Delta p \simeq h/\Delta q$. It is therefore only possible to give the probability of the particle hitting the screen at the point A.

A2.2. A Hypothetical Microscope

Suppose we have a microscope with perfect lenses and can detect the position of a particle at the point A by allowing a single photon which has been scattered by the particle to pass into the microscope (Figure A2.2).

With perfect lenses the smallest interval which can be resolved is $\Delta q = \lambda/(2 \sin \alpha)$ and this will represent the uncertainty in the position of the particle. (λ is the wavelength of the light and α the aperture of the lens.) Now the deflection of a photon by a particle

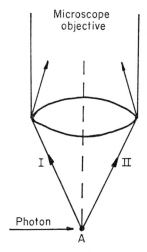

FIGURE A2.2   The scattering of a photon into a microscope objective by a particle situated at the point A.

is accompanied by a change in the momentum of the particle (Compton effect). For the extreme paths (I and II) which the photon could take and still pass through the microscope, the change in momentum of the particle in the original direction of the photon is $\pm(h/\lambda)\sin\alpha$. Because of the Compton effect the wavelengths of the incident and diffracted light will not be exactly the same but the difference is very small and may be neglected. Hence, depending upon the route taken by the photon, there is an uncertainty in the momentum of the particle of

$$\Delta p \simeq (h/\lambda)2\sin\alpha$$

Consequently for the particle

$$\Delta q\,\Delta p \simeq \frac{\lambda}{2\sin\alpha}\,\frac{h}{\lambda}\,2\sin\alpha$$

$$\simeq h$$

The above 'experiments' serve to illustrate the uncertainty principle. Whatever system involving small particles is considered the result is the same; it is not possible to know simultaneously the exact position and momentum of a particle. The product of the inexactitudes can never be less than a value with the magnitude of Planck's constant h.

ALGEBRAIC STEPS IN THE CALCULATION ON THE TUNNEL EFFECT (BOX PROBLEM 3.4)

It is required to eliminate B_1, A_2, and B_2 from the four equations

$$A_1 + B_1 = A_2 + B_2 \qquad (A3.1)$$

$$\frac{i}{\lambda_1}(A_1 - B_1) = \frac{1}{\lambda_2^*}(A_2 - B_2) \qquad (A3.2)$$

$$A_2 \exp\left(\frac{2\pi a}{\lambda_2^*}\right) + B_2 \exp\left(-\frac{2\pi a}{\lambda_2^*}\right) = A_3 \exp\left(\frac{2\pi i a}{\lambda_3}\right) \quad (A3.3)$$

$$\frac{1}{\lambda_2^*}\left[A_2 \exp\left(\frac{2\pi a}{\lambda_2^*}\right) - B_2 \exp\left(-\frac{2\pi a}{\lambda_2^*}\right)\right] = \frac{i}{\lambda_3} A_3 \exp\left(\frac{2\pi i a}{\lambda_3}\right) \qquad (A3.4)$$

Adding equations (A3.1) and (A3.2) and also (A3.3) and (A3.4) gives

$$2A_2 = A_1\left[1 + \frac{i\lambda_2^*}{\lambda_1}\right] + B_1\left[1 - \frac{i\lambda_2^*}{\lambda_1}\right]$$

$$= A_3\left[1 + \frac{i\lambda_2^*}{\lambda_3}\right]\exp\left[2\pi a\left(\frac{i}{\lambda_3} - \frac{1}{\lambda_2^*}\right)\right] \qquad (A3.5)$$

Likewise, if instead of adding, equation (A3.2) is subtracted from equation (A3.1), and (A3.4) from (A3.3) the corresponding equation for B_2 is obtained.

$$2B_2 = A_1\left[1 - \frac{i\lambda_2^*}{\lambda_1}\right] + B_1\left[1 + \frac{i\lambda_2^*}{\lambda_1}\right]$$

$$= A_3\left[1 - \frac{i\lambda_2^*}{\lambda_3}\right]\exp\left[2\pi a\left(\frac{i}{\lambda_3} - \frac{1}{\lambda_1}\right)\right] \qquad (A3.6)$$

B_1 may now be eliminated from equations (A3.5) and (A3.6).

$$B_1 = \frac{\lambda_1}{\lambda_1 - i\lambda_2{}^*}\left\{A_3\left(1 + \frac{i\lambda_2{}^*}{\lambda_3}\right)\exp\left[2\pi a\left(\frac{i}{\lambda_3} - \frac{1}{\lambda_2{}^*}\right)\right] - A_1\left(1 + \frac{i\lambda_2{}^*}{\lambda_1}\right)\right\}$$

$$= \frac{\lambda_1}{\lambda_1 + i\lambda_2{}^*}\left\{A_3\left(1 - \frac{i\lambda_2{}^*}{\lambda_3}\right)\exp\left[2\pi a\left(\frac{i}{\lambda_3} - \frac{1}{\lambda_1}\right)\right] - A_1\left(1 - \frac{i\lambda_2{}^*}{\lambda_1}\right)\right\}$$

$$(A3.7)$$

Rearranging this equation gives the required relationship

$$\frac{A_1}{A_3} = \frac{1}{4}\left\{\left(1 + \frac{\lambda_1}{\lambda_3}\right)\left[\exp\left(\frac{2\pi a}{\lambda_2{}^*}\right) + \exp\left(-\frac{2\pi a}{\lambda_2{}^*}\right)\right]\right.$$

$$\left. - \left(\frac{i\lambda_2{}^*}{\lambda_3} + \frac{\lambda_1}{i\lambda_2{}^*}\right)\left[\exp\left(\frac{2\pi a}{\lambda_2{}^*}\right) - \exp\left(\frac{-2\pi a}{\lambda_2{}^*}\right)\right]\right\}\exp\left(\frac{2\pi ia}{\lambda_3}\right)$$

$$= \frac{1}{2}\left[\left(1 + \frac{\lambda_1}{\lambda_3}\right)\cosh\frac{2\pi a}{\lambda_2{}^*} - \left(\frac{i\lambda_2{}^*}{\lambda_3} + \frac{\lambda_1}{i\lambda_2{}^*}\right)\sinh\frac{2\pi a}{\lambda_2{}^*}\right]\exp\left(\frac{2\pi ia}{\lambda_3}\right)$$

From this expression the probability of penetration through the barrier would be

$$\frac{A_1 A_1{}^*}{A_3 A_3{}^*} = \frac{1}{4}\left[\left(1 + \frac{\lambda_1}{\lambda_3}\right)^2\cosh^2\left(\frac{2\pi a}{\lambda_2{}^*}\right) + \left(\frac{\lambda_2{}^*}{\lambda_3} - \frac{\lambda_1}{\lambda_2{}^*}\right)^2\sinh^2\left(\frac{2\pi a}{\lambda_2{}^*}\right)\right]$$

TRANSFORMATION OF CARTESIAN INTO POLAR COORDINATES

It is customary to express the position of a point P in terms of the cartesian coordinates x, y, and z, but when dealing with wave mechanical problems it is often essential to employ polar coordinates r, θ, and ϕ. From an examination of the diagram we see that the relationships between these two sets of coordinates is

$$x = r \sin \theta \cos \phi$$

$$y = r \sin \theta \sin \phi$$

$$z = r \cos \theta$$

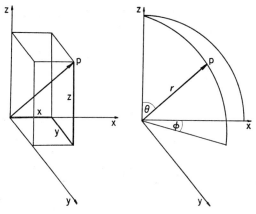

FIGURE A4.1   The cartesian and polar coordinates of a point P.

The reverse transformations are,

$$r = (x^2 + y^2 + z^2)^{1/2}$$

$$\tan \theta = \frac{(x^2 + y^2)^{1/2}}{z}$$

$$\tan \phi = \frac{y}{x}$$

Partial derivatives may be obtained from these. For example,

$$\frac{\partial r}{\partial x} = \tfrac{1}{2}(x^2 + y^2 + z^2)^{-1/2}(2x) = \frac{x}{r} = \sin \theta \cos \phi$$

$$\frac{\partial \theta}{\partial x} = 1 + \frac{z^2}{x^2 + y^2}\frac{1}{2}\left(\frac{x^2 + y^2}{z^2}\right)^{-1/2}\frac{2x}{z^2} = \frac{\cos \theta \cos \phi}{r}$$

$$\frac{\partial \phi}{\partial x} = \left(\frac{y^2}{x^2 + y^2}\right)\frac{1}{y} = \frac{\sin \phi}{r \sin \theta}$$

The other partial derivatives may be obtained in a similar manner and a complete list is given below

$$\frac{\partial r}{\partial x} = \sin \theta \cos \phi; \quad \frac{\partial r}{\partial y} = \sin \theta \sin \phi; \quad \frac{\partial r}{\partial z} = \cos \theta$$

$$\frac{\partial \theta}{\partial x} = \frac{\cos \theta \cos \phi}{r}; \quad \frac{\partial \theta}{\partial y} = \frac{\cos \theta \sin \phi}{r}; \quad \frac{\partial \theta}{\partial z} = -\frac{\sin \theta}{r}$$

$$\frac{\partial \phi}{\partial x} = -\frac{\sin \phi}{r \sin \theta}; \quad \frac{\partial \phi}{\partial y} = \frac{\cos \phi}{r \sin \theta}; \quad \frac{\partial \phi}{\partial z} = 0$$

A4.1. Conversion of the Laplacian Operator ∇ into Polar Coordinates

The Laplacian operator which occurs in the Schrödinger equation is

$$\nabla^2 = \frac{\partial^2}{\partial x^2} + \frac{\partial^2}{\partial y^2} + \frac{\partial^2}{\partial z^2}$$

and the variable upon which it operates is the wave function ψ. The first derivative of ψ with respect to x is

$$\frac{\partial \psi}{\partial x} = \frac{\partial \psi}{\partial r}\frac{\partial r}{\partial x} + \frac{\partial \psi}{\partial \theta}\frac{\partial \theta}{\partial x} + \frac{\partial \psi}{\partial \phi}\frac{\partial \phi}{\partial x}$$

$$= \sin \theta \cos \phi \frac{\partial \psi}{\partial r} + \frac{\cos \theta \cos \phi}{r}\frac{\partial \psi}{\partial \theta} - \frac{\sin \phi}{r \sin \theta}\frac{\partial \psi}{\partial \phi}$$

The second derivative may be obtained by differentiating this equation with respect to x but as the resulting expression is long and its simplification tedious it will not be reproduced. The second differentials of ψ with respect to y and z are similarly obtained and if the three equations are added the Laplacian operator becomes

$$\nabla^2 = \frac{\partial^2}{\partial r^2} + \frac{2}{r}\frac{\partial}{\partial r} + \frac{1}{r^2}\frac{\partial^2}{\partial \theta^2} + \frac{\cot\theta}{r^2}\frac{\partial}{\partial\theta} + \frac{1}{r^2\sin^2\theta}\frac{\partial^2}{\partial\phi^2}$$

$$= \frac{\partial^2}{\partial r^2} + \frac{2}{r}\frac{\partial}{\partial r} + \frac{1}{r^2\sin\theta}\frac{\partial}{\partial\theta}\left(\sin\theta\frac{\partial}{\partial\theta}\right) + \frac{1}{r^2\sin^2\theta}\frac{\partial^2}{\partial\phi^2}$$

$$(A4.1)$$

Conversion of the Laplacian Operator into the Spherical Coordinate r

Some solutions of the Schrödinger equation are only dependent upon the distance r. In this case $\partial\psi/\partial\theta$ and $\partial^2\psi/\partial\phi^2$ are both zero so the appropriate form of equation (A4.1) is

$$\nabla^2 = \frac{d^2}{dr^2} + \frac{2}{r}\frac{d}{dr} \qquad (A4.2)$$

This transformation may be obtained directly as follows: Since ψ is only dependent upon r,

$$\frac{d\psi}{dx} = \frac{d\psi}{dr}\frac{dr}{dx} = \frac{x}{r}\frac{dr}{dx}$$

and

$$\frac{d^2\psi}{dx^2} = \frac{1}{r}\frac{d\psi}{dr} - \frac{x}{r^2}\frac{d\psi}{dr}\frac{dr}{dx} + \frac{x}{r}\frac{d^2\psi}{dr^2}\frac{dr}{dx}$$

$$= \frac{1}{r}\frac{d\psi}{dr} - \frac{x^2}{r^3}\frac{d\psi}{dr} + \frac{x^2}{r^2}\frac{d^2\psi}{dr^2}$$

Similar second differentials are obtained with y and z respectively replacing x. Adding the three equations

$$\nabla^2\psi = \frac{d^2\psi}{dx^2} + \frac{d^2\psi}{dy^2} + \frac{d^2\psi}{dz^2}$$

$$= \frac{3}{r}\frac{d\psi}{dr} - \frac{x^2+y^2+z^2}{r^3}\frac{d\psi}{dr} + \frac{x^2+y^2+z^2}{r^2}\frac{d^2\psi}{dr^2}$$

and remembering that $x^2 + y^2 + z^2 = r^2$

$$\nabla^2\psi = \frac{2}{r}\frac{d\psi}{dr} + \frac{d^2\psi}{dr^2}$$

This is equation (A4.2) above.

Conversion of Angular Momentum Operators into Polar Coordinates

The angular momentum operator for momentum about the x axis is (equation (4.3))

$$\mathbf{M}_x = \frac{h}{2\pi i}\left(y\frac{\partial}{\partial z} - z\frac{\partial}{\partial y}\right)$$

In polar coordinates this becomes

$$\mathbf{M}_x = \frac{h}{2\pi i}\left[r\sin\theta\sin\phi\left(\frac{\partial r}{\partial z}\frac{\partial}{\partial r} + \frac{\partial\theta}{\partial z}\frac{\partial}{\partial\theta} + \frac{\partial\phi}{\partial z}\frac{\partial}{\partial\phi}\right)\right.$$
$$\left. - r\cos\theta\left(\frac{\partial r}{\partial y}\frac{\partial}{\partial r} + \frac{\partial\theta}{\partial y}\frac{\partial}{\partial\theta} + \frac{\partial\phi}{\partial y}\frac{\partial}{\partial\phi}\right)\right]$$
$$= \frac{h}{2\pi i}\left[(r\sin\theta\sin\phi\cos\theta - r\cos\theta\sin\theta\sin\phi)\frac{\partial}{\partial r}\right.$$
$$\left. + (-\sin^2\theta\sin\phi - \cos^2\theta\sin\phi)\frac{\partial}{\partial\theta} + (-\cot\theta\cos\phi)\frac{\partial}{\partial\phi}\right]$$
$$= \frac{h}{2\pi i}\left[-\sin\phi\frac{\partial}{\partial\theta} - \cot\theta\cos\phi\frac{\partial}{\partial\phi}\right]$$

The other momentum operators $\mathbf{M}_y$ and $\mathbf{M}_z$ may be transformed into polar coordinates by identical procedures yielding

$$\mathbf{M}_y = \frac{h}{2\pi i}\left[\cos\phi\frac{\partial}{\partial\theta} - \cot\theta\sin\phi\frac{\partial}{\partial\phi}\right]$$
$$\mathbf{M}_z = \frac{h}{2\pi i}\left[\frac{\partial}{\partial\phi}\right]$$

To obtain the function which gives the square of the angular momentum the above operators have to be applied twice. Considering the operator $\mathbf{M}_x$ in Cartesian coordinates we obtain

$$\mathbf{M}_x^2 = \mathbf{M}_x\mathbf{M}_x = \frac{h}{2\pi i}\left(y\frac{\partial}{\partial z} - z\frac{\partial}{\partial y}\right)\frac{h}{2\pi i}\left(y\frac{\partial}{\partial z} - z\frac{\partial}{\partial y}\right)$$
$$= -\frac{h^2}{4\pi^2}\left(y^2\frac{\partial^2}{\partial z^2} - 2yz\frac{\partial^2}{\partial y\,\partial z} - y\frac{\partial}{\partial y} - z\frac{\partial}{\partial z} + z^2\frac{\partial^2}{\partial y^2}\right)$$

Or in polar coordinates

$$\mathbf{M}_x{}^2 = \frac{h}{2\pi i}\left[-\sin\phi\,\frac{\partial}{\partial\theta} - \cot\theta\cos\phi\,\frac{\partial}{\partial\phi}\right]$$

$$\times \frac{h}{2\pi i}\left[-\sin\phi\,\frac{\partial}{\partial\theta} - \cot\theta\cos\phi\,\frac{\partial}{\partial\phi}\right]$$

$$= \frac{h^2}{4\pi^2}\left[\sin^2\phi\,\frac{\partial^2}{\partial\theta^2} + 2\cot\theta\sin\phi\cos\phi\,\frac{\partial^2}{\partial\theta\,\partial\phi}\right.$$

$$\left. - \csc^2\theta\sin\phi\cos\phi\,\frac{\partial}{\partial\phi} + \cot\theta\cos^2\phi\,\frac{\partial}{\partial\theta} + \cot^2\theta\cos^2\phi\,\frac{\partial^2}{\partial\phi^2}\right]$$

The same procedure may be employed to obtain $\mathbf{M}_y{}^2$ and $\mathbf{M}_z{}^2$. Finally the operator giving the square of the total angular momentum will be

$$\mathbf{M}^2 = \mathbf{M}_x{}^2 + \mathbf{M}_y{}^2 + \mathbf{M}_z{}^2$$

$$= -\frac{h^2}{4\pi^2}\left[\frac{1}{\sin\theta}\frac{\partial}{\partial\theta}\left(\sin\theta\,\frac{\partial}{\partial\theta}\right) + \frac{1}{\sin^2\theta}\frac{\partial^2}{\partial\phi^2}\right]$$

THE ORTHOGONALITY OF
WAVE FUNCTIONS

In Section 3.1 it was shown that the wave functions for a particle in a box are orthogonal. This can be proved to be the case for any two eigenfunctions of an electron. That is

$$\int \psi_a \psi_b \, d\tau = 0 \qquad \text{(A5.1)}$$

where ψ_a and ψ_b are two orbitals for the system and the integration is over the whole of space for a single electron. Physically this means that the two solutions are completely independent of each other.

For the individual quantum states the Schrödinger equations are

$$\nabla^2 \psi_a + \frac{8\pi^2 m}{h^2} (E_a - V)\psi_a = 0$$

and

$$\nabla^2 \psi_b + \frac{8\pi^2 m}{h^2} (E_b - V)\psi_b = 0$$

The potential term may be eliminated if the first of these equations is multiplied by ψ_b, the second by ψ_a, and the resulting equations subtracted. This gives

$$\psi_b \nabla^2 \psi_a - \psi_a \nabla^2 \psi_b + \frac{8\pi^2 m}{h^2} (E_a - E_b)\psi_a \psi_b = 0$$

If this equation is now integrated over the whole of space we obtain

$$\int (\psi_b \nabla^2 \psi_a - \psi_a \nabla^2 \psi_b) \, d\tau = - \frac{8\pi^2 m}{h^2} (E_a - E_b) \int \psi_a \psi_b \, d\tau \quad \text{(A5.2)}$$

Since

$$\nabla^2 = \frac{\partial^2}{\partial x^2} + \frac{\partial^2}{\partial y^2} + \frac{\partial^2}{\partial z^2}$$

the left-hand side of the equation will contain the term

$$\int_{-\infty}^{+\infty} \left(\psi_b \frac{\partial^2}{\partial x^2} \psi_a - \psi_a \frac{\partial^2}{\partial x^2} \psi_b \right) dx$$

which on integration by parts gives

$$\left[\psi_b \frac{\partial}{\partial x} \psi_a - \psi_a \frac{\partial}{\partial x} \psi_b \right]_{-\infty}^{+\infty} - \int_{-\infty}^{+\infty} \left(\frac{\partial \psi_b}{\partial x} \frac{\partial \psi_a}{\partial x} - \frac{\partial \psi_a}{\partial x} \frac{\partial \psi_b}{\partial x} \right) dx$$

The second of these parts is obviously zero; now consider the first part. Because the limits are $\pm\infty$ the wave function must be zero at these values of x as this is a condition for an acceptable solution of the Schrödinger equation. Hence this first term is also zero. Similarly the other terms on the left-hand side of equation (A5.2), involving $\partial^2/\partial y^2$ and $\partial^2/\partial z^2$, are zero. Consequently,

$$(E_a - E_b) \int \psi_a \psi_b \, d\tau = 0$$

If the states belong to different eigenvalues $E_a - E_b \neq 0$ and the integral itself must be zero, which proves equation (A5.1) for these conditions.

It is possible that ψ_a and ψ_b represent degenerate wave functions in which case $E_a - E_b = 0$ and equation (A5.1) need not necessarily be true. If ψ_a and ψ_b are degenerate however any linear combination of them will also be an eigenfunction with the same energy and it is therefore always possible to *arrange* for the wave functions to be orthogonal. If for instance

$$\int \psi_a \psi_b \, d\tau = c$$

then by replacing the degenerate functions ψ_a and ψ_b by ψ_a and $\psi_b - c\psi_a$ they will be orthogonal because

$$\int \psi_a (\psi_b - c\psi_a) \, d\tau = \int \psi_a \psi_b \, d\tau - c \int \psi_a^2 \, d\tau$$
$$= \quad c \quad - \quad c$$
$$= \quad 0$$

The solutions of the wave equation for the hydrogen atom considered in Chapter 7 are all orthogonal.

THE VARIATION THEOREM

It is required to prove that

$$\xi = \frac{\int \psi^* H \psi \, d\tau}{\int \psi^* \psi \, d\tau} \geqslant E$$

or if the wave function is normalized that

$$\xi = \int \psi^* H \psi \, d\tau \geqslant E$$

where ξ is the average energy associated with the approximate wave function ψ and E is the true energy of the lowest state of the system.

Consider the integral

$$\int \psi^*(H - E)\psi \, d\tau = \int \psi^* H \psi \, d\tau - E \int \psi^* \psi \, d\tau$$

$$= \xi - E$$

Hence we have to prove that this integral is positive. This may be done by expanding ψ in terms of a series of normalized orthogonal functions which are themselves solutions of the wave equation

$$H\psi = E\psi.$$

Let $\psi = \Sigma_{n=1}^{\infty} a_n \phi_n$. The expressions for ϕ need not be known but as they are eigenfunctions

$$H\psi = \Sigma a_n H \phi_n = \Sigma a_n E_n \phi_n$$

and

$$\int \psi^*(H - E)\psi \, d\tau = \Sigma a_m^* \phi_m^* \Sigma a_n(E_n - E)\phi_n \, d\tau$$

$$= \Sigma\Sigma a_m^* a_n(E_n - E)\phi_m^* \phi_n \, d\tau$$

$$= \Sigma a_m^* a_n(E_n - E)$$

This follows because when $m \neq n$ the ϕ's are orthogonal and $\int \phi_m{}^* \phi_n \, d\tau = 0$, and when $m = n$ the ϕ's are normalized and $\int \phi_n{}^* \phi_n \, d\tau = 1$. Since $a_m{}^* a_n$ is positive and $E_n - E$ is zero or positive (by definition E is the lowest energy state) the summation must be positive. Consequently

$$\int \psi^*(\mathbf{H} - E)\psi \, d\tau = \xi - E \geqslant 0$$

Appendix 7

Slater Wave Functions

Slater wave functions are approximations to the radial part of one electron wave functions. The approximation is to allow for the resultant coulombic interaction with the other electrons by employing an effective nuclear charge Z' in place of Z. The symmetry of the wave functions also differ from the exact solutions found

TABLE A7.1. SLATER WAVE FUNCTIONS

n	l	State	ψ
1	0	$1s$	$\left(\dfrac{Z'^3}{\pi}\right)^{1/2} e^{-Z'r}$
2	0	$2s$	$\left(\dfrac{Z'^5}{96\pi}\right)^{1/2} r\, e^{-Z'r/2}$
2	1	$2p_x$	$\left(\dfrac{Z'^5}{32\pi}\right)^{1/2} x\, e^{-Z'r/2}$
3	0	$3s$	$\left(\dfrac{2Z'^7}{5 \times 3^9\pi}\right)^{1/2} r^2\, e^{-Z'r/3}$
3	1	$3p_x$	$\left(\dfrac{2Z'^7}{5 \times 3^8\pi}\right)^{1/2} xr\, e^{-Z'r/3}$
3	2	$3d_{z^2}$	$\left(\dfrac{Z'^7}{2 \times 3^9\pi}\right)^{1/2} \dfrac{3z^2 - r^2}{\sqrt{3}}\, e^{-Z'r/3}$
3	2	$3d_{xy}$	$\left(\dfrac{Z'^7}{2 \times 3^9\pi}\right)^{1/2} 2xy\, e^{-Z'r/3}$
3	2	$3d_{x^2-y^2}$	$\left(\dfrac{Z'^7}{2 \times 3^9\pi}\right)^{1/2} (x^2 - y^2)\, e^{-Z'r/3}$

The necessary modifications for the other p and d orbitals are obvious.

for a hydrogen-like atom as they do not possess spherical nodes.

Slater wave functions[1-3] are given in Table A7.1. The effective nuclear charge Z' is obtained by reducing the actual nuclear charge by a screening factor σ, i.e. $Z' = Z - \sigma$. To obtain σ the orbitals are considered in the following order

$$1s; \quad 2s, 2p; \quad 3s, 3p; \quad 3d; \quad 4s, 4p; \quad 4d; \quad 4f; \quad 5s, 5p$$

the s and p orbitals being grouped together. The screening factor is the sum of contributions from the inner electrons as follows:

1. Nothing from an electron in a group outside the one being considered.
2. 0·35 (0·30 for $1s$) for all other electrons in the same group.
3. 1·00 for all other electrons in inner shells except that if the electron being considered is in an s or a p orbital then only 0·85 is contributed by each electron in the *next* inner shell.

These rules apply even if some of the inner electrons are missing (X-ray spectra) but have to be used with great care if the principal quantum number is 4 or more.

The screening constants listed above have been obtained by comparing the Slater functions with the results of more elaborate calculations on atoms. We should note some other limitations. The orbitals do not have the correct number of spherical nodes but this is frequently of no importance. The orbitals of different symmetries are orthogonal but those of the same symmetry are not. This could be a serious limitation but it is possible to replace them by orthogonalized orbitals. Instead of ψ_{1s}, ψ_{2s}, and ψ_{3s} for example ψ_{1s}, $\psi_{2s} + \lambda\psi_{1s}$, and $\psi_{3s} + \mu\psi_{2s} + \nu\psi_{1s}$ are taken where the parameters λ, μ, and ν are fixed so that

$$\int \psi_{1s}(\psi_{2s} + \lambda\psi_{1s})\, d\tau = 0$$

and

$$\int \psi_{1s}(\psi_{3s} + \mu\psi_{2s} + \nu\psi_{1s})\, d\tau = 0$$

These orthogonal orbitals now also possess the correct number of spherical nodes. It generally makes no difference to a determinantal wave function whether the original Slater wave functions or the orthogonalized ones are used.

As an example of Slater wave functions the carbon $1s$, $2s$, and $2p$ functions are

$$\psi_{1s} = 7\cdot66\, e^{-10\cdot8r}$$
$$\psi_{2s} = 2\cdot06r\, e^{-3\cdot07r}$$
$$\psi_{2p_x} = 3\cdot58x\, e^{-3\cdot07r}$$

If these are orthogonalized the $1s$ and $2p_x$ functions are unchanged but the $2s$ function has to be replaced by

$$\psi_{2s}{}' = 1{\cdot}953r\,e^{-3{\cdot}07r} - 1{\cdot}595\,e^{-10{\cdot}8r}$$

The radial distributions for these orbitals $4\pi r^2\psi^2$ are plotted in Figure A7.1 together with the resultant distribution of all the electrons in the carbon atom. For this resultant curve, and for the $2p$ function, the distribution has been averaged over all angles.

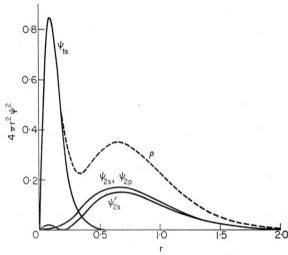

FIGURE A7.1   Slater wave functions for a carbon atom.

Contour surfaces of uniform charge density have been published for Slater orbitals (e.g. Ogryzlo and Porter[4]).

Integration formulae and tables for functions of the forms

$$\int \psi_a\psi_b\,d\tau, \quad \int x\psi_a\psi_b\,d\tau, \quad \int \psi_a\nabla^2\psi_b\,d\tau, \quad \int \frac{\psi_a\psi_b}{r}\,d\tau, \text{ etc.}$$

have been given[5-18] and greatly simplify the use of Slater functions in calculations.

BIBLIOGRAPHICAL REFERENCES

1. Slater, J. C., *Phys. Rev.*, 1930, **36**, 57.
2. Duncanson, W. E., and Coulson, C. A., *Proc. Roy. Soc. Edinburgh*, 1944, **62**, 37.
3. Löwdin, P. O., and Appel, K., *Phys. Rev.*, 1956, **103**, 1746.

4. Ogryzlo, E. A., and Porter, G. B., *J. Chem. Educ.*, 1963, **40**, 256.
5. Coulson, C. A., *Proc. Camb. Phil. Soc.*, 1942, **38**, 210.
6. Mulliken, R. S., Rieke, E. A., Orloff, D., and Orloff, H., *J. Chem. Phys.*, 1949, **17**, 1248.
7. Thorne, C. J., Barker, R. S., and Eyring, H., *Tables of Quantum Mechanical Integrals, Studies in Applied Mathematics*, Nos. 10, 14, 16, University of Utah.
8. Roothaan, C. C. J., *Special Technical Report, Laboratory of Molecular Structure and Spectra*, University of Chicago, 1955.
9. Roothaan, C. C. J., *J. Chem. Phys.*, 1951 **19**, 1445.
10. Ruedenberg, K., Roothaan, C. C. J., and Jaunzemis, W., *Technical Report, Laboratory of Molecular Structure and Spectra*, University of Chicago, 1952–53.
11. Kotani, M. *et al.*, *Proc. Phys. Math. Soc. Japan*, 1938, **20**, extra vol. 1940, **22.**
12. Kotani, M. *et al.*, *J. Phys. Soc. Japan*, 1953, **8**, 463.
13. Kotani, M. *et al.*, *J. Phys. Soc. Japan*, 1953, **9**, 553.
14. Kotani, M. *et al.*, *Table of Molecular Integrals*, Maruzen, Tokyo, 1955.
15. Murai, T., and Araki, G., *Progr. Theor. Phys. Kyoto*, 1952, **8**, 615.
16. Scrocco, E., and Salvetti, O., *Ricerca Sci.*, 1953, **23**, 98.
17. Barnett, M. P., and Coulson, C. A., *Phil. Trans. Roy. Soc.*, 1951, A**243**, 221.
18. Preuss, H., *Integraltafeln zur Quantenchemie*, Springer-Verlag, Berlin, 1956.

COVALENT AND IONIC RADII, ELECTRONEGATIVITIES, AND IONIZATION POTENTIALS

TABLE A8.1

Element		Z	r_{cov} (Å)	r_{ionic} (Å)	Electro-negativity		Ionization Potential (eV)	
					Pauling	S.R	1st	2nd
Aluminium	Al	13	1·25	0·45	1·5	1·94	6·0	18·8
Antimony	Sb	51	1·41		1·9	3·37	8·6	18·6
Argon	Ar	18	1·91			1·00	15·8	27·6
Arsenic	As	33	1·21		2·0	3·91	10·5	20·3
Barium	Ba	56	1·98	1·29	0·9	1·02	5·2	10·0
Beryllium	Be	4	0·89	0·30	1·5	1·91	9·3	18·2
Bismuth	Bi	83	1·52	1·16	1·9	3·78	8·5	16·8
Boron	B	5	0·80	0·20	2·0	2·84	8·3	25·1
Bromine	Br	35	1·14	1·95	2·8	4·53	11·8	19·1
Cadmium	Cd	48	1·41	0·92	1·7	2·59	9·0	16·8
Caesium	Cs	55	2·35	1·67	0·7	0·49	3·9	23·4
Calcium	Ca	20	1·74	0·94	1·0	1·22	6·1	11·9
Carbon	C	6	0·77		2·5	3·79	11·3	24·4
Cerium	Ce	58	1·65	1·02 (+3)			6·6	
				0·87 (+4)				
Chlorine	Cl	17	0·99	1·81	3·0	4·93	13·0	23·8
Chromium	Cr	24	1·17	0·55 (+3)	1·6	3·02	6·6	16·6
Cobalt	Co	27	1·16	0·78 (+2)	1·8	3·38	7·9	17·5
Copper	Cu	29	1·17	0·69 (+2)	1·9	2·43	7·7	20·3
				0·95 (+1)				
Fluorine	F	9	0·72	1·33	4·0	5·75	17·4	35·0

TABLE A8.1 (*continued*)

Element		Z	r_{cov} (Å)	r_{ionic} (Å)	Electro-negativity		Ionization Potential (eV)	
					Pauling	S.R	1st	2nd
Gallium	Ga	31	1·25	0·62	1·6		6·0	20·4
Germanium	Ge	32	1·22		1·8	3·59	8·1	15·9
Gold	Au	79	1·34		2·4	3·39	9·2	20·0
Hafnium	Hf	72	1·44	0·86 (+4)	1·3		5·5	15
Helium	He	2				1·00	24·6	54·4
Hydrogen	H	1	0·36	1·54 (−1)	2·1	3·55	13·6	
Indium	In	49	1·50	0·92 (+3)	1·7	2·86	5·8	18·8
Iodine	I	53	1·33	2·19	2·5	3·84	10·4	19·1
Iron	Fe	26	1·17	0·75 (+2)	1·8	3·27	7·9	16·3
				0·53 (+3)				
Krypton	Kr	36				1·00	14·0	26·4
Lanthanum	La	57	1·69	1·22	1·1	1·96	5·6	11·4
Lead	Pb	82	1·54	1·17	1·8	3·67	7·4	15·0
Lithium	Li	3	1·23	0·68	1·0	0·74	5·4	75·6
Magnesium	Mg	12	1·36	0·65	1·2	1·56	7·6	15·0
Manganese	Mn	25	1·17	0·80 (+2)	1·5	3·15	7·4	15·7
Mercury	Hg	80	1·44	1·05	1·9	3·47	10·4	18·7
Molybdenum	Mo	42	1·29	0·68 (+4)	1·8		7·2	
Neon	Ne	10				1·00	21·6	41·1
Nickel	Ni	28	1·15	0·68	1·8		7·6	18·2
Niobium	Nb	41	1·34	0·70	1·6		6·8	14·1
Nitrogen	N	7	0·75		3·0	4·49	14·5	29·6
Osmium	Os	76	1·26	0·67 (+4)	2·2		8·7	
Oxygen	O	8	0·74	1·45	3·5	5·21	13·6	35·1
Palladium	Pd	46	1·28	0·50	2·2		8·3	20·0
Phosphorus	P	15	1·10		2·1	3·34	11·0	19·7
Platinum	Pt	78	1·26	0·52 (+2)	2·2		9·0	19·4
Potassium	K	19	2·03	1·33	0·8	0·56	4·3	31·8
Radium	Ra	88		1·52	0·9		5·3	10·1
Radon	Rn	86				1·00	10·7	
Rhenium	Re	75	1·28		1·9		7·9	
Rhodium	Rh	45	1·25	0·69	2·2		7·7	18·2
Scandium	Sc	21	1·44	0·83	1·3	1·88	6·6	12·9
Selenium	Se	34	1·17	2·02 (−2)	2·4	4·25	9·8	21·3
Silicon	Si	14	1·17	0·41	1·8	2·62	8·1	16·3
Silver	Ag	47	1·34	1·13	1·9	2·30	7·6	22·0
Sodium	Na	11	1·57	0·98	0·9	0·70	5·1	47·3
Strontium	Sr	38	1·91	1·10	1·0	1·10	5·7	11·0
Sulphur	S	16	1·04	1·90	2·5	4·11	10·4	23·4
Tantalum	Ta	73	1·34	0·73			6	
Tellurium	Te	52	1·37	0·89 (+4)	2·1	3·62	9·0	21·6

TABLE A8.1 (*continued*)

Element		Z	r_{cov} (Å)	r_{ionic} (Å)	Electro-negativity		Ionization Potential (eV)	
					Pauling	S.R	1st	2nd
Thallium	Tl	81	1·55	1·05 (+3)	1·8	3·58	6·1	20·3
				1·49 (+1)				
Thorium	Th	90	1·65	1·10 (+4)	1·3			
Tin	Sn	50	1·40	0·74 (+4)	1·8	3·10	7·3	14·5
Titanium	Ti	22	1·32	0·64 (+4)	1·5	2·27	6·8	13·6
Tungsten	W	74	1·30	0·68	1·7		8·0	
Uranium	U	92	1·42	0·89 (+4)	1·7		4	
Vanadium	V	23	1·22	0·64 (+4)	1·6	3·12	6·7	14·2
				0·40 (+5)				
Xenon	Xe	54				1·00	12·1	21
Yttrium	Y	39	1·62	1·06	1·2	1·75	6·6	12·3
Zinc	Zn	30	1·25	0·70	1·6	2·84	9·4	17·9
Zirconium	Zr	40	1·45	0·87	1·4	2·26	7·0	14·0

ELECTRONIC STRUCTURES OF ATOMS IN THEIR GROUND STATES

TABLE A.9.1. ELECTRONIC STRUCTURES OF ATOMS IN THEIR GROUND STATES

Element	Atomic Number	1s	2s	2p	3s	3p	3d	4s	4p	4d	4f	5s	5p	5d	5f	6s	6p	6d	7s
H	1	1				
He	2	2				
Li	3	2	1			
Be	4	2	2			
B	5	2	2	1		
C	6	2	2	2		
N	7	2	2	3		
O	8	2	2	4		
F	9	2	2	5		
Ne	10	2	2	6		
Na	11	2	2	6	1	
Mg	12	2	2	6	2	
Al	13	2	2	6	2	1
Si	14	2	2	6	2	2
P	15	2	2	6	2	3
S	16	2	2	6	2	4
Cl	17	2	2	6	2	5
A	18	2	2	6	2	6

370

Z	Element	1s	2s	2p	3s	3p	3d	4s	4p	4d	5s
19	K	2	2	6	2	6		1			
20	Ca	2	2	6	2	6		2			
21	Sc	2	2	6	2	6	1	2			
22	Ti	2	2	6	2	6	2	2			
23	V	2	2	6	2	6	3	2			
24	Cr	2	2	6	2	6	5	1			
25	Mn	2	2	6	2	6	5	2			
26	Fe	2	2	6	2	6	6	2			
27	Co	2	2	6	2	6	7	2			
28	Ni	2	2	6	2	6	8	2			
29	Cu	2	2	6	2	6	10	1			
30	Zn	2	2	6	2	6	10	2			
31	Ga	2	2	6	2	6	10	2	1		
32	Ge	2	2	6	2	6	10	2	2		
33	As	2	2	6	2	6	10	2	3		
34	Se	2	2	6	2	6	10	2	4		
35	Br	2	2	6	2	6	10	2	5		
36	Kr	2	2	6	2	6	10	2	6		
37	Rb	2	2	6	2	6	10	2	6		1
38	Sr	2	2	6	2	6	10	2	6		2
39	Y	2	2	6	2	6	10	2	6	1	2
40	Zr	2	2	6	2	6	10	2	6	2	2
41	Nb	2	2	6	2	6	10	2	6	4	1
42	Mo	2	2	6	2	6	10	2	6	5	1
43	Tc	2	2	6	2	6	10	2	6	6	1

Element	Atomic Number	1s	2s	2p	3s	3p	3d	4s	4p	4d	4f	5s	5p	5d	5f	6s	6p	6d	7s
Ru	44	2	2	6	2	6	10	2	6	7		1							
Rh	45	2	2	6	2	6	10	2	6	8		1							
Pd	46	2	2	6	2	6	10	2	6	10									
Ag	47	2	2	6	2	6	10	2	6	10		1							
Cd	48	2	2	6	2	6	10	2	6	10		2							
In	49	2	2	6	2	6	10	2	6	10		2	1						
Sn	50	2	2	6	2	6	10	2	6	10		2	2						
Sb	51	2	2	6	2	6	10	2	6	10		2	3						
Te	52	2	2	6	2	6	10	2	6	10		2	4						
I	53	2	2	6	2	6	10	2	6	10		2	5						
Xe	54	2	2	6	2	6	10	2	6	10		2	6						
Cs	55	2	2	6	2	6	10	2	6	10		2	6			1			
Ba	56	2	2	6	2	6	10	2	6	10		2	6			2			
La	57	2	2	6	2	6	10	2	6	10		2	6	1		2			
Ce	58	2	2	6	2	6	10	2	6	10	2	2	6			2			
Pr	59	2	2	6	2	6	10	2	6	10	3	2	6			2			
Nd	60	2	2	6	2	6	10	2	6	10	4	2	6			2			
Pm	61	2	2	6	2	6	10	2	6	10	5	2	6			2			
Sm	62	2	2	6	2	6	10	2	6	10	6	2	6			2			
Eu	63	2	2	6	2	6	10	2	6	10	7	2	6			2			
Gd	64	2	2	6	2	6	10	2	6	10	7	2	6	1		2			

Element	Z	1s	2s	2p	3s	3p	3d	4s	4p	4d	4f	5s	5p	5d	6s	6p	7s
Tb	65	2	2	6	2	6	10	2	6	10	9	2	6		2		
Dy	66	2	2	6	2	6	10	2	6	10	10	2	6		2		
Ho	67	2	2	6	2	6	10	2	6	10	11	2	6		2		
Er	68	2	2	6	2	6	10	2	6	10	12	2	6		2		
Tm	69	2	2	6	2	6	10	2	6	10	13	2	6		2		
Yb	70	2	2	6	2	6	10	2	6	10	14	2	6		2		
Lu	71	2	2	6	2	6	10	2	6	10	14	2	6	1	2		
Hf	72	2	2	6	2	6	10	2	6	10	14	2	6	2	2		
Ta	73	2	2	6	2	6	10	2	6	10	14	2	6	3	2		
W	74	2	2	6	2	6	10	2	6	10	14	2	6	4	2		
Re	75	2	2	6	2	6	10	2	6	10	14	2	6	5	2		
Os	76	2	2	6	2	6	10	2	6	10	14	2	6	6	2		
Ir	77	2	2	6	2	6	10	2	6	10	14	2	6	9	2		
Pt	78	2	2	6	2	6	10	2	6	10	14	2	6	9	1		
Au	79	2	2	6	2	6	10	2	6	10	14	2	6	10	1		
Hg	80	2	2	6	2	6	10	2	6	10	14	2	6	10	2		
Tl	81	2	2	6	2	6	10	2	6	10	14	2	6	10	2	1	
Pb	82	2	2	6	2	6	10	2	6	10	14	2	6	10	2	2	
Bi	83	2	2	6	2	6	10	2	6	10	14	2	6	10	2	3	
Po	84	2	2	6	2	6	10	2	6	10	14	2	6	10	2	4	
At	85	2	2	6	2	6	10	2	6	10	14	2	6	10	2	5	
Rn	86	2	2	6	2	6	10	2	6	10	14	2	6	10	2	6	
Fr	87	2	2	6	2	6	10	2	6	10	14	2	6	10	2	6	1
Ra	88	2	2	6	2	6	10	2	6	10	14	2	6	10	2	6	2

TABLE A9.1. ELECTRONIC STRUCTURES OF ATOMS IN THEIR GROUND STATES (continued)

Element	Atomic Number	1s	2s	2p	3s	3p	3d	4s	4p	4d	4f	5s	5p	5d	5f	6s	6p	6d	7s
Ac	89	2	2	6	2	6	10	2	6	10	14	2	6	10		2	6	1	2
Th	90	2	2	6	2	6	10	2	6	10	14	2	6	10		2	6	2	2
Pa	91	2	2	6	2	6	10	2	6	10	14	2	6	10	2	2	6	1	2
U	92	2	2	6	2	6	10	2	6	10	14	2	6	10	3	2	6	1	2
Np	93	2	2	6	2	6	10	2	6	10	14	2	6	10	4	2	6	1	2
Pu	94	2	2	6	2	6	10	2	6	10	14	2	6	10	5	2	6	1	2
Am	95	2	2	6	2	6	10	2	6	10	14	2	6	10	6	2	6	1	2
Cm	96	2	2	6	2	6	10	2	6	10	14	2	6	10	7	2	6	1	2
Bk	97	2	2	6	2	6	10	2	6	10	14	2	6	10	8	2	6	1	2
Cf	98	2	2	6	2	6	10	2	6	10	14	2	6	10	9	2	6	1	2
Es	99	2	2	6	2	6	10	2	6	10	14	2	6	10	10	2	6	1	2
Fm	100	2	2	6	2	6	10	2	6	10	14	2	6	10	11	2	6	1	2
Md	101	2	2	6	2	6	10	2	6	10	14	2	6	10	12	2	6	1	2
No	102	2	2	6	2	6	10	2	6	10	14	2	6	10	14	2	6		2
Lw	103	2	2	6	2	6	10	2	6	10	14	2	6	10	14	2	6	1	2

The lanthanides and actinides have alternative states with very similar energies so the configurations given above may not represent the true ground electronic arrangement in each case.

Author Index

Allen, H. C., 182, 209
Allen, L. C., 179
Almenningen, A., 185, 199
Alonso, J. I. F., 296
Altmann, S. L., 223
Andrew, E. R., 292
Appel, K., 363
Araki, G., 364
Arnold, J. R., 184
Arrhenius, S., 311

Bacher, R. F., 180
Badger, R. M., 292, 333
Bak, B., 199, 236, 288
Baker, J. W., 338
Baker, W., 288
Balk, P., 297
Ballhausen, C. J., 279
Ballik, E. A., 145
Barker, R. S., 364
Barnett, M. P., 364
Barrow, G. M., 337
Bartell, L. S., 182, 209
Bastiansen, O., 185, 199, 236
Bates, D. R., 139
Battiste, C. M., 288
Baudet, J., 296
Bawn, C. E. H., 38
Bayliss, N. S., 186
Beach, J. Y., 239
Becher, H. J., 304
Becker, F., 284
Bell, C. L., 337
Bell, R. P., 38
Bennett, M. A., 276
Bernal, J. D., 335
Bernstein, H. J., 221, 344
Berthier, G., 296
Bethe, H., 270
Bloch, F., 121
Bohr, N., 6
Bonham, R. A., 182, 209
Born, M., 53

Brauman, J. I., 321
Breslow, R., 286, 288
Brockway, L. O., 239
Brown, D. A., 276
Brown, H. C., 318
Brown, R. D., 228, 317, 321, 326
Brown, W. G., 193, 342, 343
Burnelle, L., 227, 230

Caldow, G. L., 220
Cardwell, H. M. E., 337
Carrington, A., 272, 344
Chalvet, O., 326, 328, 329
Chambers, V. C., 255
Chapman, A. C., 304
Chatt, J., 277
Christensen, D., 288
Clar, E., 294
Cleveland, F. F., 277
Clinton, W. L., 290
Cole, T., 218
Condon, E. U., 37, 275
Coolidge, A. S., 143
Costain, C. C., 342
Cotton, F. A., 276
Cottrell, T. L., 217
Coulson, C. A., 14, 162, 183, 191, 210, 212, 220, 223, 227, 230, 236, 238, 239, 290, 293, 296, 304, 319, 320, 321, 332, 335, 363, 364
Cox, E. G., 238
Craig, D. P., 265, 305, 306
Crawford, B., 253
Crawford, V. A., 338
Cross, P. C., 175
Cruickshank, D. W. J., 240, 265
Cumper, C. W. N., 182, 236

Dailey, D. P., 233
Dalgarno, A., 53
Danielsson, U., 335
Daudel, R., 321, 326, 328, 329
Davidson, N. R., 218

375

Subject Index

Numerals in **bold** type refer to Chapters, other references are to pages. When topics are considered on successive pages only the first page is quoted.

Date Due

Demco 293-5